D0231701

PHYSIOLOGICAL ASPECTS
OF CROP YIELD

PHYSIOLOGICAL ASPECTS OF CROP YIELD

Proceedings of a symposium sponsored by the University of Nebraska, the American Society of Agronomy, and the Crop Science Society of America, and held at the University of Nebraska, Lincoln, Nebr., January 20-24, 1969. Financial support for the symposium came from The Rockefeller Foundation. Publication assistance was provided through the International Biological Program.

Editorial Committee

JERRY D. EASTIN, Chairman

Plant Physiologist, Cereal Crops Research Branch, Crops Research Division, Agricultural Research Service, US Department of Agriculture, and Associate Professor, Department of Agronomy, University of Nebraska, Lincoln, Nebraska.

F. A. HASKINS

Professor, Department of Agronomy, University of Nebraska, Lincoln, Nebraska

C. Y. SULLIVAN

Associate Professor, Department of Horticulture and Forestry, University of Nebraska, Lincoln, Nebraska

C. H. M. VAN BAVEL

Professor, Institute of Life Sciences, Texas A & M University, College Station, Texas

Managing Editor: RICHARD C. DINAUER

Published by
American Society of Agronomy
Crop Science Society of America
Madison, Wisconsin USA
1969

FOREWORD

This volume is the outgrowth of an international symposium held at Lincoln, Nebraska, January 20-24, 1969. It was sponsored by the University of Nebraska in cooperation with the American Society of Agronomy and the Crop Science Society of America with partial financing by the Rockefeller Foundation and the International Biological Program.

The symposium planning committee was broadly based and was able to bring specialists from many parts of the world to the conference. Thus, the technical presentations were drawn from outstanding authorities backed up by a clear perspective of social needs. This was a happy combination which contributed greatly to the success of the conference and is shown on the printed pages of this book. Happy, too, is the realization that in this symposium the most basic of inquiry into the physiology of plants is brought to bear on solving problems of the yield of economic plants vital to man's existence, both now and in the long view ahead. Empiricism, successful in past decades will, we are convinced, be augmented and in some cases be replaced by the new understanding of the physiology of yield in plants.

We sometimes hear that research is less enjoyable and rewarding now than formerly, partly because it is so fragmented. The output is so great that no one can keep up with more than a mere fraction of research reports and relating one part with another is often difficult. We believe the symposium presented here in book form has bridged some of these chasms.

There is no reason why science cannot be put to work somewhere to assist man in his eternal quest to control his environment and satisfy his basic needs and ambitions. However, there are many examples of misguided or abortive "advances" which produce short-term or local gains at the risk of much larger long-term losses. Hence, as was brought out at the symposium, a certain level of technology must be evaluated in terms of its cost, its worth, and the goals men hold. The societies which sponsored this undertaking are dedicated to the encouragement of excellent science and to the dissemination of knowledge. We believe this book represents a positive and useful effort toward both.

July 1969

L. P. Reitz, President, CSSA
W. L. Nelson, President, ASA

PREFACE

Mounting world population pressures and accompanying malnutrition problems pose grave concerns in the minds of thoughtful men. The nature, scope, and impending gravity of this situation has been ably characterized by Dr. J. J. Harrar, President of the Rockefeller Foundation. In a stimulating address during the symposium, Dr. Harrar identified the two principal approaches toward alleviating malnutrition as (i) increased food production per unit land area and (ii) population control. This symposium was concerned with the first approach.

Despite the considerable genetic sophistication incorporated into current plant breeding techniques, C. M. Donald describes plant breeding approaches as being largely empirical (Advances in Agronomy, Vol. 15) because our knowledge and use of yield-related physiological and morphological characters is meager. Crop physiologists and biochemists must continue to provide plant breeders with criteria for tailoring crops to different environments, and plant breeders in turn must recognize and use these criteria in their programs.

Plant production processes must be better understood if maximum economic yields are to be realized and exploited. The competitive advantage of any biologic organism in the field, be it crop plant or pest, is dictated by its relative response to the prevailing environment. Environmental physiology research has scarcely touched on interdependencies amongst and control of the major physiologic processes dictating competitive advantage. Quantitating the environment and plant morphologic characters simultaneously with major physiologic process rates may provide much essential perspective concerning the order of these yield limiting factors. The subsequent exploitation of these yield-related factors will depend on their detailed characterization at cellular and molecular levels.

Life processes, in the final analysis, are the sum total of biochemical reactions at cellular and molecular levels. The manner in which these reactions interrelate dictates the efficiency with which light energy is trapped in the plant, converted to chemical energy, and elaborated into storage products useful to man. A significant, increased rate of progress in breeding for yield will depend on expanded, interrelated advances in disciplines such as environmental physiology, systems analyses, simulation and bioinstrumentation, anatomy and morphology, cell biology, and genetics. This symposium was keyed to reviewing and highlighting selected aspects of knowledge in some of these diverse disciplines in an attempt to bridge some of the gaps between essential field and molecular level research pertaining to higher crop yields.

The Rockefeller Foundation approved a five-year grant in 1966 to the Nebraska Agricultural Experiment Station in support of a research program entitled "The Physiology of Yield and Management of Sorghum in Relation to Genetic Improvement." A sum was included in the grant budget to assist in financing a symposium concerning the application of physiological principles in the improvement of crop yields.

Arrangements were made for the American Society of Agronomy and the Crop Science Society of America to cooperate with the University of Nebraska in sponsoring the symposium. The symposium planning committee members were Drs. F. A. Haskins (chairman), J. M. Daly, Jerry D. Eastin, and C. Y. Sullivan, representing the University of Nebraska and appointed by Dr. H. W. Ottoson, Director of the Nebraska Agricultural Experiment Station; Dr. C. H. M. van Bavel, representing the ASA, appointed by Dr. R. S. Whitney, then President of the ASA; and Dr. R.W. Howell, representing the CSSA, appointed by Dr. A. A. Hanson, then President of the CSSA.

The symposium was held from January 20 to 24, 1969, at the Nebraska Center for Continuing Education, as one of the first events in the Centennial observance of the University of Nebraska. Registration at the symposium totalled approximately 445 persons. A total of 40 states and the District of Columbia in the USA, and 14 countries outside the USA were represented at the conference.

A complete listing of all those who have helped the planning and editorial committees is not feasible. However, the committees do wish to acknowledge publicly the excellent contributions of all speakers, invited discussants, and session chairmen. The names of the speakers and of those invited discussants who elected to submit copy for this volume are shown in the Table of Contents. Two of the invited discussants made excellent verbal presentations but chose not to submit copy for publication. They were Drs. C. B. Tanner, University of Wisconsin, and V. T. Walhood, ARS, USDA. One of the invited discussants, Dr. R. W. Allard, University of California, Davis, was unable to attend the symposium.

Chairmen of the eight half-day sessions were the following: Dr. H. H. Kramer, Purdue University; Dr. D. E. McCloud, University of Florida; Dr. C. H. M. van Bavel, Texas A and M University; Dr. G. E. van Riper, Deere and Company; Drs. R. W. Howell and F. G. Viets, ARS, USDA; and Dr. E. F. Frolik and H. W. Ottoson, University of Nebraska.

The contributions of the following in various phases of planning and conducting the symposium and/or publishing this volume also merit special mention:

Drs. Sterling Wortman and Lewis M. Roberts of the Rockefeller Foundation

Dr. A. B. Ward of the Nebraska Center for Continuing Education

Drs. D. C. Smith and F. L. Patterson, Past-Presidents of the ASA and CSSA, respectively

Drs. W. L. Nelson and L. P. Reitz, Presidents of the ASA and CSSA, respectively

Dr. Matthias Stelly and Mr. R. C. Dinauer of the ASA Hdqtrs. staff

The financial support of the Rockefeller Foundation has already been mentioned. Without it, this symposium would not have been possible. The financial contribution of the International Biological Program toward the publication of this volume also is acknowledged with thanks.

July 1969

The Editorial Committee: Jerry D. Eastin (chairman); F. A. Haskins; C. Y. Sullivan; C. H. M. van Bavel.

CONTRIBUTORS

Donald N. Baker

Soil Scientist, Soil and Water Conservation Research Division, Agricultural Research Service, U.S. Department of Agriculture, Boll Weevil Research Laboratory, State College, Mississippi

Harry Beevers

Professor of Biology, Department of Biological Sciences, Purdue University, Lafayette, Indiana

Orlin Biddulph

Professor of Botany and Director of Molecular Biophysics Laboratory, Washington State University, Pullman, Washington

Robert F. Chandler, Jr.

Director, International Rice Research Institute, Manila, Philippines

Marion Clawson

Director, Land Use and Management Program, Resources for the Future, Inc., Washington, D.C.

Harry F. Clements

Senior Plant Physiologist, Emeritus, and Consulting Plant Physiologist, Retired, Hawaii Agricultural Experiment Station and C. Brewer and Company, Ltd., Honolulu, Hawaii

Alden S. Crafts

Professor of Botany, Emeritus, Botany Department, University of California, Davis, California

O. T. Denmead

Senior Research Scientist, Commonwealth Scientific and Industrial Research Organization, Canberra, Australia

William G. Duncan

Professor of Plant Physiology, Department of Agronomy, University of Kentucky, Lexington, Kentucky

Pieter Gaastra

Doctor, Centre for Plant Physiological Research, Wageningen, The Netherlands

Norman E. Good

Professor of Plant Biochemistry and Physiology, Department of Botany and Plant Pathology, Michigan State University, East Lansing, Michigan

Richard H. Hageman

Professor of Crop Physiology, Department of Agronomy, University of Illinois, Urbana, Illinois

John B. Hanson

Professor of Plant Physiology, Department of Botany, University of Illinois, Urbana, Illinois

John Heslop-Harrison

Professor, Institute of Plant Development, University of Wisconsin, Madison, Wisconsin

Yoshiaki Ishizuka

Dean, Faculty of Agriculture, Hokkaido University, Sapporo, Hokkaido, Japan

Peter R. Jennings

Leader, Inter-American Rice Program, Centro Internacional De Agricultura Tropical, Colombia, South America

Neal F. Jensen

Professor of Plant Breeding, Department of Plant Breeding and Biometry, Cornell University, Ithaca, New York

Dov Koller

Professor, Department of Botany, The Hebrew University of Jerusalem, Israel (formerly Visiting Research Professor, Laboratory of Nuclear Medicine and Radiation Biology, University of California, Los Angeles, California)

Paul J. Kramer

Professor, Department of Botany, Duke University, Durham, North Carolina

George G. Laties

Professor, Department of Botanical Sciences, University of California, Los Angeles, California

Edgar Lemon

Research Soil Scientist, Microclimate Investigations, Soil and Water Conservation Research Division, Agricultural Research Service, U.S. Department of Agriculture, Cornell University, Ithaca, New York

R. S. Loomis

Professor, Department of Agronomy and Range Science, University of California, Davis, California

Walter E. Loomis

Formerly with Southern Illinois University, Carbondale, Illinois (now Professor of Botany, Department of Botany, Iowa State University, Ames, Iowa)

CONTRIBUTORS

K. J. McCree — Associate Professor, Institute of Life Science, Texas A & M University, College Station, Texas

Terence A. Mansfield — Doctor, Department of Biological Sciences, University of Lancaster, United Kingdom

John Lennox Monteith — Professor, School of Agriculture, University of Nottingham, Sutton Bonington, Loughborough, United Kingdom

Dale N. Moss — Professor, Department of Agronomy and Plant Genetics, University of Minnesota, St. Paul, Minnesota

Yoshio Murata — Head, Division of Plant Physiology, National Institute of Agricultural Sciences, Konosu, Saitama, Japan

Werner L. Nelson — Senior Vice President, American Potash Institute, West Lafayette, Indiana

J. J. Oertli — Associate Professor of Soil Science, Department of Soils and Plant Nutrition, University of California, Riverside, California

John R. Philip — Chief Research Scientist, Commonwealth Scientific and Industrial Research Organization, Canberra, Australia

Ralph O. Slatyer — Professor of Biology, Research School of Biological Sciences, Australian National University, Canberra, Australia

George F. Sprague — Research Agronomist, Crops Research Division, Agricultural Research Service, U.S. Department of Agriculture, Plant Industry Station, Beltsville, Maryland

Volkmar Stoy — Doctor, Swedish Seed Association, Svalöf, Sweden

Carroll Arthur Swanson — Professor of Plant Physiology, Faculty of Organismic and Developmental Biology, Ohio State University, Columbus, Ohio

Akira Tanaka — Professor of Plant Nutrition, Faculty of Agriculture, Hokkaido University, Sapporo, Japan

J. W. Tanner

Professor, Department of Crop Science,
Ontario Agricultural College, University
of Guelph, Guelph, Ontario, Canada

Gillian N. Thorne

Doctor, Rothamsted Experimental Station,
Harpenden, Herts, United Kingdom

E. Bruce Tregunna

Assistant Professor, Botany Department,
University of British Columbia, Vancouver, British Columbia, Canada

Paul E. Waggoner

Chief Climatologist, The Connecticut Agricultural Experiment Station, New Haven,
Connecticut

William A. Williams

Professor of Agronomy, Department of
Agronomy and Range Science, University
of California, Davis, California

Israel Zelitch

Head, Department of Biochemistry, The
Connecticut Agricultural Experiment Station, New Haven, Connecticut

CONTENTS

Discussion   PETER R. JENNINGS   286

Discussion   WERNER L. NELSON   287

13   Development, Differentiation, and Yield   291

JOHN HESLOP-HARRISON

Discussion   NORMAN E. GOOD   321

Discussion   WALTER E. LOOMIS   324

14   Cultural Manipulation for Higher Yields   327

WILLIAM G. DUNCAN

Discussion   HARRY F. CLEMENTS   339

Discussion   E. B. TREGUNNA   341

Systems Analysis of Natural Resources and Crop Production

MARION CLAWSON

Resources for the Future
Washington, D. C.

Human history is a seamless web; every event has its antecedents, its contemporaries, and its consequences. Each event arises out of the past, each is associated with other events at the time, and each leads to new events, in an endless chain. Indeed, there is difficulty in isolating any single event; when did it begin, what are its boundaries, when did it end? These are some of the problems of the social scientist generally, and of the historian in particular.

Nature is equally a seamless web. Every natural process or event has its cause or antecedent, each takes place within a complex matrix or environment, and each leaves its consequences, out of which in time flow other events or processes. As with human history, it is sometimes difficult to define an event or a process in nature--to mark its beginning, its boundaries, its ending. At the least, it is necessary to define and to limit both events and processes, and to put each in a setting--a chemical reaction at a specified temperature and pressure, in specified concentrations, with stated degrees of impurities present, for instance. Man has established fields of knowledge or professions, such as chemistry, agronomy, genetics, and the like; but nature knows no such categories. Increasingly, we find that the really important and difficult problems lie at the crossroads of two or more of our self-established professions, rarely squarely within any one field of knowledge.

I. REQUIREMENTS OF CROP PRODUCTION

At the risk of gilding the lily, let me point out that this concept of the seamless web applies to crop production also. The requirements for successful crop production are several: a plant capable of producing a product desired by man, with efficiency; a soil capable of provid-

ing support to the plant and of holding at least a minimum of some moisture, preferably with some plant nutrients that it can yield up to the
plant; other sources of plant nutrients from mineral deposits in other
areas, applied as needed by the crop; enough, but not too much, water,
either falling as natural precipitation or applied as irrigation; a reasonable control of plant diseases, insect pests, weeds, and other rivals or
inhibitors; and many other factors. Each of these necessary inputs in
turn has its antecedents. All of these and other, factors must be present in at least a reasonably favorable degree; the absence or the scarcity of any one may limit the crop severely. You are each vastly more
familiar with all this than am I; I am simply refreshing our memories,
and supplying a common starting point for further consideration.

Any plant production, whether intended or not, leaves its consequences. It is not enough to produce; the product must be utilized, and
this in turn requires many steps and often an elaborate organization.
Moreover, the waste must be disposed of. A product is defined as
something man wants from the crop growth and production--something
directly useful for his needs, or indirectly so (e.g., food for his domes-
tic animals or even game animals and birds). The usefulness of a crop
output depends in large part upon the facilities man has constructed to
use it (e.g., transportation facilities of all kinds and means of storing
and preserving from harvest time until the product is needed).

But waste also results from most plant or crop production. Waste
may be simply defined as a material in the wrong place and time. My
old botany professor defined weeds as valuable plants growing in the
wrong time and place, and waste is analogous. Everything produced
(or transformed) by plants must somehow be disposed of, somewhere,
some time, in some way. The total volume of all production must show
up as wastes in solid, liquid, or gaseous form, except as there is direct
recycling of some products in the production processes. This is simply
the law of the conservation of matter applied to economic outputs. When
looked at in this way, the problems of pollution appear in somewhat different perspective; all produce, when it has served its primary purpose,
becomes waste and pollution in some form.

The animal manures resulting from large scale cattle feeding operations, or from large scale intensive broiler or egg production enter-
prises, may create a serious waste and pollution problem, given their
concentration at one place and point in time. But these materials are
also highly valuable plant nutrients, carefully saved and husbanded in
an earlier age in our country and highly valued yet in many lands. Anyone who has seen the eagerness with which women and children in some
countries scoop up freshly made cow manure, and convert it to a cake
for drying and later use as fuel, may wonder how such people would
view a modern large scale beef feeding lot. Or the plant nutrients which
wash from the soil and create such undesirable growths of algae in
nearby ponds are but a part of the valuable additions made to the soil
so that it can grow plants. You can surely add many more examples of
chemicals or other materials highly valued in one place but a liability
elsewhere. Even water falls in this category--the scarcity of the desert
leads to one evaluation, the destructiveness of the flood to another.

Modern man is industrial and urban, more than he is rural and agricultural. In the modern city, everything that comes in--food, fuel, clothing, shelter materials, water, etc.--must somehow be disposed of, by flushing down the river, by burning and discharge to the atmosphere, or by covering up as land fill. Materials management is coming to replace waste disposal, as the best term to describe what is involved. Increasingly, we realize that production, or the placing of a desired good in the hands of the consumer, is not the end of the technological and economic processes involved. Until the waste is somehow disposed of, and preferably to a place and in a condition where it can enter the productive cycle anew, the production-consumption process is not ended.

In my youth, I learned about the hydrologic and the nitrogen cycles-- how water was evaporated, transported by clouds, precipitated from them, and how it behaved on the land and in water bodies, and similarly how the nitrogen moved from atmosphere to various forms on earth and in plants and animals, and back again to the air. These particular cycles are still valid, but incomplete as a means of describing production of desired plant and animal materials and of disposing of them as wastes. It is now clear that there are cycles for all basic elements and for their compounds. Many cycles are complex, the paths variable, and the time length may be far beyond human control, or possibly human comprehension. Discoveries in recent decades of substantial deposits of metals or relatively simple metallic compounds on the ocean floor has opened new vistas about this matter of materials cycles. For a long time, we considered iron, copper, lead, tin, and other metals as exhaustible materials, or stock resources, not subject to replacement, while such other materials as wood fiber were considered replaceable or flow resources. But now we know that the so-called stock resources do not disappear, though their cycles may be such that we cannot recapture them readily. The lead we mine from a deposit does not disappear forever, merely because it is discharged into the atmosphere when the gasoline in which it was dissolved is burned.

II. ASPECTS OF NATURAL RESOURCES

The quantity and quality of natural resources readily available for use has been the subject of much concern by many people for many centuries; but I think it can reasonably be argued that there has been a rising tide of popular interest in the subject in recent years. In particular, the quality aspects of the problem have had increasing emphasis, with much concern over water and air pollution, over landscape degradation, over natural beauty, and all the rest of it. In one sense, everyone understands what is meant by natural resources, yet I suggest there may indeed be some lack of common understanding of at least some aspects of the term.

In my research, I have found it helpful to use a definition of natural resources which includes four parts: (i) Any quality or characteristic of nature, (ii) which we know how to use, (iii) economically, and (iv) to a desired end.

A. Qualities of Nature

In an earlier day, we tended to define natural resources only in terms of tangible assets such as soils, forests, and mineral deposits. We developed intensive and complex ways of measuring such resources, and of describing them. There is a whole language to describe soils, for instance--the old measures, such as A, B, and C horizons, or clay, loam, and sand, and others, to which I was exposed in my youth, are no longer adequate, but they were helpful in their time. Likewise, mineral deposits can be measured in various ways, even estimated prior to underground explorations, and described in terms of concentrations of desired materials, presence of other chemicals, and the like. Or forests can be measured in terms of volume and grade of various tree species, and evaluated in terms of costs of getting out the logs, of sawmill outturn, and the like.

All of these, and associated attributes of these resources are still important, at least under many circumstances. But we are learning that many other attributes of nature may be highly valuable also. Since World War II, for instance, the importance of an amenity climate in which people like to live, and hence a place where skilled workers are likely to be attracted, has become a major natural resource for Florida and the Southwest generally. The capacity of an airshed to absorb gaseous wastes, and to carry them off, has become a major natural resource for many cities. Resources long known, such as uranium, may suddenly acquire a wholly new meaning. Or combinations of forest and water bodies, long known and somehow appreciated, may acquire new importance as recreation resources. Water temperature, not of enough importance to warrant measurement in one era and under one set of conditions, may become critical as one evaluates an area for potential outdoor swimming, for instance. I think that literally any quality or characteristic of nature may become a natural resource, in the human use sense of the term, under some conditions.

B. Technology

The second part in my definition of natural resources is technology, or the ability to use what we know exists. Until we do know how to use some quality of nature, it is really not a natural resource. Petroleum was not a natural resource to the Plains Indians in 1800; they did not suspect its occurrence in the earth, would have had no means of extracting it if they had known about it, and would not have known what to do with large supplies of it if they had somehow extracted them. Neither, might it be added, was this same petroleum a natural resource to the first white trappers and fur traders in the same area--their knowledge was no better than that of the Indians.

This type of example can be multiplied many times. There are many examples in the case of soils, which you know better than I--soils too heavy to be worked with sources of power and implements then available, or soils lacking in some essential, though perhaps minor, chemical element, and many others. A forest species valueless at one period acquires value when we learn how to work its wood; oil shale and tar sands become valuable minerals when we learn how to extract the oil from them. When we learn how to make penicillin, and learn how valuable it is for many purposes, the mold which produces it quickly is recognized as a valuable part of nature, when earlier it had been unknown. I shall not try to list or catalogue examples of the influence of new technology on resource availability; I have not the knowledge to do so, and my point is valid without more examples to illustrate it.

Technology and modern science have been particularly valuable to the economically advanced countries. They have had the economic resources to invest in research and their research has generally, and naturally, been directed toward the solution of their problems. And they have had the capital and the managerial competence to utilize their research results productively. Science and technology have been less helpful, or only dubiously helpful thus far, for the economically less advanced countries. The latter have not been able to conduct much research of their own, imported research is often only partially applicable, and they have been unable fully to exploit such research as there was. Indeed, Gunnar Myrdal (1957) goes so far as to assert that science and technology have worsened the position of the economically less advanced countries; their raw materials are less valuable in international trade simply because science and technology have developed substitutes for them--artificial rubber for natural rubber, plastics for metals, etc.

But, even within a generally economically advanced country such as the United States, technology has greatly shifted the importance of different qualities of nature and of the regions in which each is dominant. Because of thin soils, steep slopes, small fields, and related characteristics the hill and mountain lands from the Appalachians westward are vastly less valuable today because of technology which has shown us how to get more output from the deeper, more nearly level, larger fields in the lowlands and plains; or the value of some sandy soils that respond to fertilizers has risen, while that of other soils has fallen because they lacked this response.

C. Economics

Knowing that an attribute or quality of nature exists, and knowing how to make something from it that we want, are not enough in themselves. In addition, the question must always be raised: are the results worth the costs? A great many things can be done which are too costly to be sensible. During one of the gold crises of the last few years, for instance, someone calculated that gold could indeed be made by atomic conversions of lesser metals but that the gold so obtained would cost millions (or billions) of dollars per ounce. Much closer to home, figuratively and geographically for us here today, and much closer to economic practicability: there exist in this country many millions of acres of land which could be farmed, were our need for agricultural commodities great enough and were we willing to accept the low real returns

that would be involved. Indeed, much land inherently no more productive is farmed in other parts of the world.

There are always vast mineral deposits below a profitably recov-
erable level; there are extensive forest areas in the world, and even in
the United States, where the costs of getting the forest products out,
and processed, are greater than the value of the product; there are
sources of water which are too costly to utilize profitably; and so on.
There has been a lot of publicity about various schemes for moving
really large volumes of water from Alaska, or northern Canada, or the
Pacific Northwest, to the Southwest of the United States and even into
Mexico; likewise, there have been various proposals for large scale
desalting of sea water as a basis for commercial agriculture. In each
case, a physical material exists and is reasonably well known; the technological process exists and is reasonably well known. But, also in each
case, the costs are yet wholly out of line with the results. Or, to take
still a different kind of example: alcohol can be made out of wheat
[Triticum (aestivum L.) sp.] or other grain, and used to power automo-
biles, thus relieving the need for some petroleum; but the costs are
completely out of line. One does not hear much about this latter example these days, but it was actively discussed some years ago.

To an economist, these questions of value in relation to cost are
fundamental. For those commodities traded freely in open markets,
the discipline of the market is usually sufficient to sort out the poor
from the good possibilities. But natural resources are marked by a
considerable degree of public action or of public control over private
action; for example, water laws limit or govern water developments.
Although elaborate procedures have been built up in some fields of government action, to apply tests of economic rationality, one must agree
that these have been somewhat less than perfect in operation. There
are many instances in which economic tests have not been applied, and
perhaps cannot be so applied. We have not yet evaluated the quality of
natural resources very well, nor have we learned very well how to take
into account those actions which damage or benefit third parties. And
many resource outputs are common goods, available to everyone and
hence not easily priced and subject to the discipline of the market.

In spite of all the problems, economists as a professional group,
have, I believe, exhibited considerable ability in measuring the worth
of resource programs that are not subjected to market evaluations.
Indeed, their ability to do so, and the results of their analyses which
demonstrate the impracticability of many resource development proposals, have led many economists into situations of tension and criti-
cism.

D. Goals

The fourth part of my definition of natural resources is concerned
with goals, or with the purposes for which we seek to use resources.
Economists have generally assumed that maximization of income was
the goal; we have developed many tools for measuring income maxi-

mization. Generally speaking, all other factors being equal, every individual and every group does indeed prefer more to less--more money income to less, more goods and services to less, more education to less, better housing to poorer, and the like. Although at one time it was sometimes argued that people in lower income groups within this country or in other societies really did not care to maximize their incomes, this idea has been pretty well exploded by now. As T. W. Schultz (1964) has said about illiterate farmers in less developed countries: they may not be able to read, but they can count, and they do prefer more to less. Thus, income maximization as one goal of natural resource use is valid and powerful, and likely to remain so.

The difficulty comes when we assume that income maximization is the only goal of natural resource use. One may value leisure more than income. Can anyone seriously argue that trout fishing is engaged in, as a means of maximizing income? In some societies, cattle are valued as wealth and status symbols, or are clothed with religious values; they are not raised or kept for income maximization. Can any of you seriously argue that your professional activities are dominated by income-maximization calculations? I presume you prefer a large salary to a small one, but I am also sure that other criteria are often more important than salary. In pursuing a research project, do you carry your research to that precise point where marginal value product exactly equals marginal cost, and no further? I have long argued that my economist friends are poor practitioners of their own methods of analysis, when it comes to their own activities.

It may be argued that the individual who has goals other than maximum economic income does maximize something--social status, personal satisfactions, opinion of his peers or contemporaries, or others. Some ingenious economic analyses have been applied to such problems, and I have contended on other occasions that one can place an economic value on any good or service to which people respond in reasonably predictable fashion (and not necessarily in rational fashion, by your standards and mine). While I think that economic analysis can often be carried much further than it has been, I also think we must never lose sight of the matter of goals or ends, in our resource use, and we must recognize that others may have goals very different from our own.

Perhaps I can illustrate with a couple of current examples. In the last few years, we have heard much about natural beauty, and many people have wakened to the fact that we have often needlessly destroyed much that was beautiful in our environment. I judge that in the future we shall give much more attention to natural beauty than we have in the past. It may be argued this is sound economics--I think it probably is; or it may be argued that a value can be placed on the beauty so preserved or enhanced--I think probably it can be. But the real motivation is not income enhancement, but rather our standards of personal and social behavior, and our goals as to what we should seek from our environment. Or, to take a different illustration, for the past 20 years the world has seen a rather large scale effort by the higher income countries to help the lower income ones develop their economies. It may be argued that this is good business for the richer countries--and

I think it is; but the major motivation arises from other sources, primarily our moral concern with fellowman.

Perhaps you will not agree with me, but I find this fourfold definition of natural resources a useful one to guide me in my research and in my writing about natural resources. I find the definition useful, as a means of putting many facts and ideas into some kind of order or system. I find it particularly helpful in avoiding consideration of some aspects of natural resources to the exclusion of other equally important aspects.

III. NATURAL RESOURCES AND THEIR USE AS SYSTEMS

"System" and "systems analysis" are the "in" terms of our generation; one must talk in such terms, if one is to be up-to-date or pretends to be, and if one is to hold his place in professional circles. While there has been some nonsense spoken and written in the name of systems and systems analysis, yet in fact these are highly useful terms and concepts, and are directly applicable to natural resources.

At its best, the concept of a system provides a means of describing many interrelated factors, and of putting each into some sort of perspective; at its best, systems analysis provides powerful analytical concepts for dealing with these problems of interrelationship. It is now possible to trace or describe an event or a process as part of a larger sequence, to put it in a larger frame of current events and processes, and to trace its consequences further and more accurately. Systems analysis almost requires quantitative measurement and quantitative expression; it is not enough merely to trace sequences, but measurement or approximations as to quantities involved is almost an essential part.

Systems analysis has gotten a tremendous boost from the development of electronic data processing equipment. A relationship may have been known earlier, or at least suspected, but calculations about it were so slow as to be meaningless in solution of any real problems. Computers have changed all this. The computer may be nothing more than a fancy adding machine, but it operates at speeds differing by many orders of magnitude; complex formulae, with many variables, can be applied almost instantly to a large range of data. Moreover, computer formulations can provide explicitly for feedback, and for simultaneous adjustments of several variables, one to another, and for decisions based upon several variables interacting simultaneously.

At the same time, no natural resource system is ever final or complete; each necessarily rests upon antecedent events and processes, each (no matter how comprehensive it may be) operates within a broader framework, and each leaves its consequences for later events and processes. One can consider a system of great complexity. Some of my friends have described to me their system models of salmon fishing for instance, with formulae including hundreds of terms or variables, that they can project ahead for scores of years under alternative assumptions, as to key variables. Nevertheless, no system, however complex, can include literally all variables and all processes--nor even

all that we know, or think we know about, much less those about which
we do not know or suspect.

It is generally recognized that no system analysis can be any
stronger than the data and the formulae fed into it. The computer only
follows instructions, although these may be quite complex. If we have
to guess as to some relationship or as to some fact, then the final result is affected to some degree by that guess. If we keep this clearly
in mind, efforts to apply systems analysis to specific problems may
help us develop better understanding and better data, and this may be
a real accomplishment.

We used to describe relationships in natural resources as competitive, complementary, symbiotic, parasitic, etc. These are still
useful terms and ideas, I think. But each can now be given mathematical expression and quantitative content, in a system approach. At one
extreme, every increase in one variable may be accompanied by a proportionate decrease in another; at the opposite extreme, every increase
in one may be accompanied by a proportionate increase in the second;
and all sorts of more complicated intermediate relationships exist.
In one sense, every natural resource process is a "zero sum" game,
in the language of the systems' analysts, since all matter and all energy
are merely transformed, not created nor lost in any absolute sense. In
more human terms, many natural resource processes are far from zero
sum games, since the gains far exceed the costs and the losses. A crop
of wheat is merely transformed energy and transformed chemicals,
based upon sunlight, soil nutrients, gases from the air, and water; but
the wheat is directly useful for human welfare, while the chemicals and
the energy were not. But natural resource processes are not invariably
gains; it is wholly conceivable that man is worse off as a result of some
resource program. Even more commonly, some men are better off, while
others are worse off.

A systems approach may be applied to each of the four parts of our
definition of natural resources. You know far better than I how various
attributes of nature form a system--how chemicals in the soil, micro-
biology of the soil, water, and other elements interact; or how the various kinds of vegetation within a forest interact; or how vegetation, soil,
water, and human actions may interact to accelerate soil erosion; and
many others. One kind of technology often interacts with another; a
process may depend upon new metallurgy, or a gain in one field may
stimulate development in another; economic demands often provide the
incentive to technology, or lead to new appraisals of resource characteristics, or these in turn open up new economic possibilities; changing
goals and ideals may lead to new resources demands and uses; and so
on, the various attributes of natural resources reacting with each other
in complex systems.

Every natural resource system use or analysis requires management, or conscious decision making, at various stages. The computer
must be programmed; the crop will not grow without decisions at various stages. Though one process or event flows from others, and in turn
leads to others, yet the sequences are not invariable nor wholly automatic. Choices not only can be made--they must be made at various
intervals, and usually they cannot be avoided. Management, as a con-

scious human activity, can and must enter. It is true that "natural" processes would proceed, were man to vanish from the earth; but natural resource processes from which man hopes to benefit must have his participation. Here is where his understanding of the qualities of nature, his technology, his economics, his goals enter into the whole process; within very wide limits, he can guide the natural processes to his own ends. He is constrained by the past, and his current actions will in turn constrain his descendants, but choices are both possible and necessary.

IV. SOME EXAMPLES

This discussion of systems analysis for natural resource problems may be illustrated by a brief description of a few examples. Those which follow may not be the most important or best examples, but they are illustrative, and they have the merit (for me) of being cases about which I am at least moderately informed.

A. Water Quality

The hydrologic cycle, as noted previously, is a natural resource system long recognized as such. Water moves in the air, on the surface of the land, and within the soil and subsoil, in a complex cycle whose exact nature varies from place to place. Man can intervene in the cycle at various points--perhaps by weather modification, surely in affecting speed and relative volume of runoff, obviously in storage behind dams or in pumping from ground water, and in other ways. Until rather recently, the primary emphasis has been upon quantities of water at various stages in the hydrologic cycle, and upon how man might influence those quantities.

But water quality is also readily subject to systems analysis, as my colleagues Kneese and Bower (1968) have shown. Wastes are of many kinds, as we have noted; all life involves wastes, which must be disposed of or removed in some way. Water, particularly running water, is often a prime vehicle for waste disposal. Some persons, firms, or groups gain by use of a given water body for waste disposal by having their wastes carried away. But other persons, firms, or groups may lose as a result of these actions if they had counted on use of this water in a relatively unpolluted condition.

How may the gains be maximized and the losses minimized? A host of possibilities exist, at least in some circumstances. Sometimes the production (or consumption) processes which produced the wastes may be modified to produce less; sometimes the waste materials may be recovered and used productively. Waste discharges may be reduced by various forms of treatment, or may be timed to utilize flood or other peak stream flows. Or water supply conditions may be altered, to provide greater flows at otherwise low flow periods. The water polluters may be given financial incentive to take one or more of these actions; incentives in the form of pollution charges geared to the amount and kind of pollutants discharged to the streams. Or the polluters may be restrained from discharging wastes into water bodies by water quality standards, laws, regulations, and other public sanctions.

In this example, all four aspects of my definition of natural resources are involved. The qualities of nature include the chemical, physical, and biologic nature of the wastes; the speed with which they decay or decompose into simpler compounds; the amount of water into which the wastes are discharged; its assimilative capacity; and others. The technology of waste reduction, waste treatment, recycling of water, and others are part of the technologic aspect of the definition. Costs are involved at each stage and for each alternative; and values of the results are a critical aspect of each aspect. But so are goals. How much do we really value relatively pure water? How offensive do we find large scale pollution? More specifically, do we want our lakes and rivers clean enough for swimming, or are we content to purify enough water for a swimming pool? Are we prepared to undertake some costs, or to impose some controls, where the calculated benefits might not be worth the cost?

Kneese and Bower (1968) have set up models to show the interaction of these and other variables. The specific parameters, and to a lesser extent the formula itself, will depend upon the particular stream or water body. The model may be relatively simple or relatively complex; even the latter may not be fully adequate to deal with every situation which may arise. The model can be operated to show the effect of alternative assumptions or alternative programs.

B. Large Scale Desalting of Sea Water for Commercial Agriculture

The possibility of large scale desalting of sea water, to provide fresh water for large scale irrigation, in the Middle East or elsewhere, has attracted much attention in recent years. General Eisenhower (1968), relying heavily upon Admiral Strauss, has publicized the idea. Kaiser Engineers have made a report, applying specifically to Israel. (Kaiser Engineers and Catalytic Construction Co., January 1966. Engineering Feasibility and Economic Study for Dual-Purpose Electric Power-Desalting Plant for Israel.) The Oak Ridge Laboratory of the Atomic Energy Commission (July 1968) has made a more general proposal that might be undertaken in one or more of several locations, and which includes a large electro-chemical complex. A systems approach might well be used in evaluating each of these.

Any scheme for large scale irrigation from desalted sea water necessarily involves three separate but closely integrated phases: (i) a source of energy, (ii) a method of obtaining pure water from sea water, and (iii) a program for transferring water from the place and time schedules of desalting to the place and time schedule of application to the land. Although more than one method of obtaining pure water from sea water exists, most attention has focused on flash distillation processes; it may reasonably be assumed that no other process is more efficient (lower cost). Most attention has focused on nuclear power as a source of energy, but any source of energy would do. In the Middle East,

where vast quantities of natural gas are flared and where oil at the well-
head is cheap, non-nuclear sources of energy might well be much
cheaper. Nuclear power, in practical operation, has not yet turned out
to be the economical source of power that 5 years ago it was expected
to be. (W. E. Hoehn, 1967. The economics of nuclear reactors for
power and desalting, The RAND Corp., Santa Monica, Calif., 1967;
Philip Sporn, annual comments to Joint Committee on Nuclear Energy.)
Nuclear power plants exhibit major economies of scale; lowest cost
power is achievable only by a size of plant that produces more electricity than most countries can absorb (Landsberg, 1968). Partly as a
means of utilizing a large part of this energy, the Oak Ridge proposal
has included a large electrochemical complex.

The most neglected aspect of the whole process has been transfer-
ence of the desalted water from place and time of desalting, to the
place and time of use in the field for crop production. The desalting
will take place at the margin of the sea; the land to which the water
might be applied will lie inland and often at higher elevations. In Israel,
for example, some of the best land to which such water may be applied
is 152 m (500 feet) or more above sea level. Experience in the USA
with irrigation clearly shows that pumping and distribution of water is
far from costless. Much more serious than the place discrepancy,
however, is the time discrepancy. Both the Kaiser and Oak Ridge proposals for nuclear power flash distillation of sea water provide for
continuous operation, around the clock, for nearly 11 months annually--
1 month or more (in one uninterrupted period) shutdown is required for
servicing. You know, better than I, that farmers will not require irrigation water on this time schedule. It must be stored in surface reservoirs, in the topsoil, or in the subsoil; in each place, substantial losses
will occur as well as costs incurred, and thus the cost per unit of us-
able water will be increased.

My earlier definition of natural resources is applicable to this
idea. The relevant qualities of nature are known or can be measured:
the chemical composition of sea water is known; so is the nature of
nuclear reaction and the energy so released; the location and character
of soils can be mapped and studied for a particular project; water consumption by cultivated crops can be estimated; and so on. The relevant
technologies are fairly well known. Large scale desalting processes
may encounter serious problems of sea water intake and of discharge
of the hot bitter brines (Foster and Herlihy, 1965). The Oak Ridge proposal includes farm production technologies that have not yet proven
feasible in comparable situations elsewhere, and much of the estimated
economic feasibility of their proposal rests on such agricultural technologies.

Economics is likely to be the foundering rock for large scale desalting proposals. Atomic power is not yet "cheap"; at the best, it is
competitive with fossil fuel. How might the vast amounts of energy,
from a large scale nuclear plant, be utilized economically in countries
with relatively small present consumption of electricity and without
extensive inter-ties to other electrical systems? The costs of distillation are high; and, although the process requires a lot of energy, a large
part of the cost is not for energy. Even were energy free (and "low

cost power" can hardly get below zero), the distilled water would still be expensive. The costs of water transport and storage are likely to be high, and the value of the water for large scale commercial agriculture will be moderate if not low. The scale of the proposed projects precludes use of more than a small fraction of the water to produce flowers, out-of-season vegetables, and other specialty products. For the next 20 years, the cost of the water at the field will be one whole order of magnitude greater than its value there. (This statement draws heavily on an as-yet-unpublished article by Marion Clawson, Hans H. Landsberg, and Lyle T. Alexander.)

But the fourth aspect of our definition--the goals or ends sought-- must also be introduced here. The Oak Ridge proposal, for instance, includes a vast agro-chemical complex, a sort of enclave located within a country but not really part of it. Some proponents of this proposal have made much of this "separateness" aspect; only by setting up such an area, they argue, can the institutional, cultural, and governmental inertias that preclude modern intensive agriculture in many countries be overcome. But what lower income country wants a new, large, primarily foreign enclave, no matter how advanced technologically it may be? Many such countries had foreign plantation agriculture before the war, and few would care to introduce or re-introduce new "plantations."

The sea water desalting problem lends itself well to systems analysis. Formulae, necessarily complex and with many terms, could be devices; numerous alternatives as to size of plant, methods of operation, disposition of surplus power, transfer and storage of water, water application, cropping systems, and others could be tested, with all the feedbacks, interactions, and relationships that one could perceive. But, in this case as in all others, the results would be no better than the data and the conversion factors fed into the system analysis. Dependable results require honest and accurate components.

C. A New Crop Variety

At the risk of exposing my lack of knowledge, let me conclude with an example directly in your field of activity--the development and introduction of a new variety of some commercial crop. Let us assume that an agricultural research organization has developed, and tested in its research station, a new variety of some crop, which promises much higher yields. How can my definition of natural resources, and how can systems analysis, apply here?

First of all, the qualities of nature--in this case, the new variety-- should be studied carefully. Just what are the genetic, nutritional, growth, flowering, seed producing, reproductive, and other characteristics of this variety? How responsive is it to, or how independent of, climatic variables such as length of day, temperatures, humidity, wind, and the like? What is its comparative performance on different kinds of soil? How responsive is it to fertilizer? How vulnerable is it to plant diseases or to insects? What special cultural practices are required for successful growth of this variety?

The technological aspects of use of this crop variety would also have to be studied. Into what natural environment would its production best fit? Into what kind of a farming system would it most readily be introduced and utilized? Where, and how, would its production be more marginal, and where would it be quite unsuited? What other productive inputs (fertilizer, irrigation water, etc.) would be required? By what production processes could this new variety best be grown?

The economics of use of the new variety should also be studied. Would it pay farmers to grow it, given the costs of inputs and the value of the crop? Would special incentives be needed, to persuade farmers to grow it? Would its extensive adoption increase total production so much that price would fall? If so, would it still be profitable? For some small countries, might the new variety shift the country from a net import base to a net export base, with a consequent sharp drop in price? Might there be a conflict between farmers' interests in higher prices for a modest volume, and national interest in lower prices for a much larger volume?

The goals or objectives aspects of natural resources could not be overlooked. Presumably a new variety of a familiar crop would not encounter the cultural resistances that a wholly new crop might encounter. But a new wheat might have different baking qualities, or a new rice different cooking characteristics, that might encounter some resistance. Presumably, more output would be valued more than a lesser output, all other factors equal.

All of this could be treated in a system analysis; no particularly new or novel problems seem involved. A model could be constructed, appropriate data fed into it, alternative programs tested, and so on.

LITERATURE CITED

Eisenhower, Dwight D., 1968. A proposal for our time. Reader's Digest. 92(6): 75-79.
Foster, Albert C., and Joseph P. Herlihy. 1965. Operating experience at San Diego flash distillation plant. In Proc. First Int. Symp. on Water Desalination. US Government Printing Office, Washington, D.C.
Kneese, Allen V., and Blair T. Bower. 1968. Managing water quality: Economics, technology, institutions. Johns Hopkins Press, Baltimore.
Landsberg, Hans H. 1968. Population growth and the potential of technology. In World population--The view ahead. Bureau of Business Research, Graduate School of Business, Indiana University, Bloomington.
Myrdal, Gunnar. 1957. Rich lands and poor. Harper & Brothers, New York.
Oak Ridge National Laboratory. July 1968. Nuclear energy centers industrial and agro-industrial complexes--summary report. ORNL-4291, UC-80-Reactor Technology. Oak Ridge, Tenn.
Schultz, Theodore W., 1964. Transforming traditional agriculture. Yale University Press, New Haven, Conn.

2

Engineering for Higher Yields

YOSHIAKI ISHIZUKA

Hokkaido University
Sapporo, Japan

I. INTRODUCTION

It was difficult for me to understand the meaning of "engineering" as used in the title of my speech. I asked Dr. Haskins who told me that the term engineering is used here because one traditional role of the engineer has been the application of scientific principles in the solution of practical problems, and that in this case we want to consider the application of biological principles in both past and future increases in crop yield. Accordingly, I intend to express my thoughts on this problem, and to ask your suggestions for obtaining higher and better yields in the future. As I belong to an Asian nation, where rice is the main food, I will use the rice plant (Oryza sativa L.) as an example to illustrate my ideas. However, I am convinced that the principles which can be applied to the rice plant, will also apply to other crops such as wheat [Triticum (aestivum L.) sp.] or corn (Zea mays L.).

II. CHANGES IN RICE YIELD FROM 1000 A.D.

The yield of brown rice in 900 A.D. was approximately 1 ton/ha (Table 2-1) and in 1885, the year of the Meiji Revolution, which was the dawn of modern Japan, the yield was about 2 tons/ha. Thus, it took about 1,000 years (from 900 A.D. to 1885) to double the yield, while it took less than 100 years, from 1885 up to the present time to redouble the yield. The main reason for the relatively rapid improvement in rice yield since the turn of the century (Fig. 2-1) is the intelligent integration of the following factors:

1) New varieties developed by scientific and systematic breeding.
2) Progress of cultivation techniques.
3) Use of chemical fertilizers, especially nitrogen.
4) Use of fungicides, insecticides and herbicides.
5) Improvement of soils.

Use of these production techniques may seem only common sense to

15

Table 2-1—Change of rice yield (metric tons) in Japan since 800 A.D.

Chronicle	Acreage of rice fields, million ha	Total yield, million tons	Yield, tons/ha	Remarks
800-900	105	106	1.01	
1550	105-120	180	1.65	
1720	164	315	1.92	Systematic introduction of irrigation systems
1840	156	300	1.92	
1878-1887	258	477	1.85	
1908-1917	300	794	2.64	Scientific varietal improvement (breeding)
1938-1942	318	953	2.99	Beginning of use of chemical fertilizers
1956-1965	313	1,238	3.95	Heavy use of nitrogen integrated techniques including fungicides, herbicides, etc.

agronomists, but it is useful to keep the indicated factors in mind because they are fundamental toward obtaining higher crop yields.

III. A BLUEPRINT TO OBTAIN 6 TONS/HA OF BROWN RICE

Though the same variety and enough fertilizers are used, there still exists a great difference in rice yield among farms—even in the same region. If, within a region, the lower yields could be brought up to the levels obtained by good farmers, the yield of the region obviously would be increased. To this end, agronomists have begun to prepare a

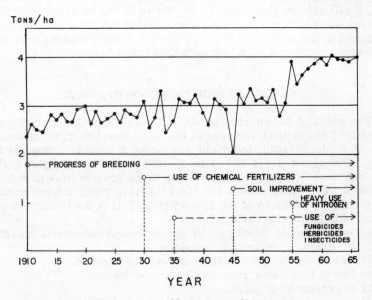

Fig. 2-1—Rice yields in Japan, 1910-1940.

Table 2-2—Yield (metric tons) of grains in some countries 1956-1958 (FAO).

Country	Yield of grain, tons/ha	Fertilizer use, kg/ha
Taiwan	2.857	163.4
Switzerland	2.895	169.2
Belgium	3.229	337.1
Netherlands	3.314	438.6
Denmark	3.462	130.0
Japan	3.633	257.4

Table 2-3—Yield (metric tons) of brown rice in some agricultural experiment stations in Japan.

Location	Latitude north	Annual mean temperature, °C	Yield brown rice tona/ha	Year
Hokkaido	43.03	7.7	7.79	1967
Tohoku	39.27	11.4	7.55	1958
Hokuriku	37.06	12.5	7.45	1962
Konosu	36.35	15.7	8.07	1959
Chugoku	34.51	15.9	7.81	1959
Shikoku	34.15	15.2	8.15	1959
Kyushu	33.12	15.7	7.62	1960

blueprint on how average farmers under normal conditions can obtain a definite yield per hectare. What figure shall we take for yield, 3 tons/ha, 5 tons/ha or 6 tons/ha? Average yields of grain of some countries are shown in Table 2-2. Based on these data, a yield of 6 tons/ha is almost twice the average grain yield in certain developed countries with intensive agriculture.

Yields of brown rice at various Agricultural Experiment Stations in Japan (Table 2-3) are considerably better than the country-wide grain yields shown in Table 2-2. These yields (7.45 to 8.15 tons/ha) are such that a goal of 6 tons/ha seems to be reasonable.

The yield of brown rice from 10 ares (1,000 m²) can be expressed theoretically by the following equation:

Yield (of brown rice) = No. of spikelets per m² (No. of ear/m² × No. of spikelets/ear) × percentage of spikelets bearing a ripe grain × average weight per grain (based on 1,000 grains) × 1,000.

For example, the following combination of yield components would result in a yield of 600 kg/10 ares (6 tons/ha):

600 kg/10 ares = 32,000 spikelets/m² (400 ears/m² × 80 spikelets/ear) × 0.85 (fraction of spikelets with a mature seed) × 0.022g (22g/1,000 grains) × 1,000.

It would seem that this blueprint would not be too difficult to follow. The number of spikelets on one ear and the weight of 1,000 grains is

Table 2-4—Analysis of the yield of rice in northern Japan.

Location	Name of variety	No. of plants/m²	No. of ears/m²	Percentage of effective tillers	Yield, tons/ha
Hoddaido	Yukara	21.8	545	66.0	7.79
Tohoku	Norin-17 ($\frac{A.E.S.}{No-17}$)	30.3	436	91.2	7.55
Hokuriku	Manryo	22.7	529	75.4	7.45

attributed to the variety. There are many varieties presently available that fulfill the condition of having at least 80 grains/ear and a 1,000 grain weight of 22 g. If we want to harvest 600 kg/10 ares from such varieties, it is necessary to have 400 ears/m², with 85% of the spikelets having mature seeds. In a good year, it is not very difficult to have 90% matured grains. However, in the case of a poor year (less sunshine and a cool summer), this declines to 80%. Therefore, 85% is a rather reasonable figure to put into the equation. The 400 ears/m² might be achieved by using a plant spacing of 20 by 20 cm. With the resulting density of 25 plants/m², each plant would need an average of 16 effective tillers to produce 400 ears/m². This is not difficult to achieve, as shown by actual data (Table 2-4) obtained in the northern part of Japan where cultivation of the rice plant is supposed to be the most difficult in the nation.

In summary, then, to obtain 6 tons/ha, we need
   1) 25 plants/m²,
   2) 16 effective tillers/plant,
   3) 80 spikelets/ear,
   4) 85% of spikelets with mature grain, and
   5) 0.022 g/seed.

When weather conditions are not extremely poor, the above blueprint can be implemented using the ordinary varieties which are widely cultivated in Japan. The application of fertilizer, however, requires some skillfulness. I wish to come back to the matter of fertilizer application a little later, and it will be discussed in greater detail by Drs. Murata and Chandler in subsequent papers.

IV. ENGINEERING FOR HIGHER YIELDS

How can the barriers against yields higher than 6 tons/ha be broken? I shall discuss this question from several points of view.

A. Plant Type

When the nutrient supply is the limiting factor for crop growth, the problem of plant type will not occur in connection with the efficiency of utilization of solar energy. However, when the supply of fertilizers is sufficient, and the price of fertilizers is low compared with the price

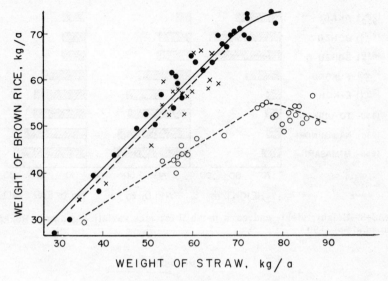

Fig. 2-2—Yields of brown rice and straw.

of crops, the concept of diminishing returns is encountered with respect to the value of added increments of fertilizer. Thus, in the case of the rice plant, the phenomenon shown in Fig. 2-2 is generally observed. Of course, it is an illusion to say that fertilizer itself will produce crops, and that crop yield depends solely on the amount of fertilizers supplied. Fertilizers are only lubricants to promote the formation of −C−C− chains.

Fundamentally, the ability to accept and transform solar energy controls the yield. Recently, this concept has prevailed among plant physiologists, and many outstanding reports have been published in Harvesting the Sun—Photosynthesis in Plant Life (A. San Pietro, F. A. Greer, and T. J. Army, 1967. Academic Press, Inc., New York), and also in the reports of the International Rice Research Institute. Accordingly, it is not necessary to dwell extensively on this problem; it will be enough to present some examples of the change in plant type in rice.

As shown in Fig. 2-3, the plant type of leading varieties propagated in Kokkaido, the northern limit area of rice cultivation in Japan, has changed considerably since 1890. The improved yields obtained since 1935 are associated with decreased plant height and increased numbers of effective tillers. The newer varieties respond more dramatically to nitrogen fertilizer than do the early varieties (Fig. 2-4).

For any variety, decisions on the density of plant population which will produce higher yields must be considered from the standpoint of leaf arrangement and Leaf Area Index (LAI). It may be supposed that an optumum LAI will produce a maximum yield.

The number of leaves on the main stem is rather fixed. For instance, in the rice plant, the number of leaves on the main stem is 13-

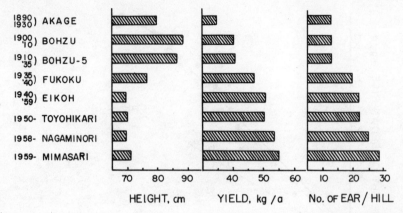

Fig. 2-3—Height, yield, and ears per hill for rice varieties grown in Hokkaido, Japan since 1890.

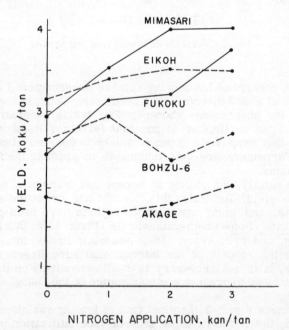

Fig. 2-4—Yield response of several rice varieties to nitrogen fetilization.

16 in Japan. Accordingly, when a rice plant population is fixed, the LAI will be governed to a great extent by the number of tillers. Therefore, "How to get an optimum LAI" becomes synonymous with "How to regulate the tillering number and position of tillers." Characteristics of tillering are varietal attributes. Theoretically, however, it is not difficult to imagine that the control of tillering may at some future time be possible through the use of agricultural chemicals.

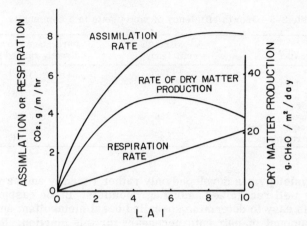

Fig. 2-5—Relationship of carbon assimilation, respiration, and dry matter production to LAI.

B. Translocation and Respiration

The second point is translocation and respiration. The latitude of Hokkaido University is about $43^\circ N$, about the same as that of New York. Rice plants suffer some damage about once every 3 years, due to a cool summer. At such times, the total weight of straw is not much different from that obtained during an ordinary good year. The difference is in the weight of ear. Apparently the translocation of assimilates is retarded by the cool temperatures, though the reduced yield is partly due to lack of fertile pollen caused by damage during formation of the pollen mother cells.

To promote translocation, a supply of energy is needed. To provide or to create energy for translocation, respiration is indispensable. At the same time, it is generally recognized that the weight of crops is the algebraic sum of the assimilates produced by photosynthesis and lost by respiration. Thus, yield = photosynehtsis - respiration (Fig. 2-5).

A simple way to obtain higher yields, it seems, is to make respiration as low as possible. Reducing respiration to a minimum would seem especially important in tropical climates where night temperatures are comparatively high and the loss of assimilates is much higher than in temperature regions where the yield of rice is comparatively high.

Several questions must be asked concerning respiration.
1) Is respiration always a negative factor in obtaining a higher yield?
2) Is a certain type of respiration indispensable for the growth of crops?
3) If the answer to question 1 is "yes," what kind of respiration has no significance for the growth of plants, how can we separate the respiration types, and how can the wasteful part of respiration be minimized?

Unfortunately, research on translocation and respiration in the field

Table 2-5—Growth efficiency of rice plants in a community.

Stage of growth	Growth efficiency, %	Percentage of respiration directly related to growth
Early stage	(60)	(100)
From booting stage to flowering	41	68
From flowering to milky stage	36	60
From milky stage to complete ripening	27	44

of plant physiology has developed only rather recently and as yet much of it is not well recognized among agronomists. In the case of animal feeding, it is easy to determine so-called basal metabolism and to calculate the amount of nutrients necessary for this function. If we want to have a definite amount of milk, for instance, we can supply the nutrients which are necessary to have that amount of milk in addition to the requirements for basal metabolism. In the case of rice plants, when the growth of a new leaf is completed, we may assume that the respiration of that leaf corresponds to basal metabolism. This value is found to be about 40% as great as respiration during the period when the leaf was under vigorous growth (or assimilation). Thus, we may conclude that respiration for growth is 60% of the total respiration of a rapidly growing leaf. If the growth efficiency at this stage is 60%, 40% of the energy consumed by respiration is for basal metabolism and 60% of that is the energy for assimilation of new materials.

This calculation is quite rough, and it will have to be subjected to more precise research in the future. Such calculations have been used by Dr. Tanaka, for example, in comparing growth efficiency and respiration at various stages of growth of the rice plant (Table 2-5). The data plainly show that the growth efficiency, in other words the percentage of respiration directly related to growth, decreases with the progress of growth. We can suggest many possible reasons for this and the effort to find the correct reasons will lead the way to obtaining higher yields.

C. Techniques of Fertilizer Application

Generally speaking, the yield of crops depends to a great extent upon the amount of fertilizer nitrogen supplied. As suggested by the data in Fig. 2-2, vegetative growth is considerably more responsive to nitrogen than is reproductive growth (grain yield). Accordingly, it is important to apply the nitrogen in such a way as to give maximum encouragement to reproductive growth.

The goal in nitrogen application is to apply adequate amounts to obtain (or to produce) a sufficient number of kernels as estimated previously (for instance, 30,000 kernels/m^2), and to reduce the nitrogen supply after obtaining this number in order to prevent the growth of ineffective new tillers. Later, then, appropriate amounts of nitrogen can be applied to keep the upper three leaves always active, and thus to promote the ripening of grain. However, it is not very easy to accomplish this in practice, because plant growth will be influenced by climate, and the buffer action of soils also will make it difficult to deliver the nitrogen to the crop in a way synchronized to promote a high yield. Further research on split applications of nitrogen fertilizer is needed.

D. Minor Elements

For a yield of 6 tons/ha, the problem of minor element deficiency is not serious, except in special cases such as sandy or calcareous soils. However, if we want to realize an even higher yield, this problem becomes more important. At this stage, the problem is not only the presence or absence of minor elements, but also their interaction. Because space is limited only one illustration, the interaction between zinc and manganese, will be given. As shown in Fig. 2-6, the deficiency of zinc becomes more serious when the supply of manganese increases and vice versa.

E. Soils

When we have a particular crop variety which has an ideal plant type, from the standpoint of utilization of solar energy, and when the supply of fertilizers is abundant, the factors which control crop growth will be some properties of the soil. If the soil is deficient in a property that is essential for crop growth, then the crop yield will be limited by that property. In such a case, the soil is of great significance in influencing crop yield. To achieve higher yields, it is necessary to use large amounts of fertilizer. Ideal varieties must be responsive to fertilizers; that is, they must be capable of absorbing large amounts of fertilizers and of using the absorbed fertilizer in producing increased amounts of grain. Unfortunately, heavy applications of fertilizer can lead to significant increases in the concentration of the soil solution, and this situation can result in decreased vigor of root growth, as shown in Fig. 2-7. In this instance root growth has been inhibited almost completely in areas adjacent to the site of urea application. To obtain higher yields, plant physiologists have begun to pay keen attention to the character of the leaf and stem. We also need to pay the same attention to the character of the root system, and soils must be evaluated with respect to their ability to support and encourage good root growth.

We might say that two categories of agriculture exist in the world; one is soil-dependent agriculture and the other is fertilizer-dependent agriculture. In the former case, the standard of soil evaluation is the natural supply of nutrients, that is the potentiality of soil to provide its own nutrients to crops. Here, the definition, "soil fertility," is quite clear.

However, in the case of fertilizer-dependent agriculture, the power of the soil to supply nutrients becomes a rather minor factor. Rather, the ability of soils to absorb fertilizers and deliver them to crops, or

Fig. 2-6—Interaction of zinc and manganese.

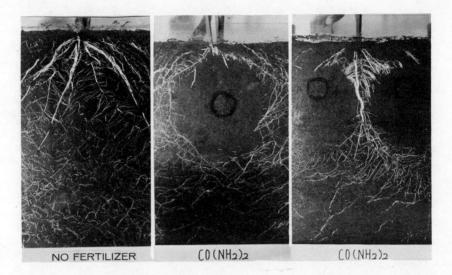

NO FERTILIZER $CO(NH_2)_2$ $CO(NH_2)_2$

Fig. 2-7—Influence of urea application on root growth. Sites of urea application are shown by the circles.

the exchange capacity as well as the exchange energy of soils, and their buffer action, all play important roles in the production of higher yields. Also, certain physical and biochemical soil properties promote vigorous growth of roots, and others retard root growth. These factors must be taken into consideration in soil evaluation.

Clearly, in the case of fertilizer-dependent agriculture, the concept of soil fertility must approach the concept of "soil productivity." The methods of soil evaluation, and the approaches commonly used in research on soils, must be re-examined.

V. CONCLUSIONS

Just as "Rome was not built in a day" a higher yield of crops also will not be obtained in a day or two. It requires integration of agricultural sciences, techniques, education and extension.

When crop yields are low, for instance 1 ton/hectare, it is not difficult to bring them up to 2 tons/ha. But, when the yield of crops is comparatively high, for instance 4-5 tons/ha, it will be quite difficult to make further rapid progress.

However, the record shows that progress can be achieved. The purpose of this paper is not to give a final solution, but to point out problems to be further considered. I would appreciate having these problems discussed, and I hope that such discussion will lead to further progress.

The sciences of crop physiology and plant nutrition are vital in improving the world's supply of food; thus, they play an important role in bringing peace to the world.

3

Productivity and the Morphology of Crop Stands: Patterns With Leaves

R. S. LOOMIS and W. A. WILLIAMS

University of California
Davis, California

The primary productivity of communities made up of autotrophic green plants is initially dependent upon photosynthesis. The patterns of chlorophyll display at each level of community organization reveal features which can be related to light interception and photosynthetic activity, and hence, to production. Studies on the comparative morphology of such displays should reveal principles useful for designing more efficient crops. It is important that we identify these principles since existing patterns are not necessarily the most efficient for intensive agriculture—a consequence of natural selection, even under a strong influence of man, having occurred principally in poverty environments and having emphasized many parameters of fitness in addition to primary productivity.

The most detailed information about chlorophyll patterns is perhaps available at the cytological level. The elements of the patterns at this level include the arrangement of pigment molecules into basic photosynthetic units, with apparatus for charge separation and for compartmentalization of products, reactants, and enzyme systems. It appears that the apparatus is basically similar for all species, at least among higher plants, although important differences in carbon pathway and chloroplast structure have been revealed for major ecological groups.

At a higher level, we know less about how patterns in leaf anatomy, including chloroplast localization within cells, relate to basic capability for assimilating CO_2. Light distribution within the leaf and resistances to gaseous fluxes are involved and these aspects vary with environment, as between sun and shade positions within a canopy (Björkman and Holmgren, 1963).

Our attention will be focused here on the patterns apparent at a yet higher level of organization—the assemblage of photosynthetic elements within plant communities. It appears legitimate to speak of a morphology at this level—indeed, also of the ontogeny and phylogeny of the pat-

27

terns. The impetus for research on such patterns comes from two sources. One is the increasing recognition by ecologists of the importance of primary production in the functioning of ecosystems. The second is from agriculturalists. As limitations related to pests, nutrients and water are alleviated, more attention to basic limitations on yield has been required, i.e., to the production capabilities of the plant communities. Although canopy architecture may affect productivity in various ways, our discussion will be directed principally towards its influence through light distribution.

I. COMMUNITY ORGANIZATION

A. Density of the Vegetative Cover

The most obvious feature of foliage canopies as related to production is the density of the foliage canopy. Ecologists have long made a practice of estimating percent cover and of relating this to production. Less than full cover permits solar radiation to escape interception by the photosynthetic apparatus. This is a problem of considerable importance with cultivated crops during early stages of growth. As examples, Shibles and Weber (1965, 1966) and Williams et al. (1965a) found that when cover is scant, production is directly related to the fraction of light intercepted. With annual crops, it usually takes a very long time for even a densely sown crop to achieve as much as 75% interception (Santhirasegaram and Black, 1968).

Chlorophyll and leaf area indices have both been used to characterize the amount of photosynthetic material in the cover. Aquatic ecologists (e.g., Steeman Nielsen, 1957; Talling, 1961) pioneered in the use of chlorophyll estimation to describe the community. The result was that depth distributions of chlorophyll, light, and production rate were found to be roughly related, but not well enough to estimate standing crop or metabolic density from chlorophyll indices (Goldman and Carter, 1965). Chlorophyll indices have been measured for a number of terrestrial communities (Brougham, 1960; Bray, 1960; Okubo et al., 1968), but correlations with production are generally poor.

For both aquatic and terrestrial systems, photosynthetic capability of the elements increase with chlorophyll concentration up to a saturation level (Gabrielsen, 1948). This level for leaves is about 3 mg chlorophyll $(a + b)$ dm^{-2} surface. At this level, changes in chlorophyll concentration strongly affect the extinction coefficient of the leaves, but the absolute amount of light absorbed is little affected (Kasanaga and Monsi, 1954). Most higher plant leaves contain at least the level of chlorophyll required for saturation of their CO_2 assimilating capacity, and the "excess" chlorophyll is not correlated with production. Further, the response of a leaf in assimilating CO_2 becomes a diminishing returns response with increasing light flux (Fig. 3-5, left). Thus, chlorophyll indices require, for quantitative purposes, the application of two curvilinear relations. When one considers that the distribution of chlorophyll of higher plant leaves is essentially in sheets whose surfaces (epidermis) are restrictive to CO_2 exchange, and whose lateral dimensions largely determine light interception, it becomes clear that area indices of leaves are a more functional basis for describing canopy morphology.

The use of leaf area as the description parameter was pioneered by English scientists who applied the techniques of "growth analysis" to agricultural communities. They were led to the concept of crop growth rate (C, net dry matter production) being equal to net assimilation rate of leaves (E, mean rate of net photosynthesis of all leaves) times the leaf area index (L, area of leaf per unit area of ground).

$$C = EL. \tag{1}$$

Considerable attention has been given to variations in E, but this is a dependent variable and is not particularly useful in community analysis except to consider its rate of decline with increasing L; its value is always small at the highest values of C. However, this approach also caused a focus on L as a parameter of community structure, and the leaf area index of Watson (1947) has become a basic description tool.

When C is related to total leaf density, L, two kinds of relationships have been found. In one, C increased as L increased up to some optimum value of L (L_{opt}), and then declined (Watson, 1958; Black, 1963). In the other cases, a plateau response has been found with C remaining constant as L increased (Brougham, 1956; Shibles and Weber, 1965; Williams et al. 1965b). The breaking point of such curves generally occurs at an L level sufficient to provide full cover. This level has been designated $L_{critical}$ or L_{95} (L required to intercept 95% of sunlight) by some workers. Watson and his associates have related seasonal yields to leaf area duration, D, the integral of L over time, but it appears to us that the integral of percent cover would be a better index.

B. Horizontal Patterns Among Leaves

Full cover could be provided by one continuous sheet of leaves. However, horizontal distributions are such that L = 3 or more is needed for complete interception of light. Leaf distributions may range from uniform (with regular or mosaic patterns), to random, and to contagious distributions (clumped or aggregated patterns). Greig-Smith (1964) summarizes a number of techniques for determining the type of pattern. The quadrant size and variance-mean ratio techniques are worthy of comment.

Contagious and regular patterns in foliage may be of several size scales. The individual plants, branches, leaves, and leaflets each serve as aggregation centers in contagious patterns. By varying the size of a series of quadrats for systematic sampling, one can deduce the aggregate sizes from the variance among quadrats. However, it is most convenient to increase quadrat size in a geometrical series, and this results in low sensitivity (Kershaw, 1957).

The variance mean ratio technique based on inclined point quadrats

Table 3-1—Proportions of gap and variance-mean ratios (relative variance) to
vertical point quadrats for six model stands of $L_{horizontal} = 1$
(Warren Wilson, 1967)

| | Proportion of gap | | |
Stand	Observed	Expected if random	Relative variance
1	0.22	0.37	0.49
2	0.31	0.37	0.74
3	0.37	0.37	0.98
4	0.42	0.37	1.20
5	0.48	0.37	1.53
6	0.57	0.37	1.96

has been employed by Warren Wilson (1959, 1961, 1965). His method, with vertical points as an example, consists of comparing ratios of the variances of foliage contacts to their means. Mean and variance are equal in Poisson distributions (ratio equals 1.0). Experimental ratios less than 1.0 indicate regular distributions, and those greater than 1.0 indicate contagious distributions. A number of interesting observations with this technique were made by Warren Wilson. In pure stands, leaf distributions for white clover (Trifolium repens L.) and English ivy (Hedera) were strongly regular, and for grasses such as Lolium were strongly contagious (Warren Wilson, 1967). When mixed in swards, clover and ryegrass (Lolium spp.) tended individually to be random; but collectively they were regular (Warren Wilson, 1959). Thus, various species were not independently arranged, and distribution of the subordinate species occurred in the gaps of the dominant grass.

Further, different patterns may be revealed with different inclinations of the quadrat (Warren Wilson, 1965). Alfalfa foliage (Medicago sativa L.) was random to points between 0 and 60° elevation, but contagious at higher angles. Warren Wilson concluded that this was due to plants being erect causing leaves to occur in vertical columns. Vertical points sampled either dense or less dense regions, whereas inclined points averaged these regions.

The implications of variations in pattern to productivity can be seen in Table 3-1 where observed and expected (from random basis) proportions of gaps are given for six of Warren Wilson's model canopies with horizontally displayed L = 1. Gaps to vertical points range from 22 to 57% of the ground area for variance ratios characteristic of real communities. It seems that the contagious pattern of grasses is relatively inefficient in light interception per unit L. However, Saeki, Iwaki, and Monsi (Monsi, 1968) have proposed a "cluster" foliage model as being particularly efficient. The argument is that widely dispersed clusters of leaves would have a smaller extinction coefficient than would dispersed foliage, and hence more leaves could be illuminated at large L. As L increases, the additional leaves are added to existing clusters; thus the extinction coefficient decreases with increasing L as proposed by Verhagen et al. (1963) for an ideal foliage.

Warren Wilson (1961) comments that while the clumping of grasses is offset to some extent by a narrow width of leaves and the tendency of the clumps to open upwards, the clumping could represent an adaptive feature to xeric environments.

With agricultural crops, a basic pattern is imposed upon the community by grouping plants in rows or other regular patterns, and by controlling the population density. This has certain obvious influences on canopy morphology, particularly in affecting the time to achieve full cover and in introducing a hedgerow characteristic to the surface of the canopy. Some of these influences have been examined experimentally (e.g., Shaw and Weber, 1967; Baker and Meyer, 1966; Heinicke, 1963) and theoretically (Jahnke and Lawrence, 1965). One general conclusion is that north-south rows give a better pattern of light interception and higher yields than do east-west rows. Optimum row spacing will be influenced by the potential size and character of the individual plants, and by latitude. In the discussion which follows, our attention will be given principally to variations in pattern found when plants are uniformly or randomly spaced.

C. Vertical Separation of Leaves

The influence of variations in the vertical density of leaves is also relatively unexplored. Nichiporovich (1961) has discussed this in relation to skylight occlusion by a leaf of a given width (w) and various distances (d) from a receiver point. The occluded solid angle $\gamma = 2 \tan^{-1}$ (w/2d) (Fig. 3-1, left). Since the tangent function is hyperbolic, one can determine a breaking point in the curve of γ versus w/d; at w/2d = 0.5, 53° or about one-third of the sky is occluded whereas, at w/2d = 0.25, $\gamma = 28^{\circ}$. Further decreases in w/d narrow γ only slowly. Thus, leaf size in relation to vertical separation strongly influences the solid angle occlusion and hence the skylight pattern within a canopy. Large but widely separated leaves like those of sunflower (Helianthus annuus L.) may actually create a diffuse light pattern quite similar to a shorter community with small leaves like alfalfa (Anderson, 1966b). Most plants seem to have evolved with mechanisms for maintaining d < 2w ($\gamma = 28^{\circ}$), but in breeding for dwarf varieties of cultivated species the relation has been overlooked. Thus, the short internode types of grain sorghum (Sorghum vulgare Pers.) frequently have their wide leaves very close together in relation to width. "Better" canopy structure would result if leaf width was reduced or if the leaves were whorled to reduce the contagious distribution resulting from the opposite and alternate arrangement.

The same geometry applies to gap size (Fig. 3-1, right). From earth, the sun's disc subtends a mean solid angle of 32' (ca. $\overline{0.5^{\circ}}$). Thus a gap admitting direct sun to a leaf low in the canopy must have a solid angle to that receiver point of greater than 0.5° to admit the full flux of direct sun. Gaps with widths (w) less than about 0.01 of the distance (d) between gap and receiver point (tan 32' = 0.0093) will produce sunflecks of varying illuminances less than direct sun. This is particularly evident in deep woodland canopies where sunflecks as bright as full sun may be rare (Evans, 1966). The same situation would occur in herba-

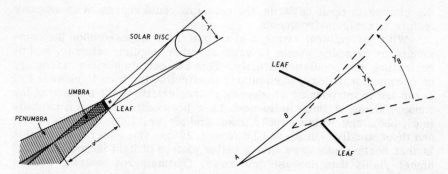

Fig. 3-1—Geometry of gaps and penumbra in relation to the distance between leaves. <u>Left</u>: Diffusion of shadow edges by penumbral effects. The angular width of the penumbra is 32'. The same model can be used to visualize the portion of sky (solid angle, γ) occluded to a receiver point distance d from a leaf of width w. <u>Right</u>: Angular size of gaps (γ), admitting direct and diffuse sunlight to receiver points A and B, in relation to separation of leaves. With γ less than 32', the full disc of the sun will not be seen at the receiver point and sunflecks of varying irradiances result.

ceous stands scaled to have dense canopies of small or finely divided leaves. The finite size of the sun also causes penumbral effects on shadows (Fig. 3-1, <u>left</u>). If the solid angle of the sun is 0.5°, then the penumbra has a width of about 0.01 of the distance from shading leaf to the receiver. If leaves are widely spaced vertically or are very narrow [as with conifers and asparagus (<u>Asparagus officinalis</u> L.)] shadow edges will be quite diffuse—in fact all distinctions between sunlight and diffuse light may be lost. Duncan et al. (1967) point out that their theoretical model will not simulate such light environments, and, as far as we know, this feature has not been included in any model.

D. Vertical Distribution of Leaves and Light Interception

Monsi and Saeki (1953) introduced to the western world the idea of measuring for herbaceous communities the amount of leaf area in each of several horizontal strata. This has been an especially powerful approach since, analogous to algal suspensions, it was found that light attenuation at any depth can usually be related to interposed L by a simple analytical expression, the Bouguer-Lambert law:

$$I = I_o e^{-KL}, \tag{2}$$

where I and I_o are light fluxes to horizontal receivers at points within and above the canopy, L is leaf area index from the top of the canopy, and K is an extinction coefficient. Variations in K have been related to variations in canopy structure, especially to angle of leaf display (Monsi and Saeki, 1953; Kasanaga and Monsi, 1954; Monsi, 1968; Loomis et al., 1968; and Takeda, 1961; among others). This relationship is well illus-

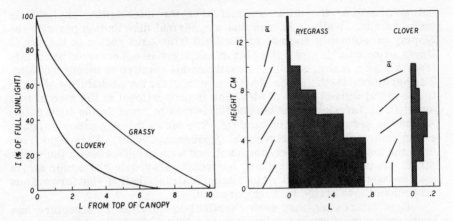

Fig. 3-2—Left: Attenuation of sunlight in clovery and grassy swards as a function of L (after Stern and Donald, 1962). Right: Vertical distribution of L and mean foliage angle $\bar{a}$ as determined with point quadrats for ryegrass and clover (after Warren Wilson, 1959).

trated through the comparative morphology of ryegrass and subterranean clover (Trifolium subterraneum L.) stands. Stern and Donald (1962) found that sunlight was diminished much more strongly per unit LAI in clovery stands than in grassy stands (Fig. 3-2, left). Approximate extinction coefficients calculated from these data are 0.60 for clover and 0.25 for grass.

Warren Wilson (1959) used the frequency, with which horizontal and vertical needles contacted leaves on passage through various strata of closely analogous stands, to estimate the mean foliage angle, $\bar{a}$. His results (Fig. 3-2, right) illustrate clearly the difference in display by such species which account largely for the differences in light attenuation—perennial ryegrass tends toward erect leaves and white clover toward horizontal leaves.

E. Foliage Angle

Mean foliage angle alone may not provide an adequate description of the canopy morphology for some communities. The distribution of α should also be known. Nichiporovich (1961) and deWit (1965) obtained distributions of leaf angle weighted by area for entire canopies (without measuring vertical distribution).

These foliage descriptions serve to characterize some major differences in canopy morphology. For example, Nichiporovich found cucumber (Cucumis sativus L.) and clover to be highly planophile (horizontal leaves predominating) in contrast to timothy (Phleum pratense L.) and maize (Zea mays L.) with erectophile canopies. His distribution for maize corresponded to the surface elements of a sphere.

He concluded that such a distribution with L = 4 would be optimal, but his supporting argument, based principally on the spherical distribution providing the minimum leaf area for intercepting skylight, is unconvincing. While it is true that a spherical distribution permits the display of elements normal to the light from each region of the sky (2 times over with L = 4), the flux of skylight is not received uniformly from all sky zones, and it is usually small relative to direct sunlight. Furthermore, in the lower stories of canopies, the probability of a gap to the sky at a given angle of elevation is proportional to the size of that angle (i.e., inverse to the chance for leaves to occur in the light path.) As may be seen clearly in upward fish-eye views through canopies, gaps occur principally near the vertical (Anderson, 1966b). When light from near the zenith is relatively abundant, and with erect leaves in the upper strata providing abundant gaps, horizontal leaves in the lower strata may be useful. This could yield a spherical distribution—but for reasons other than those stated by Nichiporovich.

It is interesting that such "vertical-to-horizontal" structure has been suggested frequently (Watson and Witts, 1959; Verhagen et al., 1963; Blackman, 1962) as an efficient pattern, yet tests with models have failed to confirm the view (Loomis et al., 1967).

Canopy morphology may vary widely for a particular species as illustrated in Fig. 3-3, left, by comparisons of several fully developed maize crops. The Russian (R) and Estonian (E) communities were strongly erectophile, the Netherlands (N) one weakly plagiophile (median angles dominant), while those from Davis, California (D) were strongly planophile. Udagawa et al. (1968) describe a strongly plagiophile maize community. Genotypes and environments were all different; and it cannot be determined from the original publications whether similar stages of development and densities are compared. Yet, it is evident that the range of distributions observed for this one species is very great.

Herbaceous communities also may show marked changes in canopy structure during growth. Particularly striking are deWit's (1965) data for perennial ryegrass (Fig. 3-3, right), in which the proportion of horizontal leaves increased during growth. The changes for maize are less dramatic. Loomis et al. (1968) noted that the upper leaves of maize shifted to a more horizontal habit after tasseling, but the maize variety studied by Ross and Nilson (1967b) increased in percentage of erect leaves while the proportion at medium inclinations decreased at about the same stage of growth. In comparison, the maize communities studied by Udagawa et al. (1968) and deWit (1965) changed less during development; the same seems true for sugar beet (Loomis et al., unpublished). Nevertheless, structural changes between juvenile and mature canopies are obvious for many species. In particular, dicotyledonous species frequently show an early dominance of horizontal leaves—an advantageous feature for maximizing light interception by the small leaf area displayed by young crop stands.

F. Stratified Analyses of Foliage Angle

Only two extensive studies with stratified analyses of leaf angle distributions are known to us. Loomis et al. (1968) reported on time course changes in maize over a wide range of population densities, and

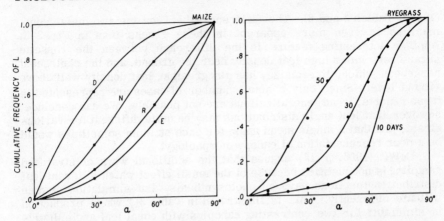

Fig. 3-3—Left: Cumulative frequency of leaf angles, for four maize communities. D—Davis, California (Loomis et al., 1968); N—Netherlands (after deWit, 1965); R—Russia (data of Nichiporovich, 1961); and E—Estonia (data of Ross and Nilson 1967b). Right: Cumulative frequency of leaf angles for ryegrass communities on June 10, after 10, 30, 50 days of growth (after deWit, 1965).

Ross and Nilson (1967a,b) made an excellent study on maize and horsebeans.

Figure 3-4 illustrates the two maize communities, horsebean (Vicia faba L.), and sugar beet (Beta vulgaris L.). The drawings for the Estonian work were derived by assuming that the vertical distributions of L per stratum given by Ross and Nilson (1967a; Table 1, col. 2, maize; and Table 5, col. 5, horsebean) are for the same communities for which they later give fractional distribution data for leaf angle

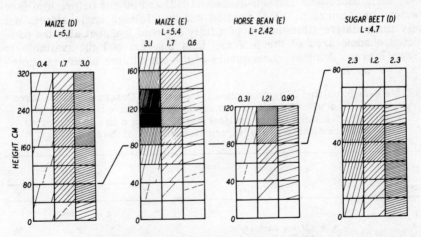

Fig. 3-4—Stratified leaf angle distribution for maize, horsebean, and sugar beet communities. Maize (D),Davis, California (Loomis et al., 1968); maize (E) and horsebean,Estonia(data of Ross and Nilson 1967a,b); the sugar beet was grown at Davis (previously unpublished data of Loomis et al.) The data are condensed and simplified from their original form.

(1967b; Tables 3 and 6). The differences between the two maize communities is even more apparent in these graphs than in Fig. 3-3. Another interesting feature is the difference between the rossette sugar beet, with a high leaf density near the ground, and the caulescent horsebean which, like maize, has its greatest leaf density well above ground level. Since only a small number of cases are represented in these reports, broad generalizations are not possible. We can conclude, however, that leaf angle distributions may be quite different for various strata, and that a single mean angle for each stratum sometimes would be a poor representation of canopy morphology.

DeWit (1965, p. 13) argues that the additional work of stratified sampling is not justified because of the small'effect which different leaf distribution functions have on photosynthesis. But simulation studies indicate differently. This is illustrated in Table 3-2 where production is simulated for two contrasting canopies with equal leaf angle distribution functions (considering each angle class occurs at the same frequency for the whole canopy). The canopy with horizontal leaves in the upper strata (clover) is less efficient at all values of L than the inverted canopy (grass), and the relative difference becomes greater as L increases. Thus, other factors being equal, stratified sampling may be essential if one wishes to compare the efficiency of various productive structures.

G. Light Distribution Models

The actual flux of light received by each individual leaf must be known in order to estimate its photosynthesis, a consequence of the curvilinear response of photosynthesis to increasing light flux (Fig. 3-5, left). Moreover Boysen-Jensen (1932) and others before him (see review by Anderson, 1964) pointed out that foliage angle affects not only the relative illumination of a fully exposed leaf, but also the projected shadow area of the leaf and thus the flux of light available to lower leaves. Another consequence of the curvilinear nature of photo-

Table 3-2—Simulated daily production rates with the Duncan model for three communities with $\bar{\alpha} = 45^\circ$. Communities B and C have the same leaf distribution functions but the vertical distribution of α has been inverted. All stands have 10 leaf layers each with 0.1 of the total L.

Stand	Description	Production rate, when L =		
		2	4	8
		g m^{-2} day^{-1}		
A	$\alpha = 45^\circ$ for each layer	30	38	38
B	$\alpha = 90^\circ$ for the top layer decreasing to 0° at the bottom	32	41	47
C	$\alpha = 0^\circ$ for the top layer increasing to 90° at the bottom	29	35	34

38° N Lat., July 1. $P_{max} = 60$, $R_{leaf} = 2$, and $R_{24\ hours} = .3\ P$.

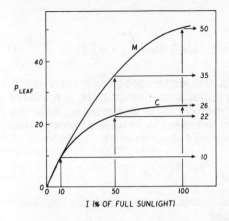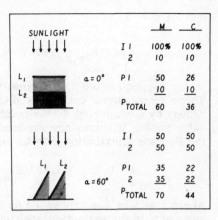

Fig. 3-5—Left: Leaf photosynthesis for maize (M) and clover (C) as a function of illumination. These species illustrate different degrees of light saturation in full sunlight. Right: Simple models and calculations of community photosynthesis for maize (M) and clover (C) with two leaf distributions of L = 2. With $\alpha = 0^\circ$, illumination (I) amounts to 100% and 10% of full sunlight. With $\alpha = 60^\circ$, I amounts to 50% of full sunlight. P_1 and P_2 at the various illumination levels were obtained from Fig. 3-5, left as indicated by the arrows.

synthetic light response curves is that higher production and hence, more efficient light utilization is achieved by illuminating many leaves at a modest level of light than by exposing a few leaves to full sun (Fig. 3-5, right).

Thus, a key problem is to relate the distribution of sun flecks and diffuse light within the community to the morphology of the community. In this way the light environment of each photosynthetic organ can be characterized. These considerations led to development of mathematical models which would predict light distribution within canopies. Monsi and Saeki (1953) and Kasanaga and Monsi (1954) developed expressions of the general form of equation (2) for homogeneously arranged leaves of uniform inclination α, where the extinction coefficient, K, was a variable computed from geometrical considerations of α, β (the elevation angle of the light source), and L. K was found to approach 1 for horizontal leaves (even exceeding 1.0 in nonrandom mosaic arrangements) and to decline as α increased.

Warren Wilson (1960) with Reeve has outlined a geometrical theory for the probability of contacting leaves of given leaf angle by an inclined point. Saeki (1963) and Anderson (1966a) showed the correspondence between this theory and that of Monsi and Saeki (1953). The point quadrat probabilities can be taken to represent the average shadow area F' cast in the direction β, of a large number of leaves of area F. For $\alpha \leq \beta$,

$$[F'/F]_{\alpha,\beta} = \cos \alpha \sin \beta; \qquad (3)$$

and for $\alpha > \beta$,

$$[F'/F]_{\alpha,\beta} = \sin \beta \, \cos \alpha \, [1 + \frac{2}{\pi} \, (\tan \theta_o - \theta_o)], \tag{4}$$

where θ_0, expressed in radians, is the angle whose $\cos = \cot \alpha \, \tan \beta$. These expressions can be used to estimate the sunlit area of a foliage canopy by considering β, the point quadrat angle of elevation, to be the solar angle. If leaves are randomly arranged in horizontal strata, then the Poisson distribution may be employed (Duncan et al., 1967) and

$$I = I_o \, \exp \, (-L \, [F'/F]_{\alpha,\beta} \, /\sin \beta) = I_o \, \exp \, (-KL) \tag{5}$$

where I and I_0 are expressed as horizontal areas illuminated by direct sun and K is the extinction coefficient.

This function for K is plotted against α and β by Anderson (1966a) and Loomis et al. (1967); $K = 1$ when $\alpha = 0$, and is a constant as long as $\alpha \leq \beta$. This means that for many canopies, values of K, measured when most of the light comes from high elevations, can be used in character- ize the canopy. As we have seen, a random distribution as assumed here approximates many real communities and serves as a benchmark with which to compare over- and under-dispersed foliages.

In Fig. 3-6 are illustrated the variations in sunlit foliage area re- sulting from application of equation (5) to a foliage providing complete cover (Warren Wilson, 1967). Such area is greatest when α and β are both large; but for small values of β the area is greatest for more horizontal leaves. Actual illumination of each unit of area will vary according to the sine of the angle of incidence. Interestingly, as long as $\alpha \leq \beta$, the sunlit area is independent of β, being equal to $\sec \alpha$. For example, with $\alpha = 0$ sunlit leaf area equals 1.0.

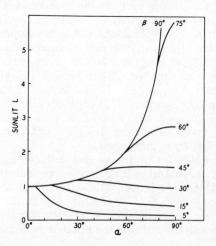

Fig. 3-6—Sunlit (skylight not considered) foliage area in canopies with randomly displayed leaves of various inclinations. β is solar elevation. (After Warren Wilson, 1967.)

The equations shown for direct sun also suffice to describe the penetration of diffuse light from a particular point in the sky. Hanau's equations (Duncan et al., 1967) offer a more complete solution, however, and permit calculation of illumination on either or both surfaces of a leaf of any angle from any zone of a hemispherical sky. (In most models it is assumed that illumination of the lower surface of a leaf is equally effective in photosynthesis to illumination of the upper surface). The relative brightness of sun and total sky can be obtained fairly readily, but there is little information on the brightness of different regions of the sky under various meteorological conditions. Anderson (1966a) discusses the Moon and Spencer's Standard Overcast Sky which is azimuthally uniform but brightest at the zenith, while Duncan et al. (1967) like Monsi and Saeki (1953) have used a uniform sky. We are now working on approximating any sky comprised of varying proportions or clear, cloudy, and smoggy conditions. Preliminary results indicate that productivity levels and optimum canopy structure differ appreciably for various sky conditions.

Most models have for simplicity ignored the contributions of diffuse light originating from reflections and transmission within the canopy. This light can be important to production as has been indicated by computer simulation (Duncan et al., 1967).

As an alternative to the geometrical solution given in equation (5), solutions may be based on measured light "transmission" or "penetration" coefficients. As an example, the following function was developed by Kasanaga and Monsi (1954) for illumination penetrating the Nth layer of horizontal leaves:

$$I = I_0 M^N, \tag{6}$$

where $M = 1 - (1-T)L$, and T is the light transmission coefficient. By coupling these expressions with a function for the photosynthesis response to light, they made production calculations which agreed reasonably well with measured values.

Monteith (1965) extended this approach to deal with inclined leaves by introducing a parameter s equal to the fraction of light which passes a unit leaf layer without interception. Thus, s is 0 for a continuous sheet of foliage normal to a distant point-light source and 1.0 for leaves parallel to the light rays. The resulting equation for illumination penetrating the Nth layer is

$$I = I_0 \left[s + (1-s)T\right]^N. \tag{7}$$

If each layer consists of a unit L, (i.e., $N = L$) then

$$I = I_0 \exp\left\{L \ln\left[s + (1-s)T\right]\right\}, \tag{8}$$

and by analogy to equation (2), the extinction coefficient is

$$K = - \ln \left[s+(1-s)T \right]. \tag{9}$$

Taking s = 0.7 for grass and 0.4 for prostrate-leaved plants, Monteith calculated several light distributions that were applied with appropriate photosynthetic functions to give a reasonable fit to measured production curves. Variations in s have a large effect on calculated productivity. Warren Wilson (1967) points out, that s taken as a constant for a given canopy implies that the source of all light was from the zenith, with I_O varying to stimulate changes in solar inclination. We should note that the empirical s integrates all variations in leaf distribution. To answer questions about canopy morphology and yield, a model must simulate s from the leaf distribution. Thus, this approach is much less useful in its application than is Monsi and Saeki's original geometrical solution for inclined leaves.

Model construction has reached a point where many of the parameters which affect light distribution within canopies can be considered together. Such models give discrete solutions and thus for optimization, the parameters must be varied systematically and the entire simulation rerun repeatedly. Until the sophistication of the models is improved and until they can be coupled with microclimate models, it is difficult to justify efforts to deduce an "ideal" foliage for each crop at each latitude and date. However, specific solutions to simple comparisons can be reached. The vertical distribution of leaves, and within each stratum, the distribution within various angle classes are revealed to be of critical importance.

Thus far, models for evaluating nonrandom (contagious or mosaic) distributions within layers, or for assigning leaf elements to individual plants (for studies on competition), are still in their infancy. These features are obviously of considerable importance in real communities. Ultimately, we can hope to simulate row and spacing effects, interspecific and (as a basis for examining the course of evolution) intraspecific competition.

H. Azimuthal Orientations

Ross and Nilson (1967b) gave attention to azimuthal orientation of leaves by employing a device to determine to which of 48 sky zones (each 15° elevation by 45° azimuth) the normal to a portion of a leaf pointed. When planted in rows (direction unspecified), maize had a significant azimuthal tendency toward east-west orientation of leaves; horsebeans had little azimuthal orientation. The observation with maize is of special interest because of Peters' (1961) attempts at seed-oriented plantings of this crop to provide a strongly mosaic leaf arrangement for maximizing light interception.

Nichiporovich (1961) and Loomis et al. (1968) failed to observe this east-west tendency in their maize communities, but Udagawa et al. (1968) found maize leaves to be somewhat elongated in the direction of their northeast-southwest rows. Apparently a strong azimuthal orientation is an inherited characteristic in some crops. We have observed strong east-west orientation of leaves by a few varieties of both maize

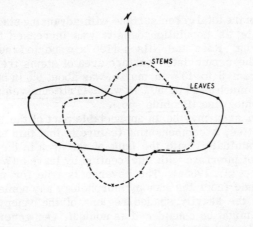

Fig. 3-7—Azimuthal distribution of maize leaves and stems. The mean of leaves 4, 5, 9, and 10 from first foliage leaf, and the stem axis at ground level are plotted (previously unpublished data of Loomis et al.).

and sorghum regardless of row direction (Fig. 3-7). Our tentative suggestion is that the effect is related to solar path as much as to row direction and plant density. Solar orientations of leaves are not uncommon. Heliotropic movements by sunflower and the occurrence of "compass" plants such as Silphium are well known; but the potential of these traits for affecting productivity remains to be studied.

I. Nonleaf Structures

Light interception by nonphotosynthetic tissues is an additional feature of canopy morphology. In woodlands, the importance of trunks and branches to the light environment of understory plants is apparent; but the role of stems and branches has been felt to be of less importance in herbaceous communities and is generally ignored. While stems are the most obvious component of the morphology, it also may be useful to consider other tissues. El-Sharkawy and Hesketh (1965) found that subtraction of nongreen vein areas from leaves of certain species brought their photosynthetic rates per unit area more closely into line with those of other species. On a different scale, light interception by flower structures may be appreciable. As an example, Duncan et al. (1967) found that about 9% of the daily isolation may be intercepted by tassels of a maize crop at commercial densities (50,000 plants/ha) and 18% may be intercepted at twice that density.

With herbaceous plants, stem (and with grasses the sheaths which enclose them), petioles and inflorescence parts may contain appreciable chlorophyll, and thus represent productive as well as light intercepting structures. While the role of cereal awns and glumes in photosynthesis has been well documented, little is known about the photosynthetic rates associated with most other such organs. Their relative abundance is not necessarily small. In maize (Williams et al., 1965a), the surface areas of culms with sheaths, treated as elliptical cylinders, varied from 9 to 18% of the total green surface with advancing stages of growth, but varied little as population density was increased from 6,700 to 700,000 plants/ha. Ross and Nilson (1967a) reported the fraction of L found as L_{es} (the accumulated surface area of stems treated as cylinders) varied from 5 to 13% in maize, was about 9% in horsebean, and increased to as much as 40 or 50% in wheat (Triticum vulgare L.), white clover, and bromegrass (Bromus spp.).

While stem area may be an appreciable part of the total in herbaceous communities, a compensating feature is that this area is usually distributed pyramidally, with the bulk of the area in the lower strata; hence it does not interfere with interception by leaves (Warren Wilson, 1965; Williams et al., 1965a). The reverse is true for many grasses.

If we exclude from the canopy morphology any nonleaf structures which occur in the heavily shaded regions of the canopy, some of the leaf area itself might be considered as nonleaf. Our general conclusion is that more attention needs to be given to nonleaf components of canopies.

II. RELATION OF CANOPY MORPHOLOGY TO PRODUCTION

Establishing relationships between canopy morphology and yield presents a number of difficulties. Agriculturalists have been principally concerned with economic yield, and variation in parameters affecting partitioning of production becomes confounded with variations in production rate. Translocation, respiration, and hormonal controls on partitioning, as discussed in later chapters, determine the correlation between primary productivity and economic yield. Time dependency also causes problems in interpreting integrative characters such as grain yield. It is well to recall the importance of rate of leaf area development and of leaf area duration (Watson, 1952; Nichiporovich, 1966). The shorter the season, the more dependent crop yield will be upon the rate at which full cover is reached, and on the efficiency of the canopy at small values of L. Thus, a short-season crop such as cantaloup (Cucumis melo L. var. reticulatus Nand.) develops only a small leaf area but one containing highly dispersed horizontal leaves.

Beyond these factors, canopy morphology affects more than just visible light distribution among leaves, and photosynthesis. The patterns of leaf distribution influence air circulation, canopy roughness and hence the efficiency of eddy turbulence. These factors in turn affect CO_2, H_2O vapor, and heat transfer. Since leaf disposition also determines the receipt and loss of short and long wave radiation, canopy architecture in effect determines microclimate. Modeling efforts are being made on each of these aspects, and before long canopy architecture will be assessed on a much broader basis than on just light distribution.

A. Simulations of Crop Productivity

DeWit (1965), Monteith (1965), and Duncan et al. (1967) all reached similar basic conclusions, through simulations, regarding the influence of variations in α and L. That is, when L is small, horizontal leaves

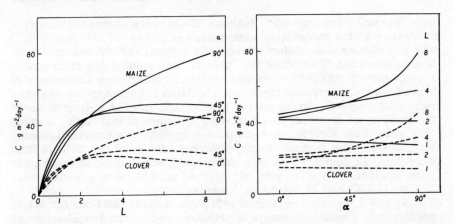

Fig. 3-8—Simulations of daily crop growth rates (C) for maize and clover communities of various L and a combinations. Solar and skylight data of 38° N. latitude for July 1. <u>Left</u>: C as a function of L for various values of a. <u>Right</u>: The same data plotted with C as a function of a for various values of L.

are advantageous; at large values of L, more erect leaves give greater production. Further, optimal L, or at least a pronounced optimum, is not evident providing the lower leaves adapt physiologically to the shade environment. The Duncan model is the most flexible with regard to input and the most rigorous as to theory. This model was used to compute the production rates illustrated in Fig. 3-8. Photosynthesis rate is computed for each hour of the day and then summed and corrected for respiration to give an estimate of daily production. With β_{max} for the day at 74°, inclined leaves show a marked advantage only when L exceeds 2 to 4, and erect leaves only when L approaches high values of 8 or more. This was true for the photosynthetic functions of both maize and clover (Fig. 3-5, <u>left</u>; i.e., whether or not the individual leaves light saturated with less than full sun), but crossover points and daily production rates are quite different. Also, leaf photosynthetic rate is revealed as a powerful determinant of crop growth rate.

The influences of varying sky conditions, latitude, physiological functions and leaf optical properties have been explored briefly with this model. Figure 3-8 serves to summarize much of what can now be said about an ideal foliage for light interception in latitudes up to 50 or 60°. Azimuthal distributions, nonrandom patterns, including those of row effects and genotypic mixtures, could be considered and remain to be examined. One point made clear from Fig. 3-8 is that simulations are essential to the proper design and interpretation of field experiments on patterns with leaves.

B. Some Experimental Results

The hypothesis that erect leaves should confer tolerance to crowding is widely accepted and several tests of its validity have been attempted. Pendleton et al. (1968) developed genetic isolines of maize with "normal" and "upright" leaves. These were compared for grain production with a moderately high density of plants (59,000 plants ha^{-1}) with L reaching 4.0. Unfortunately, the normal variety was intolerant of high densities. Thus while the "upright" line yielded 41% more grain, a large part of this difference was related to differences in numbers of barren plants, a circumstance. more related to carbohydrate status of individual plants at silking than to crop growth rate. A second phase of the experiment demonstrated a striking influence of leaf angle. Leaves of a planophile variety were positioned upright by mechanical means. With L = 4.1, the normal display intercepted 99% of the incident light near noon as compared to 90% intercepted when leaves above the ear were upright, and 84% with all leaves upright. Grain yields were 10,700, 12,200, and 11,400 kg ha^{-1}, respectively.

At L = 4, simulation models with physiological functions for maize predict only a small advantage in primary productivity from upright as compared to horizontal leaves (Fig. 3-8). Considering only the data on light interception, and remembering that C is usually found to vary directly with percent cover, we would expect that C would have declined with increasing proportions of upright leaves. Thus, it appears that the grain yield advantage with upright leaves was not the result of greater C. Rather, as Pendleton et al. suggest, greater illumination of leaves adjacent to the developing ears may have been the cause of a greater proportion of the assimilate being accumulated by the grain.

In Ontario, Stoskopf (1967) compared grain yields from "droopy" and "upright" winter wheats. The upright selections from New York may have been slightly less suited to the environment than the well adapted "droopy" control, and gave lower yields. However, the yield increase obtained from narrow as compared with wide row spacings was greatest with the upright types. Data on maturity dates, L, and biomass were not given. Here again it is impossible to draw very general conclusions from the data. Did the communities attain L values at which erect leaves might increase C, or, indeed, with this latitude, time of year, and sky conditions, would erect leaves confer an advantage at any L? The weight of the Guelph researchers' experience points towards affirmative answers.

Watson and Witts (1959) compared an erect-leaved sugar beet with several prostrate-leaved wild progenitors. E for the sugar beet declined less as L increased, indicating perhaps that the increase in mutual shading was least with erect leaves. In these experiments, as Monteith (1965) points out, L was small (2 to 3) and the real advantage of the sugar beet may have been due principally to greater dispersion of leaves (longer petioles and hence greater percent light interception than with the wild beet?). At L = 2 to 3, the simulations illustrated in Fig. 3-8 predict a slight advantage for horizontal leaves.

These experiments are among the better efforts, but they illustrate some of the problems in establishing cause and effect relations between canopy morphology and agronomic yield. Many more careful and detailed experiments are needed. We need to distinguish the role of physiological processes (e.g., partitioning efficiency, photosynthetic capability, and respiration) from advantages conferred by changes in the patterns among leaves. The definition of an "ideal" foliage canopy depends upon our establishing guiding principles about the interactions of these factors within particular environments. Obviously, we cannot explore each point of possible significance adequately or quickly enough by experiments with genetic isolines or mechanical manipulations. The modeling efforts described earlier assume an essential role since many aspects of production processes can now be investigated through simulations.

ACKNOWLEDGMENTS

Portions of the original data reported here were obtained through research supported by the National Science Foundation (GB 4192) and by the California sugar beet industry.

LITERATURE CITED

Anderson, Margaret C. 1964. Light relations of terrestrial plant communities and their measurement. Biol. Rev. 39:425–486.

Anderson, M. C. 1966a. Some problems in the characterization of the light climate in plant communities. In: R. Bainbridge, G. C. Evans, and O. Rackham (ed.). Light as an ecological factor. Symp. Brit. Ecol. Soc. 6:77–90. John Wiley, New York.

Anderson, Margaret C. 1966b. Stand structure and light penetration. II. A theoretical analysis. J. Appl. Ecol. 3:41–54.

Baker, D. N., and R. E. Meyer. 1966. Influence of stand geometry on light interception and net photosynthesis in cotton. Crop Sci. 6:15–19.

Björkman, O., and P. Holmgren. 1963. Adaptability of the photosynthetic apparatus to light intensity in ecotypes from exposed and shaded habitats. Physiol. Plant. 16:889–914.

Black, J. N. 1963. The interrelationship of solar radiation and leaf area index in determining the rate of dry matter production of swards of subterranean clover (Trifolium subterranean L.). Aust. J. Agr. Res. 14:20–38.

Blackman, G. E. 1962. The limit of plant productivity. Ann. Rep. East Malling Res. Sta. for 1961. p. 39–50.

Boysen Jensen, P. 1932. Die Stoffproduktion der Pfanzen. G. Fischer, Jena.

Bray, J. R. 1960. The chlorophyll content of some native and managed plant communities in central Minnesota. Can. J. Bot. 38:313–333.

Brougham, R. W. 1956. Effect of intensity of defoliation on regrowth of pasture. Aust. J. Agr. Sci. 7:377–387.

Brougham, R. W. 1960. The relationship between the critical leaf area, total chlorophyll content, and maximum growth-rate of some pasture and crop plants. Ann. Bot. 24:463–474.

DeWit, C. T. 1965. Photosynthesis of leaf canopies. Agr. Res. Rep. no. 663, Central Agr. Publ. Doc., Wageningen.

Duncan, W. G., W. A. Williams, and R. S. Loomis. 1967. Tassels and the productivity of maize. Crop Sci. 7:37–39.

Duncan, W. G., R. S. Loomis, W. A. Williams, and R. Hanau. 1967. A model for simulating photosynthesis in plant communities. Hilgardia 38:181–205.

El-Sharkawy, M., and J. Hesketh. 1965. Photosynthesis among species in relation characteristics of leaf anatomy and CO_2 diffusion resistances. Crop Sci. 5:517–521.

Evans, G. C. 1966. Model and measurement in the study of woodland light. In: R. Bainbridge, G. C. Evans and O. Rackham (eds.). Light as an ecological factor. Symp. British Ecol. Soc. 6:53-76. John Wiley, New York.

Gabrielsen, E. K. 1948. Effects of different chlorophyll concentrations on photosynthesis in foliage.leaves. Physiol. Plant. 1:5-37.

Goldman, C. R., and R. C. Carter. 1965. An investigation by rapid carbon-14 bioassay of factors affecting the cultural entrophication of Lake Tahoe, California-Nevada. J. Water Poll. Cont. Fed. 37:1044-1059.

Greig-Smith, P. 1964. Quantitative plant ecology. Butterworths, Washington, D.C.

Heinicke, D. R. 1963. The microclimate of fruit trees: II. Foliage and light distribution patterns in apple trees. Amer. Soc. Hort. Sci., Proc. 83:1-11.

Jahnke, S., and D. B. Lawrence. 1965. Influence of photosynthetic crown structure on potential productivity of vegetation, based primarily on mathematical models. Ecology 46:319-326.

Kasanaga, H., and M. Monsi. 1954. On the light-transmission of leaves, and its meaning for the production of matter in plant communities. Jap. J. Bot. 14: 304-324.

Kershaw, K. A. 1957. The use of cover and frequency in the detection of pattern in plant communities. Ecology 38:291-299.

Loomis, R. S., W. A. Williams and W. G. Duncan. 1967. Community architectecture and the productivity of terrestrial plant communities, p. 291-308. In: A. San Pietro, F. A. Greer, and T. J. Army (ed.) Harvesting the sun. Academic Press, New York.

Loomis, R. S., W. A. Williams, W. G. Duncan, A. Dovrat, and F. Nunez A. 1968. Quantitative descriptions of foliage display and light absorption in field communities of corn plants. Crop Sci. 8:352-356.

Monsi, M., and T. Saeki. 1953. Über den Lichtfaktor in den Pflanzengesellshaften und seine Bedeutung für die Stoffproduktion. Jap. J. Bot. 14:22-52.

Monsi, M. 1968. Mathematical models of plant communities, p. 131-149. In F. E. Eckardt (ed.) Functioning of terrestrial ecosystems at the primary production level. UNESCO, Paris.

Monteith, J. L. 1965. Light distribution and photosynthesis in field crops. Ann. Bot., N.S. 29:17-37.

Nichiporovich, A. A. 1966. Aims of research on the photosynthesis of plants as a factor in productivity. In A. A. Nichiporovich (ed.) Photosynthesis of productive systems. Transl. edition. Israel Prog. Sci. Transl., Jerusalem.

Okubo, T., H. Oizumi, M. Hoshino and S. Nishimura. 1968. Chlorophyll amount for analysis of matter production in forage crops, p. 43-46. In Photosynthesis and utilization of solar energy - Level III experiments. Japanese IBP/PP Group. Tokyo.

Pendleton, J. W., G. E. Smith, S. R. Winter, and T. J. Johnston. 1968. Field investigations of the relationship of leaf angle in corn (Zea mays L.) to grain yield and apparent photosynthesis. Agron. J. 60:422-424.

Peters, D. B. 1961. Water use by field crops. Plant Food Rev. 7(1):14.

Philip, J. R. 1965. The distribution of foliage density with foliage angle estimated from inclined point quadrate observations. Austral. J. Bot. 13:357-366.

Ross, Y. K., and T. Nilson. 1967a. The vertical distribution of biomass in crop stands. In A. A. Nichoporovich (ed.) Photosynthesis of productive systems. Translated edition. Israel Prog. Sci. Trans., Jerusalem. pp. 86-95.

Ross, Y. K., and T. Nilson. 1967b. The spatial orientation of leaves in crop stands and its determination. In A. A. Nichiporovich (ed.) Photosynthesis of productive systems. Translated edition. Israel Prog. Sci. Trans., Jerusalem. p. 75-85.

Saeki, T. 1963. Light relations in plant communities, p. 79-94. In L. T. Evans (ed.) Environmental control of plant growth. Academic Press, New York.

Santhirasegaram, K., and J. N. Black. 1968. The distribution of leaf area and light intensity within wheat crops differing in row direction, row spacing, and rate of sowing; a contribution of the study of undersowing pasture with cereals. J. Brit. Grassland Soc. 23:1-12.

Shaw, R. E., and C. R. Weber. 1967. Effects of canopy arrangement on light interception and yield of soybeans. Agron. J. 59:155-159.

Shibles, R. M., and C. R. Weber. 1965. Leaf area, solar radiation interception and dry matter production by soybeans. Crop Sci. 5:575-577.

Shibles, R. M., and C. R. Weber. 1966. Interception of solar radiation and dry matter production by various soybean planting patterns. Crop Sci. 6:55-59.

Steeman Nielsen, E. 1957. The chlorophyll content and the light utilization in communities of plankton algae and terrestrial higher plants. Physiol. Plant. 10:1009-1021.

Stern, W. R., and C. M. Donald 1962. The influence of leaf area and radiation on the growth of clover in swards. Austral. J. Agr. Res. 13:615-623.

Stoskopf, N. C. 1967. Yield performance of upright-leaved selections of winter wheat in narrow row spacing. Can. J. Plant Sci. 47:597-601.

Szeich, G., J. L. Monteith, and J. M. Dos Santos. 1964. Tube solarimeter to measure radiation among plants. J. Appl. Ecol. 1:169-174.

Takeda, T. 1961. Studies on the photosynthesis and production of dry matter in the community of rice plants. Jap. J. Bot. 17:403-437.

Talling, J. F. 1961. Photosynthesis under natural conditions. Ann. Rev. Plant Physiol. 12:133-154.

Udagawa, T., Z. Uchijima, T. Horie, and K. Kobayashi. 1968. Canopy structure of the corn plant, p. 20-24. In Photosynthesis and utilization of solar energy Level III experiments. Jap. IBP/PP Group. Tokyo.

Verhagen, A. M. W., J. H. Wilson, and E. J. Britten. 1963. Plant production in relation to foliage illumination. Ann. Bot. N.S. 27:627-640.

Warren Wilson, J. 1959. Analysis of the spatial distribution of foliage by two-dimensional point quadrats. New Phytol. 58:92-101.

Warren Wilson, J. 1960. Inclined point quadrats. New Phytol. 59:1-8.

Warren Wilson, J. 1961. Influence of spatial arrangement of foliage area on light interception and pasture growth. Proc. 8th Int. Grassl. Cong. pp. 275-279.

Warren Wilson, J. 1965. Stand structure and light penetration. I. Analysis by point quadrats. J. appl. Ecol. 2:383-390.

Warren Wilson, J. 1967. Stand structure and light penetration. III. Sunlit foliage area. J. appl. Ecol. 4:159-165.

Watson, D. J. 1947. Comparative physiological studies on the growth of field crops. I. Variation in net assimilation rate and leaf area between species, and within and between years. Ann. Bot. N.S. 11:41-76.

Watson, D. J. 1952. The physiological basis of variation in yield. Adv. Agron. 4:101-145.

Watson, D. J. 1958. The dependence of net assimilation rate on leaf area index. Ann. Bot. N.S. 22:37-55.

Watson, D. J., and K. J. Witts. 1959. The net assimilation rates of wild and cultivated beets. Ann. Bot. N.S. 23:431-439.

Williams, W. A., R. S. Loomis, and C. R. Lepley. 1965a. Vegetative growth of corn as affected by population density: I. Productivity in relation to interception of solar radiation. Crop Sci. 5:211-215.

Williams, W. A., R. S. Loomis, and C. R. Lepley. 1965b. Vegetative growth of corn as affected by population density. II. Components of growth, net assimilation rate, and leaf area index. Crop Sci. 5:215-219.

3 ...DISCUSSION

DONALD N. BAKER

Agricultural Research Service, USDA
Boll Weevil Research Laboratory
State College, Mississippi

Little needs to be added to Drs. Loomis' and Williams' presentation. They have done a very creditable job of reviewing a complex subject. There are, however, two related questions pertaining directly to these models of photosynthesis by plant communities which merit consideration. The first concerns experimental verification and the second deals with the matter of systems applications.

Evidently, not every one who is capable of making contributions in the development of these models is equipped or has the time to verify them experimentally by making short term measurements of photosynthesis in intact stands. Such measurements are not by any means impossible, but they are not easy to do either. So, the question is, would such an effort be justified, is it necessary, or can we be confident of the essential correctness and completeness of our models as they are now?

These models are designed to account for the effects of leaf angle, sun angle, etc., on photosynthesis by the stand. Two physical factors are handled very well, stand geometry and the angle of incidence of the radiation. Such a model then, should provide the diurnal variation of stand photosynthesis by the minute. What concerns me is that most efforts at experimental verification have been done by dry weight measurements over days. This gets one into the technical problem of plant sampling, but it also requires an accounting for day and night respiration by the crop. Plant sampling and the measurement of dry weight increases over several days time would seem to be a rather crude way of testing a model designed to estimate increments of carbon assimilation over minutes.

Concerning the application of these models, many agronomists are interested in simulating crop growth and development, using classical systems engineering methods. Stand photosynthesis is one of the basic subsystems about which we have to be concerned. Recently Dr. Hesketh and I have been incorporating our photosynthesis and respiration data into a model for the study of potential fruit development. This is a study of the distribution of photosynthesis. Without going into the derivation, I can give the result as follows:

$$\frac{dW}{dt} = P - RW, \qquad (1)$$

where W is fruit weight in mg/dm^2 ground area, t is time in days, P is gross photosynthate in mg/dm^2 ground area/day, and R is the respiration rate in mg/g dry wt/day. We are defining P as follows,

$$P = P' - R_{vn}, \qquad (2)$$

where P' and R_{vn} are daytime net carbon exchange and night respiration loss by the vegetative tissue. R is the day plus night fruit respiration. R_{vn} equals slightly less than 10% of a typical day's net photosynthesis (P') in cotton, and total daily (24 hr) vegetative respiration equals 28% of P. Equation (1) applies to a determinate crop but for cotton it had to be modified as follows:

$$\frac{dW}{dt} = P - RW + P \left\{ 1 - \exp\left[-R(t-55)\right] \right\} \qquad (3)$$

where 55 days are required to mature a fruit. We've used experimental respiration and photosynthesis data to obtain an iterative solution to this expression. The result was a time course for the development of a theoretically possible fruit load for the 1966 growing season, and it was, to us, amazingly similar to behavior to the real system. It also gave us an estimate of the theoretical maximum yield.

This estimate of potential yield is based on carbohydrate supply. We've also obtained an estimate of potential yield from another system of equations based on carbohydrate demands by the fruit. The problem there is stated as follows:

$$\frac{dC}{dt} = \frac{dW}{dt} + RW \qquad (4)$$

where all symbols are defined as above except C which represents the carbohydrate need. Integration over time yields a total carbohydrate requirement and a final fruit weight. The conversion ratio obtained from these values, then, multiplied by the supply of photosynthete gives an estimate of yield. In this connection, we have found that 44% of the fruit carbohydrate requirement is for respiration. I would note in passing that this potential yield estimate is somewhat more precise in that it accounts for changes in the respiration rate of the fruit as a function of time.

Both of these approaches depend on an accurate estimate of the rate of photosynthesis. We have been using experimental data. This is satisfactory for some purposes, but the claim is made (and in a sense I think it is justified) that our present approach is not general enough. So, we need to move toward the application of an organization of "fundamental" relations.

3 ... DISCUSSION

J. W. TANNER

University of Guelph
Guelph, Ontario, Canada

Actual experimental data illustrating the importance of plant morphology to plant yield is difficult to find. I would like to cite some data and relate some observations which I feel are relevant to the discussion. C.J. Gardener, formerly a graduate student at Guelph, selected three high yielding barley varieties (Hordeum vulgare L.) and three low yielding barley varieties to determine, if possible, the physiologic reasons for their yield differences. It became apparent very early in the study that morphology was one of the major effects as the three high yielding varieties had narrow, upright leaves while the three low yielding varieties had wide dropping leaves. (These were relative but obvious differences.)

The higher yielding (upright) varieties showed slower initial growth rates, required a longer period before reaching 95% light interception, but had higher crop growth rates (C) subsequent to 95% light interception. The higher yielding varieties also exhibited a better distribution of light within the canopy.

Further, a comparison of the 1964 and 1965 data indicated that when the LAI's were high the more upright types showed higher C values; when the LAI's were low the upright and drooping had almost identical C values (Table 3D-1). This experimental data supports the theoretical prediction derived from Duncan's model (Duncan, 1967).

With this study in mind we proceeded to rank the material in the wheat (Triticum aestivum L.), oat (Avena sativa L.), and barley nurseries for yield, using only the attributes leaf angle and width as selection criteria. Approximately 300 varieties and lines were evaluated as high, medium, or low yielders. When these visual evaluations were checked with performance, it was shown that this method properly catagorized all of the 50 high-yielding strains except two. Twenty other varieties, classed as high-yielding by this visual method, did not fall into this category. The results of this visual evaluation indicated that for Ontario conditions these two leaf characteristics could provide useful criteria in selection for yield.

Further observations (Table 3D-2) of upright leaf types in variety trials proved to be equally enlightening. At one location where weeds were controlled chemically, a short wheat strain with extreme upright leaves yielded equal to the check varieties. At another location, where no herbicide treatment was used the strain was greatly reduced in yield. Weed growth between the rows was markedly more profuse than in the floppy-leaf types. A tall, leafy variety, developed at this latter location,

Table 3D-1—Relationship between LAI and C (crop growth rate) for
erectophile and planophile barley plants

Year*	LAI		C, $g\ m^{-2}\ day^{-1}$	
	Erectophile	Planophile	Erectophile	Planophile
1964	9 3	9. 5	30 6	25. 7
1965	3. 2	3. 5	23. 6	23. 9

* 1964 normal moisture, above normal temperature during vegetative period; 1965
much below normal moisture, near normal temperature during vegetative period.

Table 3D-2—Effect of weed competition on yield of wheats
of differing morphologies

	Location A		Location B	
	Yield	Height	Yield	Height
	kg/ha	cm	kg/ha	cm
Check I	3,767	114	3,329	114
Short upright	3,787	86	2,132	79
Tall leafy*	3,181	112	3,094	119
Check II	4,029	112	2,885	114

* Developed at Location B. Location A — Broad-leafed weeds controlled chemically;
Location B — Broad-leafed weeds present.

showed little reduction in yield at the weedy location. At one location
the results would indicate that the short upright variety should be discarded immediately, while the results at the other location would indicate future possibilities.

These observations emphasize the fact that selections made from a
breeding program reflect the environment in which the nursery was
evaluated. In the example cited here, weed competition at the one location represented a selection pressure in favor of tall leafy types, i.e.
performance was based primarily on the plants' ability to compete with
weeds. However the competition with weeds in this instance was no less
of a deterrent in selecting for yield than was the selection and evaluation
of rice (Oryza sativa L.) strains under a low nitrogen regime (as indicated by previous speakers) or, in all likelihood, the 100 cm (40-inch)
row commonly used in corn (Zea mays L.) breeding programs.

4

Physiological Significance of Internal Water Relations to Crop Yield

R. O. SLATYER

Australian National University
Canberra City, Australia

I. INTRODUCTION

The overall effects of water deficits on crop yield are known to everybody. Moderate water deficiencies can result in stunting, distorted development, and much reduced crop yields, and prolonged drought can cause complete crop failure.

Despite these visible symptoms of deficiency, a clear and unambiguous statement as to the effect of deficits on crop yield is difficult to make, for a variety of reasons. Firstly, despite the importance of the phenomenon to agriculture in most of the food producing countries of the world, relatively little attention has been devoted to its water deficits. Secondly, and in part this is a reason for the relative lack of effort, plant water status is a highly dynamic parameter, strongly influenced by conditions in the soil and atmospheric microenvironment, and also regulated to different degrees in different situations and with different species, by physiological factors. It therefore constitutes a difficult parameter to examine experimentally. Thirdly, as is the case with most types of lesion, water deficits affect the growth and development of crops in many ways, both directly and indirectly. Consequently, it is frequently difficult to assign cause and effect relationships with confidence.

Partly because of these complications, perhaps only two valid generalizations can be made as a basis for this paper:

1) In most crops growth and development proceed completely unimpaired, and crop yield is maximal, only when high water status is maintained throughout the life of the crop.
2) The deleterious effects of water deficits are usually most pronounced in tissues and organs which are in stages of most rapid growth and development.

It follows from the second point that there are periods of growth when there is relatively greater or lesser sensitivity to water stress,

53

as far as economic crop yield is concerned. To give some idea of the significance of this phenomenon, it need only be stated that with some crops it is a practice on farms to impose stress at certain growth stages with a view to influencing development and improving the economic (though not necessarily the maximum) yield. Clearly this example already gives causes for concern as to the validity of the first generalization!

II. DEVELOPMENT OF INTERNAL WATER DEFICITS

The phrase "internal water deficit" means that the water potential (Ψ) of the cell, tissue, or organ under consideration has dropped below the reference value of zero potential, where it would be at equilibrium with pure, free water. At zero water potential, the individual cells are fully turgid; as the water potential drops, cell turgor pressure drops and, when the cell water potential reaches the level at which cell turgor pressure is zero, the cell is quite flaccid. A leaf containing cells at this level of water potential can be expected to be completely wilted as long as its structural characteristics permit wilting to occur.

It is often said that internal water deficits develop in plants because transpiration exceeds absorption. Although this statement is true, in the most general terms, the rate of absorption relative to that of transpiration is not the only factor affecting the internal water deficit. A proper understanding of the manner in which internal water deficits develop requires a more detailed examination of the diurnal and day-to-day changes which occur in transpiration, absorption, and soil and plant water potential, and the reasons for these changes.

The level of plant water potential, and hence of internal water deficit, is influenced by two main factors: (i) the level of the soil water potential, and (ii) the diurnal lag of absorption behind transpiration. In turn each of these factors is influenced by other factors, both environmental and physiological.

For absorption to occur a gradient of water potential must extend from soil to leaf. (Although, in various segments of the transpiration pathway, component potentials rather than the total water potential may control water transport, the generalization that flow is controlled by total water potential is acceptable for the purposes of this discussion.) It follows that as soil water content (and soil water potential) is progressively reduced during a period of rainless weather, there is a concomitant drop in the level of plant water potential. That is, plant water potential cannot be higher than soil water potential (except in the rare situation of absorption of atmospheric water by shoots of plants), hence there is a base level of plant water potential and internal water deficit which is limited by the level of soil water potential.

Superimposed on this base level is the additional water deficit, and plant water potential drop, associated with the daily rhythm of transpiration and absorption. At the beginning of each day transpiration initially removes water from the leaves, and reduces leaf water potential (Ψ_{leaf}) below its dawn value, without compensating absorption. Although absorption commences as soon as potential gradients extend

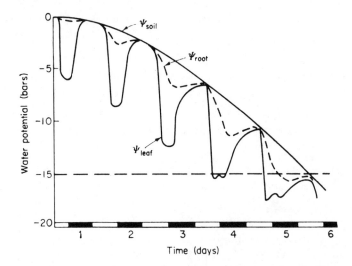

Fig. 4-1—Schematic representation of changes in leaf water potential (Ψ_{leaf}), root surface water potential (Ψ_{root}) and soil water potential (Ψ_{soil}) as transpiration proceeds from a plant rooted in initially wet soil (Ψ_{soil}) = 0). The same evaporative conditions are assumed to prevail each day. The horizontal dashed line indicates the value of Ψ_{leaf} at which wilting occurs (from Slatyer, 1967).

down to and across the soil-root interface, the quantitative lag of total absorption behind total transpiration, and hence the magnitude of the internal water deficit, continues to increase until the rate of absorption equals the rate of transpiration and is only reduced when it becomes more rapid.

The interrelationships between these two phenomena are illustrated schematically in Fig. 4-1 from Slatyer (1967). Assuming that the same evaporation conditions prevail each day, the upper limiting curve shows the progressive decline in the water potential of the soil mass, Ψ_{soil}, as the soil dries from an initially wet condition ($\Psi_{soil} = 0$). The other curves show the water potential at the root surface, Ψ_{root}, and in the leaves, Ψ_{leaf}, assuming that transpiration proceeds for 12 hours and then ceases for 12 hours.

From the diagram, the progressive decline in soil water potential from day to day, which limits the level of plant water potential, and hence provides a lower limit for the internal water deficit, can clearly be seen. Also evident is the manner in which leaf and root water potential drop below this limiting value each day and tend to recover to the equilibrium value ($\Psi_{soil} = \Psi_{root} - \Psi_{leaf}$) each night.

It can be seen that when the soil is wet (days 1, 2), only small differences in ($\Psi_{soil} - \Psi_{root}$), i.e., small internal water deficits, are needed to sustain flow. As soon as transpiration falls in the evening there is a rapid recovery of Ψ_{plant} and hence a rapid elimination of the diurnal water deficit. As Ψ_{soil} continues to fall, however (days 3, 4), the hydraulic conductivity of the soil declines rapidly so that larger values of ($\Psi_{soil} - \Psi_{root}$) are required to maintain flow at the desired

level. By day 4 partial stomatal closure retards flow below potential
levels, but even so recovery at night to the point where Ψ_{leaf} = Ψ_{soil}
becomes progressively slower.

As leaf water content and Ψ_{leaf} decline, leaf cell turgor also declines and, depending on cell volume/turgor pressure relationships and
the structural characteristics of the leaves concerned, they will gradually become wilted. There is good evidence that, in those leaves which
do exhibit complete wilting, this occurs at the point when cell turgor
pressure reaches zero (see Slatyer 1957a, 1957b; Gardner and Nieman,
1964).

Slatyer (1957a) proposed that at the point where Ψ_{leaf} had dropped
to a stage at which cell turgor pressure was zero, and when Ψ_{leaf} =
Ψ_{root} = Ψ_{soil}, the plant would be in a state of permanent wilting and the
soil water content would be the permanent wilting percentage. This
point is indicated in Fig. 4-1 by the line drawn horizontally across the
diagram at an arbitrary level of -15 bars, but it should be recalled that
the actual soil water potentials at which permanent wilting occurs can
vary over a wide range (Slatyer, 1957b).

Most physiological processes are affected by water deficits severe
enough to cause permanent wilting. Some processes are sensitive to
much smaller and more transient deficits. Clearly, transpiration, even
in wet soil, cannot occur without the development of at least small water
deficits, so it is virtually impossible to grow plants without some exposure to water stress. In the following discussion, most attention will
be devoted to stresses which are severe enough to cause at least moderate wilting for short periods of time.

III. EFFECTS OF WATER DEFICITS ON SOME PHYSIOLOGICAL PROCESSES

The growth and development of a plant depends, in the simplest
terms, on the progressive initiation of tissue and organ primordia and
on the differentiation and expansion of the component cells until the
characteristic form of the plant is realized. Associated with this phenomenon (basically genetically controlled) is an interconnected web of
metabolic events which involve the uptake of nutrients from soil and air,
the synthesis of metabolites and structural materials, and the transport
of substances within the plant body.

Since all plant processes take place in what is effectively an aqueous medium, and since water is involved as a transporting agent or as
a reactant in many of these processes, it is not surprising that reduced
water uptake and dehydration can have deleterious effects on most physiological processes.

A consideration of the effect of water deficits on physiological
processes cannot ignore the role of plant development in influencing
the character of plant metabolism. Although reproductive development
will be separately considered later in the paper, some general aspects
of water deficits and plant development will be mentioned at this stage.

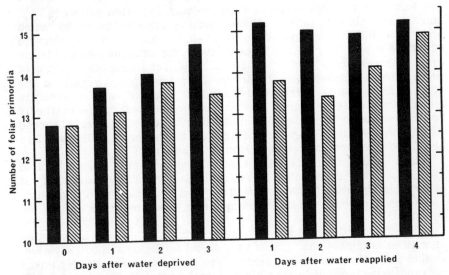

Fig. 4-2—Numbers of foliar primordia in Lupin apices during water deprival and upon rewatering (shaded columns) compared with well watered controls (solid columns) (after Gates, 1968).

A. Water Deficits and Growth Processes

Both the initiation and differentiation of vegetative and reproductive primordia in the apical meristems, and the enlargement of the cells thus differentiated, are very sensitive to water stress.

The effect on primordial initiation appears to be superficially similar to that of dormancy, in the sense that initiation can be completely suspended without the potential for subsequent development being impaired, as long as the stress is not too severe or too protracted. Fig. 4-2 from Gates (1968) provides a good illustration of this point, using apical development of Lupin as experimental material. The virtual cessation of appearance of new primordia, as soon as stress was imposed, followed by renewed development upon relief of stress, is a phenomenon that has frequently been referred to in water stress literature (see for example Gates 1955a, 1968; Slatyer, 1967).

Cell division is also sensitive to stress, but the observation that leaves of plants which have undergone periods of stress may contain a similar number of cells to unstressed controls (Petinov; cited by Slatyer, 1965) suggests that the capacity for resumed activity upon relief of stress may remain unimpaired. As distinct from the situation with primordial initiation, however, where complete suspension may occur, cell division may continue during stress, though at a much reduced rate, until quite severe conditions exist (Gardner and Nieman, 1964). This provides the opportunity for a relatively rapid resumption of expansion growth when stress is removed.

The renewed development upon re-watering often proceeds at a more rapid rate than in the controls, enabling stressed plants to "catch up." This phenomenon, evident in Fig. 4-2, has also been demonstrated on a field scale. Morton and Watson (1948), for example, showed that a crop of sugar beets (Beta vulgaris L.), subject to repeated cycles of water stress interspersed by irrigations, developed, overall, at the same rate as the well irrigated controls. Even so, where stress is more severe or is protracted, the rate of development can be markedly reduced, delayed flowering and maturation frequently being observed (Salter and Goode, 1967). In addition, the character of both vegetative and floral development can be seriously affected.

Cell enlargement, the other essential component of growth, is also affected at very slight stress levels. In fact, this is usually the first observable symptom of water deficits, and is a main cause of the stunting which is perhaps the most common sign of water stress under field conditions.

The main difference between the long-term effect of reduced rates of cell enlargement, and that of primordial initiation and cell division, is that cell enlargement is a plastic type of phenomenon, closely linked with the laying down of fairly rigid cell wall materials (Plaut and Ordin, 1964). In consequence, slower rates of enlargement are generally associated with smaller final cell size, so that "catching up," of the type referred to with regard to primordial initiation, is largely precluded.

In some species cell enlargement is so sensitive to water deficits that stem elongation or leaf enlargement can be inhibited by small diurnal water deficits that occur even with well watered plants on days of high radiation incidence (see for example Loomis, 1934). A more general response is one of a progressive decline in rates of cell enlargement as water deficits develop. Slatyer (1957a) suggested that rate of cell enlargement is more or less proportional to turgor pressure, but this is seldom a simple relationship (Lockhart, 1965) and enlargement may cease when turgor pressure levels are still at the level of several bars (Boyer, 1968).

Associated with these reduced rates of organ development and cell enlargement are many indirect effects on physiological processes, since nutrient inflow, and protein and carbohydrate synthesis and metabolism, are immediately affected by reduced developmental activity of cells and tissues. A key implication to final biological yield follows from the effect of reduction in cell expansion on total leaf area. This reduces the size of the photosynthesizing surface and can be expected to reduce crop growth rate unless leaf area is not limiting net assimilation rate.

The effect of water stress on the continued development of tissues which are already mature, or approaching maturity, resembles that of hastened senescence. One of the earliest signs of stress is the migration of phosphorus from older leaves to the stems and meristematic tissue (Williams and Shapter, 1955; Gates, 1957). This is closely followed by the movement of nitrogen, suggesting progressive protein hydrolysis and breakdown of normal cell function. Furthermore the stomata tend to remain closed and become nonfunctional (Slatyer and Bierhuizen, 1964).

Little is known of the effects of water deficits on root development.

Although it is sometimes stated that root development is enhanced relative to shoot development during stress, there is little quantitative information on this point (Weaver, 1926; Troughton, 1962; Salim, Todd, and Schlehuber, 1965).

Two types of effects can be expected, the first being a reduction in rates of meristematic activity, and of root elongation, directly associated with the level of internal water deficit; the second, an effect of suberization on the water and nutrient uptake properties of the root system as a whole.

Most research has shown a progressive reduction in rate of root elongation as water stress is imposed (Salim, Todd, and Schlehuber, 1965; Newman, 1966) and, in some cases, root elongation ceases before shoot growth. In this regard Newman's (1966) work with flax (Linum usitatissimum L.) shows a high dependence of rate of root extension on local soil water potential. Thus roots in relatively moist soil may continue to elongate even though the plant as a whole is subject to severe internal water stress. In consequence continued exploration of the soil mass by root systems might be expected until the root zone is reduced to the same general level of water potential.

The effect of water stress on suberization can be expected to vary depending on the local rates of root extension. In rapidly growing roots a nonsuberized zone of 10-20 cm may occur in some species, constituting a highly active and extensive absorbing surface. As rates of root elongation are reduced the rate of suberization exceeds the rate of elongation, and the nonsuberized zone is reduced, until it is virtually eliminated in nonelongating roots. This phenomenon, common under conditions of severe water stress, substantially reduces the effective surface of the roots and their activity as absorbing organs.

In summary, it can be stated that the effect of stress on growth tends to be most pronounced in those tissues which are in rapid stages of development, a conclusion already reached by other workers (Williams and Shapter, 1955; Gates, 1968). Primordial initiation and cell enlargement are particularly susceptible. Although cell enlargement does not appear to compensate following the removal of stress, initiation does as long as the stress has not been too severe. The developing tissues appear to enter a rejuvenating phase on relief of stress. Relative growth rates of such plants may be more rapid than those of controls (Gates, 1955a, 1955b; Williams and Shapter, 1955). This rapid growth is aided by the continued, slow cell division which has occurred, and by the availability of nutrients released from older tissues.

B. Water Deficits and Physiological Processes

The effect of water stress on such key processes as nutrient uptake, carbohydrate and protein metabolism, and translocation of ions and metabolites is intimately linked with the effects on development since, as has been mentioned above, the rate of development affects both the supply and demand situation for many physiological processes.

For example, root development affects the size and character of the absorbing system for mineral nutrients; shoot development affects the rate of carbohydrate metabolism. The source strength represented by the size and activity of the photosynthetic system and the sink strength represented by tissue which requires carbohydrate, but which is not actively photosynthesizing, influences the rate of translocation.

However, direct effects of water stress on many key processes can be identified and some of these will now be considered.

1. Water Deficits and Water Transport

First of all, water stress directly affects water transport through the plant, and hence the rate of water absorption and transpiration. Under conditions of high soil water status, with only small gradients of water potential required for transport, the water potential drop in the leaves (needed to maintain high rates of flow) is relatively small and the stomata remain open. Transpiration is then primarily determined by environmental factors, particularly the amount of energy received by the plant and the factors which affect air flow around the leaves.

As soil water content falls, however, the water potential gradients required to move water to the roots and on to the leaves increase so that leaf water potential drops to levels which induce stomatal closure. Initially this phenomenon occurs for only a short period around midday. Commonly, transpiration is reduced to a level which enables absorption to exceed transpiration so that leaf water potential rises and the stomata generally re-open after a couple of hours. (This can also occur in well watered soils, when periods of excessive evaporative demand may cause marked reduction of leaf water potential.)

As soil water content continues to fall the period each day over which partial or complete stomatal closure occurs extends—the stomata closing earlier and re-opening later each day and acting as flow regulators to minimize dehydration.

The degree to which stomatal closure, in the light, is influenced by water deficits alone is beyond the scope of the present paper. However, it should be pointed out that Meidner and Mansfield (1965) have suggested that diurnal increase in leaf temperature may induce midday closure by increasing respiration rate and the level of intercellular CO_2 concentration. The same phenomenon would tend to maintain closure until opening was induced by turgor recovery, or by photosynthetic depletion of intercellular CO_2.

A direct consequence of stomatal closure is a tendency for reduced water uptake and transport, and for reduced gas exchange by the leaves, especially of water vapor and CO_2. There is usually an increase in leaf temperature associated with a greater disposition of the absorbed energy into sensible heat transfer rather than evaporation. Perhaps the most significant effect is that on CO_2 exchange which can directly regulate photosynthesis.

2. Water Deficits and Nutrient Uptake

The effect of water stress on mineral nutrition is difficult to resolve clearly. Although mineral nutrient uptake is frequently reduced to a considerable degree in stressed plants (Williams and Shapter, 1955; Greenway, Klepper, and Hughes, 1968), nutrient uptake is not directly

Table 4-1—Absolute and relative amounts of nitrogen and phosphorus in the laminae and stems of severely stressed and unstressed tomato plants

| Plant part | Nitrogen | | | | Phosphorus | | | |
| | Control | | Stress | | Control | | Stress | |
	mg/plant	% dry weight	mg/plant	% dry weight	mg/plant	% dry weight	mg/plant	% dry weight
Laminae	137	6.1	88	5.4	14.7	0.66	8.0	0.49
Stem	51	4.2	37	3.8	7.2	0.59	4.5	0.45

* After Gates (1957).

dependent on water uptake (Russell and Barber, 1960) and soil nutrient availability, per se, is not necessarily affected by soil water stress (Wadleigh and Richards, 1951; Fawcett and Quirk, 1962) at least in the available soil water range.

Since the demand for nutrients also declines progressively, due both to the reduced rates of plant development and to the migration of nutrients out of older leaves, the key point is whether or not reduced nutrient uptake retards growth and development in a plant under stress.

Table 4-1 from Gates (1957) shows the absolute and relative levels of nitrogen and phosphorus in tomato plants (Lycopersicum esculentum Mill.) following "severe" stress. Although uptake of both elements was clearly depressed by the stress treatment, as shown by the absolute figures, the change in relative amounts is much smaller, and Gates does not comment on deficiency symptoms as such. A similar pattern emerged from a very comprehensive study of most nutrient ions (Williams and Shapter, 1955).

Although overall effects on nutrient content may not show marked changes, Gates (1957) has shown that the pattern can vary to a much greater degree when individual leaves are considered. In well watered plants, both nitrogen and phosphorus content decreased as leaf age increased. In stressed plants, nitrogen and phosphorus levels were also reduced, the younger leaves showing the greatest reduction, and phosphorus showing earlier and more pronounced reductions than nitrogen. With both nutrients there was a tendency for migration from leaf to stem as stress was imposed.

In summary it seems likely that nutrient supply may retard some aspects of growth and development during stress imposition. It is of interest to note that, upon re-watering, Gates observed a reversal of the above trends, with the preferential distribution of both nitrogen and phosphorus leading to greater uptake in the younger leaves. In the older leaves the senescence induced by stress was not completely reversed (see also Gates, 1968).

C. Water Deficits, Protein Synthesis and Nitrogen Metabolism

In general there appears to be a reasonably clear dependence of the growth rate of developing tissues and organs on protein synthesis, and a close association between protein synthesis and RNA (ribonucleic acid) content, and between RNA and DNA levels (deoxyribonucleic acid)

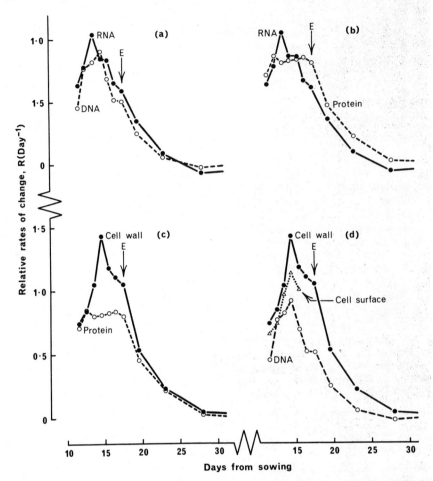

Fig. 4-3—Relative rates of change in various attributes of the fourth leaf of a wheat plant from initiation to maturation. E is time of leaf emergence. (a) DNA and RNA, (b) RNA and protein nitrogen, (c) protein nitrogen and cell wall material, (d) DNA, cell wall material and cell surface (from Williams and Rijven, 1965).

(see for example Woodstock and Skoog, 1960, 1962; Williams and Rijven, 1965). (Figure 4-3 from Williams and Rijven (1965) shows the nature of some of the associated phenomena for a developing wheat leaf (Triticum aestivum L.), although these authors are very cautious in the degree to which they associate any pair of these parameters, or assign cause and effect relationships.

From the known effects of water stress on rate of development, it can be expected that there will be associated effects on many aspects of protein synthesis. Indeed, interruption of protein synthesis and proteolysis are generally observed when stress is imposed (Zholkevich

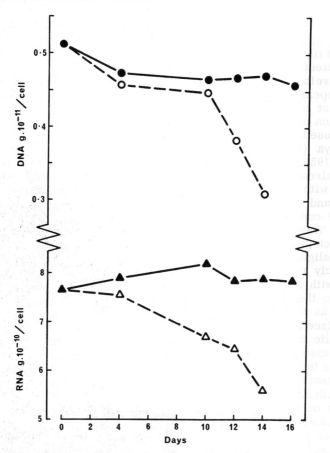

Fig. 4-4—DNA and RNA concentrations, expressed on a per cell basis, for stressed (dashed line) and unstressed (continuous line) sugar beet leaves. The progressive onset on stress caused wilting of the leaves from about day 10 onwards (after Shah and Loomis, 1965).

and Koretskaya, 1959; Chen, Kessler, and Monselise, 1964; Shah and Loomis, 1965; Ben-Zioni, Itai, and Vaadia, 1967).

Although few studies of the effects of water stress on nucleic acid metabolism have been made, the results form a fairly consistent pattern.

In the first place Shah and Loomis (1965) found a tendency for the DNA content per cell, which remained relatively constant with age in expanding beet leaves, to be reduced by water stress only if severe wilting occurred and was protracted (see Fig. 4-4). Gardner and Nieman (1964) showed a marked reduction of the rate of increase in DNA content of developing, and presumably actively dividing, cotyledonary leaves of radish at slight stress levels, but also found that there was still some increase in DNA level when severe stress was imposed. Together these results appear to be consistent with a marked sensitivity of cell division to stress, but with cell breakdown occurring only in developed tissues and under severe and prolonged stress conditions.

An effect on RNA levels (see also Fig. 4-4) tends to occur at lower stress levels and the ratio of RNA in stressed to that of unstressed leaves appears to decline progressively. Shah and Loomis (1965) concluded that RNA synthesis was impaired by stress and also that some degradation occurred in the RNA which was already formed when stress was imposed. A similar conclusion was reached by Zholkevich and Koretskaya (1959) with pumpkin roots (Cucurbita pepo). Gates and Bonner (1959) attributed the relative decline to enhanced degradation of RNA already formed rather than to impeded synthesis, because of evidence with ^{32}P-labelled RNA which showed that, while total RNA increased and total activity remained constant in the controls, total RNA remained constant in stressed plants and there was a progressive loss of label. They considered that the continued synthesis provided a base from which growth could be rapidly resumed upon rewatering.

The slightly different responses observed by these various workers is probably related in some degree to the developmental stage of the tissues with which they worked. A similar comment can probably be applied to the rather inconclusive results obtained to date by different workers as to the effect of water stress on the nucleotide composition of RNA (see for example Kessler, 1961; Shah and Loomis, 1965; West, 1966; Stutte and Todd, 1967).

The association between RNA and protein levels (see Fig. 4-3) was also found to be closely linked in stressed leaves, as shown in Fig. 4-5. On the assumption that ribosomal RNA plays a key role in protein synthesis, both Shah and Loomis (1965) and West (1966) examined the effect of stress on the level of ribosomal RNA, but no consistent pattern of change emerged from these studies, perhaps due to differences in treatments and to material studied. In beet leaves Shah and Loomis (1965) found a reduction in ribosomal RNA and a change in its nucleotide composition, with stress, whereas in corn seedling stems (Zea mays L.) West (1966) found an increase in ribosomal RNA and no change in composition. West did show, however, that polysome formation was slowed by stress and proposed that an effect of stress on messenger RNA could be a primary cause of reduced protein synthesis.

The changes reported previously in uptake and movement of nitrogen and phosphorus are consistent with the effects on nucleic acid and protein synthesis, suggesting that in expanding leaves the normal tendency to synthesize soluble nitrogen and phosphorus into more highly organized compounds was checked by water stress and that, especially in older leaves, hydrolytic breakdown processes tend to occur.

The role of certain growth substances, particularly auxins, gibberellins, and kinins, in retarding senescence, and the general similarity of many stress effects to processes associated with senescence, has provoked interest in the role of growth substances in water stress phenomena. In regard to protein synthesis, Richmond and Lang (1957) and Osborne (1965) have shown that the addition of cytokinins to the leaves of a number of annual plants has retarded chlorophyll degradation and has promoted amino acid incorporation and protein synthesis.

Recently Ben-Zioni, Itai, and Vaadia (1967) have examined the

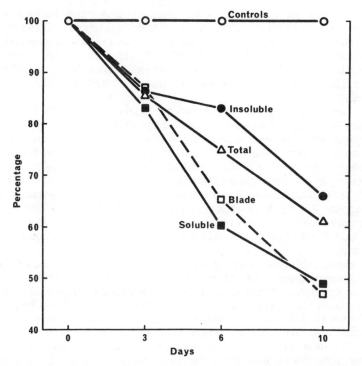

Fig. 4-5—Concentrations of total, soluble and insoluble RNA (continuous lines) and of leaf blade protein (dashed line) in leaves of stressed sugar beet plants, expressed relative to levels in non-stressed plants (after Shah and Loomis, 1965).

effect of kinetin in the incorporation of L-leucine in stressed tobacco leaves (Nicotiana tabacum L.). Even though the stress imposed was brief, and mild (about -4 bars water potential), stressed tissues showed a marked reduction in ability to incorporate L-leucine into protein, the reduction being more pronounced in older than younger leaves. Stressed plants also had lower kinin levels in the root exudate, than did control plants.

The addition of kinetin restored incorporation in stressed leaves to levels approximating that of the controls, although a higher applied kinetin concentration was required to achieve this effect, compared with levels in control plants. (It should be noted that the kinetin was applied after stress; a greater effect may have followed its application prior to stress.) These workers are cautious in assigning a causal role for kinin level in protein synthesis, and point out that reductions in both kinin levels and protein synthesis could be merely reflections of disturbed metabolism. However, the known effects of kinins on rate of senescence suggests that kinin supply to the shoot is important in the maintenance of active protein synthesis, and also suggests that studies of root development and metabolism in relation to hormone balance may provide important insights into aspects of stress physiology.

A frequently observed effect of stress is the appearance of high levels of free amino acids, especially proline, and amides (Chen, Kessler, and Monselise, 1964; Kemple and Macpherson, 1954; Mothes, 1956; Prusakova, 1960). This phenomenon was recently investigated by Barnett and Naylor (1966) who found that although amino acids were continually synthesized during water stress in bermudagrass (Cynodon dactylon (L.) Pers.) protein synthesis was inhibited and protein levels decreased.

In their experiments water stress induced a marked increase in free proline, the C^{14} level of which turned over very slowly. Stressed shoots accumulated much more proline newly synthesized from glutamic acid than did control shoots. It was suggested that the slow turnover of labelled proline may reflect an inhibition of proline catabolism.

There is no clear understanding of the significance of this rise in proline level. However, Barnett and Naylor (1966) suggested that free proline may act as a storage compound for both carbon and nitrogen during water stress, when both starch and protein synthesis are inhibited. Such a storage pool might be utilized for renewed growth upon rewatering.

Various inhibitors have also been observed to influence development. Among them CCC (2 chloroethyltrimethylammonium chloride) (see, for example, Humphries, 1968) has created considerable interest and has been claimed to increase cereal yield under stress conditions. Humphries (1968) has reviewed the literature on this phenomenon and concluded that the primary effect of CCC is to increase root growth relative to shoot growth, thus delaying the onset of stress and reducing its severity. There may be a link between the role of CCC and that of kinin since the effects of CCC on root growth may influence the supply of kinins to the shoot, perhaps leading to stress tolerance.

D. Water Deficits, Photosynthesis, and Carbohydrate Metabolism

Carbohydrate metabolism can be affected in a number of ways by water deficits. There appear to be direct and indirect effects on photosynthesis, and on a number of intermediate components and processes.

In general, net photosynthesis is progressively reduced by water stress, and negative values may develop when stress is severe (El-Sharkawy and Hesketh, 1964; Slatyer, 1967). It is assumed that this response is mediated partly by a way of impeded CO_2 supply following stomatal closure and partly by a direct effect of dehydration on the photosynthetic system. Although many experiments have been conducted with a view to assessing the relative importance of stomatal closure and dehydration (see for example Crafts, 1968), they are of questionable value unless a quantitative measurement of the gas phase resistances to CO_2 transport has been made, or treatments have been imposed which render this measurement unnecessary. In my opinion few such experiments have as yet been conducted.

One such study, conducted with cotton leaves (Gossypium hirsutum L.) (Troughton, 1969), has provided evidence that the observed reduction in net photosynthesis with increasing stress can be completely attributed to stomatal closure until quite severe stress exists. The type of

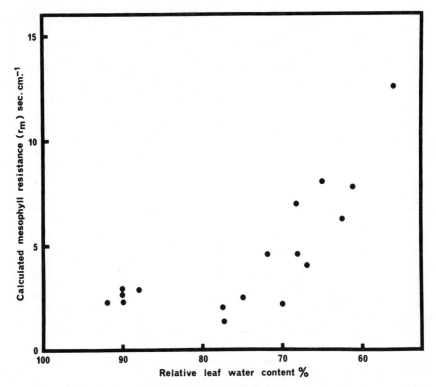

Fig. 4-6—Effect of water deficits on mesophyll resistance of cotton leaves (after Troughton, 1968).

evidence obtained is shown in Fig. 4-6 where the change in mesophyll resistance caused by reductions in relative water content is plotted. Mesophyll resistance is the slope of the curve relating CO_2 concentration (between the mesophyll cell wall surfaces and the chloroplasts) to CO_2 exchange. Any reduction in CO_2 exchange, per unit of CO_2 supplied, causes an increase in mesophyll resistance. It can be seen from Fig. 4-6 that there was no increase in mesophyll resistance in cotton leaves until relative water contents of about 75% were reached. Since cotton leaves wilt at relative water contents of around 80-85%, severe stress, corresponding to leaf water potentials of the order of -20 bars, existed before direct effects of dehydration appeared.

Although other work suggests that mesophyll resistance may change at lower stress values (Meidner, 1961, 1962) it is not certain that stomatal or temperature effects were avoided. Assuming that generalizations can be drawn from Troughton's work, the results of Baker and Musgrave (1964) who showed reductions of net photosynthesis in corn of up to 40-50% at slight stress levels, may also be attributable to stomatal closure.

If progressive stomatal closure is the primary cause of the first stages of the photosynthetic response to water stress, there should be supporting evidence from other types of experiments which indicate that the photosynthetic apparatus, and the reactions associated with respiration, are relatively unaffected until severe water stress exists.

As far as the photosynthetic apparatus is concerned, the recent work of Santarius and colleagues (Santarius and Heber, 1967; Santarius and Ernst, 1967; Santarius, 1967) with isolated chloroplasts, and with leaf tissue segments, has provided evidence that such key processes in the photosynthetic reduction of CO_2 as adenosine triphosphate (ATP) synthesis, the reduction of nicotinamide adenine dinucleotide phosphate (NADP) and the reduction of phosphoglyceric acid (PGA), were unaffected until very severe stress existed. In the leaf segments this corresponded to relative water contents of less than 50% (probably equivalent to water potentials below -25 bars). Although Santarius observed reductions in net photosynthesis, no attempt was made to control or assess stomatal effects or other aspects of the CO_2 supply system; the key results, therefore, are those just reported.

Recent experiments by Troughton and Slatyer (1969) have also provided evidence of the tolerance of gross photosynthesis to water deficits. In experiments in which photorespiration was suppressed by oxygen-free air, no effect on the mesophyll resistance of cotton leaves was observed even when relative water contents of 55% were imposed (equivalent to water potentials of about -50 bars). Since respiration was suppressed the experiment effectively demonstrated that gross photosynthesis was unaffected by stresses of this magnitude.

The effect of water deficits on respiration is somewhat obscure, partly because of the failure of many investigators to distinguish between dark respiration and photorespiration in those species in which the latter process is evident, partly because of the difficulties in measuring photorespiration, and partly because of possible differences in short term and long term effects.

With regard to dark respiration most recent studies have indicated that it is relatively unaffected by water deficits, until at least moderate water stress exists, and that a reduction rather than an increase is likely to occur. With Chlorella, for example, Greenway and Hiller (1967) found that water potentials of -10 bars did not affect respiration over periods of about 2 hours, although reductions were observed when the water potential was reduced to -20 bars. In short term (several minutes) experiments even water potentials of this level did not affect the uptake of acetate 2 - ^{14}C and also had little effect on the distribution or level of ^{14}C in the intermediates of the tricarboxylic acid (TCA) cycle, suggesting that there was no pronounced inhibition of respiratory pathways. In longer term (up to 56 hours) experiments with beet leaves, referred to above, Santarius (1967) found that dark respiration was not reduced until extremely severe stress (water potentials probably below -100 bars), existed.

The effect of water stress on photorespiration is difficult to assess because photosynthesis is proceeding at the same time. One index of an effect is a change in the CO_2 compensation point and Meidner (1961, 1962) has measured increases in this parameter, as stress was imposed in several species, suggesting that photorespiration increases even at moderate stress levels. By comparison, Troughton and Slatyer

(1969) did not observe a change in the CO_2 compensation point of cotton leaves under the stress conditions previously reported. A complicating factor in all respiration work is the marked dependence of dark respiration, and more particularly photorespiration, on temperature (Zelitch, 1967). Since stomatal closure generally induces an increase in leaf temperature, indirect effects of water stress on net photosynthesis through this means may outweigh direct effects of dehydration.

To summarize the preceding paragraphs, it can be stated that there is increasing evidence that stomatal closure, directly by impeding CO_2 supply and indirectly by increasing leaf temperature, may be the primary mechanism by which water stress leads to reduced net photosynthesis under natural conditions. Much more work remains to be done however, before this matter is resolved.

Another factor which has been observed to influence photosynthesis is the availability of suitable sinks for assimilates. When utilization of assimilates is impeded, substantial reductions of net photosynthetic rate have been observed (see for example Burt, 1964; Nösberger and Humphries, 1965).

Again, the response pattern can be expected to vary between species. In species which can store significant amounts of assimilate as starch in the leaves, any effect can be expected to be much less than in species in which there is little starch storage, such as wheat. In wheat, King, Wardlaw, and Evans (1967) have shown dramatic and pronounced effects of sink size on photosynthesis, under nonstressed conditions.

During water stress, it appears quite probable that assimilates may be accumulated at sites of photosynthesis, since expansion growth is probably restricted sooner, and to a greater degree, than photosynthesis. Wardlaw (1967, 1969) examined this phenomenon in wheat and ryegrass (Lolium temulentum). He concluded that, although leaf photosynthesis was not affected until after growth rate had been reduced, there was no evidence of sink size directly affecting the rate of photosynthesis. However, he conceded that this interpretation could be revised, and that lack of suitable sinks could retard photosynthesis under appropriate conditions.

Wardlaw (1967, 1969) also examined the translocation mechanism. in these experiments. As Table 4-2 shows, he found that the velocity of assimilate movement in the conducting system was not reduced, as

Table 4-2—Effect of progressive water stress imposition in wheat during grain development on photosynthesis and velocity of translocation

Days after water deprived	Photosynthesis	Velocity of assimilate movement	
		Flag leaf sheath	Top internode
	mg CO_2 dm^{-2} hr^{-1}	———— cm hr^{-1} ————	
0	12.40	33	45
2	13.25	42	36
4	12.30	27	39
6†	7.15	39	72

* After Wardlaw (1967).   † Leaves wilted.

long as adequate sink capacity existed, and concluded that the conducting system was remarkably resistant to water stress. Although these results conflicted with the conclusions of some other workers (Zholkevich, Prusakova, and Lizandr, 1958; Plaut and Reinhold, 1965; Hartt, 1967), which suggest a direct effect of stress on translocation, sink capacity may have been a factor in some of those experiments. The continued movement of assimilates from the green stems to the roots and buds in the perennial grass (Phalaris tuberosa) when the leaves had been shed during severe stress, indicates that the conducting tissue can be well maintained (McWilliams, 1968), even if the velocity of translocation is reduced.

Transport within the leaf does appear to be reduced by stress under some conditions. Although Plaut and Reinhold (1967) showed enhanced movement of ^{14}C applied to stressed bean leaves, Wardlaw's (1967) data and Hartt's (1967) experiments with sugarcane (Saccharum officinarum L.), show a greater retention of photosynthetic assimilates in wilted wheat leaves and a slower but prolonged movement of the assimilates out of the leaf. This result, however, may have been influenced by sink capacity because, in a subsequent experiment with perenial ryegrass, Wardlaw (1969) was able to maintain rates of movement out of stressed leaves, as long as adjacent actively photosynthesizing leaves were removed.

One of the most commonly reported effects of water deficits on carbohydrate metabolism is an increase in sucrose levels and decrease in starch levels (see for example, Iljin, 1957). These changes are frequently associated together, although there are reports of reduced polysaccharide levels not being accompanied by an increase in sugar content (Woodhams and Kozlowski, 1954).

Hiller and Greenway (1968) have recently examined more specific aspects of these phenomena in short term experiments with Chlorella. Their primary results were generally similar to those just described, water deficits (equivalent to water potentials down to -10 bars) causing a marked increase in sucrose synthesis, as measured by incorporation of applied ^{14}C-glucose into sucrose, and an immediate and pronounced suppression of polysaccharide synthesis. They also observed reduced ^{14}C incorporation into methanol soluble intermediates other than sucrose, which was more pronounced for sugar phosphates than for amino acids. Incorporation into uridine diphosphate glucose (UDPG) was depressed more than that into hexose monophosphates, especially when stress was not too severe. Generally similar reductions in sugar phosphate levels have been observed in stressed Trifolium subterraneum (Wilson and Huffaker, 1964), and in starch formation in stressed sunflower (Helianthus annuus) (Plaut and Ordin, 1964).

The question arises as to the relationship between the enhanced sucrose and reduced polysaccharide levels. Reduced starch levels have been attributed to factors such as reduced photosynthesis and increased hydrolysis as well as to decreased synthesis (see for example, Mothes, 1956; Kozlowski, 1964). Although all these factors may operate, Hiller and Greenway (1968) found little evidence of hydrolysis, at least in the short term response to stress; similar levels of ^{14}C activity in methanol-soluble compounds being observed in stressed and unstressed cells which had previously been supplied with ^{14}C-labelled bicarbonate in the light. They concluded that reduced starch formation was an indirect result of increased sucrose synthesis, rather than a direct effect of water stress on starch synthesis.

IV. EFFECT OF WATER STRESS ON GRAIN YIELD IN CEREALS

In focussing the general effects of water stress on growth and development, on to the specific problem of grain formation and crop yield, there are three key stages to be considered. The first of these is the stage of floral initiation and inflorescence development when the potential grain number is determined. The second is the stage of anthesis and fertilization when the degree to which this potential is realized is fixed. The third is the stage of grain filling when grain weight progressively increases.

Although many aspects of yield development are common to all cereals, it is difficult to generalize widely as to the effects of water stress on grain yield, because of the considerable differences which do exist, in morphogenesis generally and reproductive development in particular, between various species. In the following discussion, data will be used to illustrate both similarities and differences in development patterns.

A. Water Stress and Inflorescence Development

Dealing first with the development of the inflorescence, there is good evidence that even slight water stress can reduce the rate of appearance of floral primordia. In Lupin, as depicted in Fig. 4-2, Gates (1968) has shown that this is one of the most sensitive reactions, and a similar pattern emerges with barley (Hordeum vulgare L.) (Nicholls and May, 1963) which is probably typical for most cereals. These studies suggest that if the stress is mild, and if the period of stress is relatively brief, rate of primordial initiation, upon relief of stress, is more rapid than in the controls and the total number of spikelets formed may be unaffected. On the other hand, if the stress is severe, or prolonged, total spikelet number may be substantially reduced.

Nicholls and May (1963) provided evidence that initiation of new primordia in the barley plant concludes with the appearance of stamen initials on the first formed spikelets. This is supported by the work of Williams (1966) on unstressed wheat plants. From their observations, Nicholls and May suggest that the number of spikelets per inflorescence is determined by the balance between the rate of primordial initiation relative to that of spikelet development. Since spikelet development appeared to be less affected by stress than primordial initiation, it follows that prolonged stress at the stage of floral initiation could markedly reduce the potential number of grains per ear.

An example of this effect is given in Fig. 4-7 where data from Nicholls and May (1963) are presented. The treatments consisted of a well watered control, and two water stress treatments. All treatments

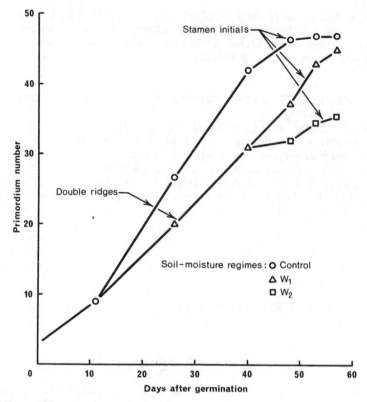

Fig. 4-7—Number of primordia formed in barley plants exposed to stress (Δ,□) compared with well watered controls (O). In the intermediate treatment (Δ) the plants were rewatered when soil water potential dropped to -5 bars (after Nicholls and May, 1963).

were well watered until about 10 days after germination. The first treatment was then deprived of water until the soil water potential dropped to -5 bars when it was rewatered, the second water stress treatment remained deprived of water (but soil water potential did not drop below -15 bars).

Compared with the control plants, the rate of primordial formation in the plants deprived of water is seen to diverge almost immediately, so that the double ridges of the first spikelet primordia did not appear until several days after floral initiation commenced in the controls. (The total number of leaf primordia initiated was, however, the same in each treatment.) Rate of initiation of floral primordia became progressively slower in the stressed plants but, upon rewatering, the rate in the "mild" stress treatment increased rapidly so that, by the time of stamen initiation, total spikelet number was almost the same as in the controls. By comparison, in the "severe" stress treatment, total spikelet number was at a much lower level at the time when development of the spike was concluded.

Although this interpretation, if it could be generally applied, would provide a simple explanation of the effects of water stress on inflorescence development in cereals, the indeterminate character of the barley inflorescence may permit this type of response to a much greater degree than in species where the spike is determinate, and the rachis terminates in an apical spikelet. The explanation appears inadequate to account for the developmental patterns observed in grain sorghum (Sorghum vulgare Pers.), for example. In experiments in which the timing and duration of stress was varied around the stage of floral initiation, but in which all treatments constituted "severe" stress (wilted for 1 week or more), Whiteman and Wilson (1965) found that the development of the inflorescence could be suspended during stress yet could be resumed on rewatering and result in a flowering head not significantly different from that of control plants.

In one experiment, in which severe stress was imposed for periods of about 1 week, on three occasions during the normal time of floral initiation, initiation was totally suspended but was resumed upon rewatering. The time at which inflorescence development was completed was delayed for approximately 10 days, as was the time to commencement of flowering (see Table 4-3). There was no reduction in head size or yield.

In another experiment, stresses were imposed at about the stage of floral initiation and persisted for 14, 21, and 28 days. Floral initiation occurred in all treatments at about the same time as in the controls (stress not being fully effective at this stage), but there was no elongation of the inflorescence in the stressed plants until rewatering. From then on, development proceeded more or less at the same rate as in the controls and emergence of flowers took place at intervals of 10, 24, and 30 days after the controls, periods corresponding fairly closely to the durations of stress.

Although sorghum is known to be a drought tolerant crop, it seems probable that, as more data are collected, differences of a similar order may emerge between other common cereals. In corn, for example, Volodarski and Zinevich (1960) have claimed that a somewhat similar phenomenon occurs to that in sorghum, retardation of ear initiation during stress being completely reversible. Unfortunately, the degree of stress imposed was not well defined and, if mild, the reversible response would be expected. However, evidence from Robins and Domingo

Table 4-3—Effect of water stress on floral initiation and time to flowering in sorghum

Period of wilting† (days from sowing)	Floral initiation (days from sowing)	Flowering (days from sowing)
Nil	23-26	58
15-21	34-37	68
19-25	34-37	68
27-35	34-37	65

* After Whiteman and Wilson (1965).
† Water was deprived well in advance of the appearance of wilting. In the last treatment sufficient stress had presumably developed prior to wilting to prevent initiation from occurring at the same time as in the controls.

(1953) and Denmead and Shaw (1960) that corn in the vegetative stage is relatively tolerant to stress, suggests that the indeterminate nature of corn ear development may lend itself to recovery of this type upon relief of stress.

From the state of spikelet initiation to fertilization of the ovules, a number of other processes, associated with the development of the inflorescence, are likely to be sensitive to water deficits, and thus cause a reduction in the number of grains per ear, or even in the number of fertile ears. Such effects have been reported in most cereals, for example in barley (Aspinall, Nicholls, and May, 1964; Skazkin and Zavadskaya, 1957; Wells and Dubetz, 1966); in oats (Avena sativa L.) (van de Paauw, 1949; Novikov, 1952, 1954; Skazkin and Lukomskaya, 1962); in wheat (Chinoy, 1962; Single, 1964; Bingham, 1967) and in corn (Robins and Domingo, 1953; Denmead and Shaw, 1960; Volodarski and Zinevich, 1960).

The effects have been attributed in some cases to specific interference with the sexual development of the spikelets, such as meiosis in the gametes (Skazkin and Lerman, 1952; Novikov, 1954; Skazkin and Zavadskaya, 1957; Bingham, 1967).

The availability of mineral nutrients and carbohydrates during the preflowering phase can also influence spikelet development, and may be an important means by which water stress effects are mediated.

Examples of this phenomenon are provided by the work of Single (1964) and Davidson (1965) with wheat. Single imposed a series of nitrogen treatments on wheat grown in nutrient culture, which involved varying the nitrogen status from severely limiting to nonlimiting conditions at various stages of development. Nitrogen deficiency prior to spikelet initiation had a predictable marked effect on spikelet number and, if the nutrient level was not increased during the later development of the inflorescence, the number of fertile florets per spikelet did not exceed one. However, an increase in the nitrogen level, after spikelet initiation but before the appearance of the flag leaf, caused a marked increase in the numeer of fertile florets and hence on final grain number.

In Davidson's experiment the leaves of the experimental plants were clipped to maintain leaf area indices (LAI's) at levels of 3 and 1, compared with levels of up to 10 in control plants. The clipping treatments commenced after floral initiation, so did not affect the number of spikelets laid down, yet grain number per spikelet was reduced from 1.57 in the controls to 0.88 and 0.76 in the two treatments, respectively.

Although water stress was not imposed in these studies, photosynthesis, and hence the supply of assimilates, was markedly reduced by the treatments which were imposed. In Single's work the supply of nitrogen to the developing inflorescence was probably also reduced, in which case additional direct effects on protein synthesis and cell development could have occurred.

These results clearly indicate the importance of stress on the progressive development of the inflorescence prior to anthesis. In some plants such as wheat, the potential for variable floret numbers provides an opportunity for compensatory effects if stress is removed. This may also apply to oats but would not apply to crops such as rye, barley, or maize in which floret number is fixed (Bonnett, 1966). On the other hand, although this type of compensation may not occur, relief of stress in many species during the stage of inflorescence development may at least permit final grain number to approach the potential represented by the number of spikelets initiated.

The effect of water stress on the floral stimulus, that is, on the number of leaves formed prior to the commencement of floral initiation, has not been investigated in much detail although it is clear that the dramatic effects associated with photoperiod are not found with water stress effects. The most pronounced effects of which I am aware are those recently reported for tobacco by Hopkinson (1968). This work showed that water stress not only delayed floral initiation but that it took place at a higher node, differences of the order of 5 nodes being recorded.

In cereals there appears to be little evidence of pronounced shifts in the number of vegetative primordia prior to floral initiation. Nicholls and May (1963) showed that, in barley, stress imposed about 10 days before floral initiation did not affect the number of vegetative primordia formed. Whiteman and Wilson (1965) with sorghum showed that as the date of onset of stress approached the normal time of floral initiation, mean leaf number could be reduced by up to 3 leaves. These workers considered that the leaf number at which floral initiation commenced may depend on the interaction between the amount of vegetative development necessary to allow the formation of a floral stimulus, and the extent to which stress may suspend development. With stress imposed well ahead of the normal time of floral initiation, there was insufficient vegetative development so that, on rewatering, leaf initiation was resumed.

By comparison, when stress was imposed closer to the normal time of floral initiation there had been sufficient vegetative development to permit the formation of a floral stimulus and, upon rewatering, floral initiation occurred at a lower leaf number. This explanation presumably requires the relatively higher leaf number, at which nonstressed plants flowered, to be influenced by a time factor which is relatively insensitive to stress, and which is associated with the passage of the floral stimulus from the leaves to the apex.

A frequently observed effect of water stress in the preflowering stage is a delay in date of flowering although some observations of advanced flowering have also been made (Salter and Goode, 1967). In sorghum, as has already been mentioned, the delay is closely related to the period of stress, but in other crops the relationship is less obvious. In wheat Chinoy (1960) showed that a period of 7 days wilting delayed anthesis by 8-18 days for eight varieties tested when applied at the preflowering stage. In this species, therefore, as compared with sorghum, post-stress development was less rapid than in control plants.

B. Water Stress and Fertilization

Stress at anthesis can markedly reduce fertilization and grain-set in most cereals. Perhaps the most sensitive crop, at this stage, appears to be corn (Robins and Domingo, 1953; Denmead and Shaw, 1960),

Table 4-4—Effect of water regime on grain yield in corn

Treatment	Yield		Shelling
	kg/ha	(lb/acre)	%
Irrigated at anthesis, plus 3 subsequent irrigations·	9,294	(8,298)	82.9
Irrigated at anthesis, plus 2 subsequent irrigations	8,930	(7,974)	81.9
Irrigated at anthesis, no subsequent irrigation	6,384	(5,700)	82.7
Wilted at anthesis, plus 2 subsequent irrigations	5,315	(4,746)	76.7
Wilted at anthesis, plus 1 subsequent irrigation	4,482	(4,002)	77.6

* After Robins and Domingo (1953).

reductions of over 50% in yield being caused by relatively brief periods of wilting (see Table 4-4).

Since water stress frequently is associated with arid atmospheric conditions, it is sometimes suggested that stress at this stage acts by way of dehydration of pollen grains. However, it also seems probable that germination of the pollen, or growth of the pollen tube from the stigma to the ovules, may be impaired.

From the work of Robins and Domingo (1953) with corn, it appears that the latter explanation was the correct one in their experiments, since adequate amounts of pollen were available from well watered plants adjacent to stressed ones. It seems likely that if the styles are wilted the germination of the pollen or the growth of the pollen tube from the stigma to the ovules may be interfered with. This could be expected to be more pronounced in corn than in other cereals.

The relative sensitivity of different species to stress at the pre-flowering and flowering stages appear to vary somewhat, but comparable stress treatments have seldom been imposed and internal water deficits have seldom been measured, so detailed comparisons are impossible.

Species which flower over an extended period, usually because of the progressive flowering of tillers which develop after the main stem, are somewhat protected from isolated periods of stress. Some compensation also occurs if stress early in the vegetative period, which may interfere with spikelet development on the main stem, serves to promote tiller development. Although tillers may not have as many spikelets as a nonstressed main stem, the total number of grains per plant may be relatively little affected by a stress which severely reduces main stem grain number (see for example Aspinall, Nicholls, and May, 1964).

C. Water Stress and Grain Filling

The third component of grain yield—weight per grain—is influenced both by pre-flowering and post-flowering conditions. In almost all cases, however, the post-flowering stage is the more important.

Yield development requires the accumulation of photosynthate in the grain. The two sources for these assimilates are photosynthesis in the ear itself and translocation from elsewhere in the plant. Although photosynthate accumulated prior to anthesis contributes to grain filling, and in some cases may provide a significant proportion of grain yield, by far the greatest contribution is usually from photosynthesis after anthesis by the ear, leaves, and stem (see for example Porter, Pal, and Martin, 1950; Thorne, 1963; Carr and Wardlaw, 1965; Allison and Watson, 1966). Figure 4-8, from Asana (1966), demonstrates this point in relation to wheat, showing that virtually all the increase in dry weight after anthesis is associated with grain filling. Clearly water stress, by reducing photosynthesis at this time, can lead to large yield decrements.

Although Wardlaw (1967, 1969) has shown fairly conclusively that there is little effect of water stress on translocation of assimilates in the conducting tissue itself, he has pointed out that translocation out of the leaves is slowed and prolonged by water stress. This phenomenon, combined with evidence that water stress hastens, rather than slows, maturation, and with the direct effect of stress on photosynthesis in the ear as well as in the leaves, contributes to lower grain weight in stressed plants.

Because grain filling is a relatively rapid process, because most of the increase in plant weight after anthesis involves grain development, and because it is a terminal process, it follows that the reduced photosynthesis at any point of the post-anthesis stage may have effects on grain weight which may not be compensated for by activity of other stages of grain filling (Aspinall, 1965).

On the other hand, there is also evidence that there may be an upper limit to grain size, and rate of grain filling, in any one phenotype

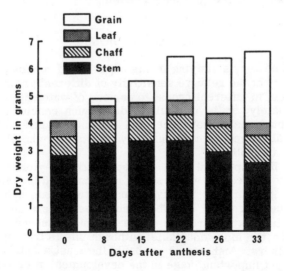

Fig. 4-8—Dry weight components of the tops of wheat plants from anthesis to maturity (after Asana, 1966).

and that, in nonstressed plants, surplus photosynthate may be available. The work of Buttrose and May (1959) in which grain removal in barley did not lead to increased weight of the remaining grains is consistent with this view. It follows that a reduction in photosynthesis, caused by water stress, may not lead to reduced grain weight until any surplus photosynthate is eliminated. In this connection Asana and Basu (1963) showed that, for wheat, reduced photosynthesis caused by stress early in the grain filling stage could be compensated for by enhanced translocation from the stem. They considered that, because of hastened senescence of leaves of stressed plants, stress occurring later in the grain filling stage could not be compensated for in this manner.

Prolonged stress throughout grain filling, even at moderate levels, almost invariably reduces grain weight (Salter and Goode, 1967). Fischer and Kohn (1966) have shown that wheat yield tends to be inversely correlated with the stress-induced rate of senescence of photosynthetic tissue after flowering. In some situations an enhanced gradient of grain weight from the base to the tip of the ear develops (Aspinall, 1965).

The relative importance of photosynthesis in the ear, the flag leaf, and elsewhere in grain filling does not appear to be a major factor in interpreting yield decrements under water stress conditions, even though it has been a subject of controversy for some time. There are, of course, important differences between species associated partly with crop morphology. For example, the role of ear photosynthesis is greater in wheat than in corn (Allison and Watson, 1966). In the presence of water stress, there is likely to be more rapid senescence of older leaves, which would lead to a flow of assimilates from them towards the ear, but would eliminate their continued role in supplying assimilates. Consequently the role of continued ear and flag leaf photosynthesis would become relatively greater.

V. CONCLUSIONS

It would be very satisfying if this paper could conclude with a succinct summary of the relative sensitivity of different growth and development stages, in different crops, to periods of water stress.

Unfortunately, it is difficult to draw such conclusions, not only because of inadequate knowledge, and because of differences between species, but also because compensatory effects can take place from one growth stage to another.

Overall it is apparent that, although maximum yield is likely to be obtained only if adequate water status is maintained throughout the life of cereal crops, mild or relatively brief stress can usually be completely compensated for by subsequent development under favorable conditions. In this regard the stage of inflorescence development appears to be the most adaptable, although this is true in some crops more than others. Anthesis is probably the least adaptable since it is such a brief yet important stage in the development of crop yield.

By comparison, severe stress, at almost any stage between floral initiation and maturity, is likely to result in marked yield decrements.

Again it appears to be generally true that the preflowering stage is the most tolerant, but at anthesis and grain filling pronounced yield reductions are likely to be induced.

Two final remarks seem appropriate if they might stimulate research activity in this area. The first concerns the extent to which studies of morphogenesis have been linked to metabolism. It seems that too many studies have concentrated on either developmental or metabolic processes without sufficient emphasis on the link between the two. Environmental physiology can play a much more meaningful role in agronomy if physiological responses to stress are studied in relation to the stage of development at which they occur. The second concerns the problem of specification of the degree of stress in experimental treatments, a point already made by Kramer (1963). A reviewer is constantly thwarted by qualitative remarks as to the onset, duration and degree of stress imposed in various experiments. I encourage prospective investigators to pay more attention to means of inducing well•defined and reproducible levels of stress, and of monitoring them so that quantitative, and comparative, data can be obtained.

ACKNOWLEDGMENT

It is desired to acknowledge the valuable assistance of Dr. Nita Mortlock in preparing the bibliography on which this review was based.

LITERATURE CITED

Asana, R. D. 1966. Physiological analysis of yield of wheat in relation to water-stress and temperature. J. Indian Agricultural Research Institute Post-Grad. School 4:17-31.

Asana, R. D., and R. N. Basu. 1963. Studies in physiological analysis of yield. 6. Analysis of the effect of water stress on grain development in wheat. Indian J. Plant Physiol. 6:1-13.

Allison, J.C.S., and D.J. Watson. 1966. The production and distribution of dry matter in maize after flowering. Ann Bot. (N.S.)30:365-381.

Aspinall, D. 1965. The effects of soil moisture stress on the growth of barley: II. Grain growth. Aust. J. Agr. Res. 16:265-275.

Aspinall, D., P. B. Nicholls and L. H. May. 1964. The effects of soil moisture stress on the growth of barley: I. Vegetative development and grain yield. Aust. J. Agr. Res. 15:729-745.

Baker, D. N., and R. B. Musgrave. 1964. The effects of low level moisture stresses on the rate of apparent photosynthesis in corn. Crop Sci. 4:249-253.

Barnett, N. M., and A. W. Naylor. 1966. Amino acid and protein metabolism in Bermuda grass during water stress. Plant Physiol. (Lancaster) 41:1222-1230.

Ben-Zioni, A., C. Itai, and Y. Vaadia. 1967. Water and salt stressed, kinetin and protein synthesis in tobacco leaves. Plant Physiol. (Lancaster) 42:361-365.

Bingham, J. 1967. Investigations on the physiology of yield in winter wheat by comparisons of varieties and by artificial variation in grain number per ear. J. Agr. Sci. 68:411-422.

Bonnett, O. T. 1966. Inflorescences of maize, wheat, rye, barley and oats: Their initiation and development. Illinois Agr. Exp. Sta. Bull. 721.

Boyer, J. S. 1968. Relationship of water potential to growth of leaves. Plant Physiol. (Lancaster) 43:1056-1062.

Buttrose, M. S., and L. H. May. 1959. Physiology of cereal grain: I. The source of carbon for the developing barley kernel. Aust. J. Biol. Sci. 12:40-52.

Burt, R. L. 1964. Carbohydrate utilization as a factor in plant growth. Aust. J. Biol. Sci. 17:867-877.

Carr, D. J., and I. F. Wardlaw. 1965. The supply of photosynthetic assimilates to the grain from the flag leaf and ear of wheat. Aust. J. Biol. Sci. 18:711-719.

Chen, D., B. Kessler and S. P. Monselise. 1964. Studies on water regime and nitrogen metabolism of citrus seedlings grown under water stress. Plant Physiol. (Lancaster) 39:379-386.

Chinoy, J. J. 1960. Physiology of drought resistance of wheat. I. Effect of wilting at different stages of growth on survival values of 8 varieties of wheat belonging to 7 species. Phyton 14:147-157.

Chinoy, J. J. 1962. Physiology of drought resistance of wheat. IV. Effect of wilting at different growth and developmental stages on plant characters determining yield of grain in 8 varieties of wheat. Phyton 19:5-10.

Crafts, A. S. 1968. Water deficits and physiological processes, p. 85-133. In T. T. Kozlowski (ed.). Water deficits and plant growth. Vol. 2. Academic Press, Inc., New York.

Davidson, J. L. 1965. Some effects of leaf area control on the yield of wheat. Aust. J. Agr. Res. 16:721-731.

Denmead, O. T., and R. H. Shaw. 1960. The effects of soil moisture stress at different stages of growth on the development and yield of corn. Agron. J. 52:272-274.

El-Sharkawy, M. A., and J. D. Hesketh. 1964. Effects of temperature and water deficit on leaf photosynthetic rates of different species. Crop Sci. 4:514-518.

Fawcett, R. G., and J. P. Quirk. 1962. The effect of soil water stress on the absorption of soil phosphorus by wheat plants. Aust. J. Agr. Res. 13:194-205.

Fischer, R. A., and G. D. Kohn. 1966. The relationship of grain yield to vegetative growth and post-flowering leaf area in the wheat crop under conditions of limited soil moisture. Aust. J. Agr. Res. 17:281-295.

Gardner, W. R., and R. H. Nieman. 1964. Lower limit of water availability to plants. Science 143:1460-1462.

Gates, C. T. 1955a. The response of the young tomato plant to a brief period of water shortage. I. The whole plant and its principal parts. Aust. J. Biol. Sci. 8:196-214.

Gates, C. T. 1955b. The response of the young tomato plant to a brief period of water shortage. II. The individual leaves. Aust. J. Biol. Sci. 8:215-230.

Gates, C. T. 1968. Water deficits and growth of herbaceous plants, p. 135-190. In T. T. Kozlowski (ed.). Water deficits and plant growth. Vol. 2. Academic Press, Inc., New York.

Gates, C. T., and J. Bonner. 1959. The response of the young tomato plant to a brief period of water shortage. IV. Effects of water stress on the ribonucleic acid metabolism of tomato leaves. Plant Physiol. (Lancaster) 34:49-55.

Gates, C. T. 1957. The response of the young tomato plant to a brief period of water shortage. III. Drifts in nitrogen and phosphorus. Aust. J. Biol. Sci. 10:125-146.

Greenway, H., and R. G. Hiller. 1967. Effects of low water potentials on respiration and on glucose and acetate uptake by Chlorella pyrenoidosa. Planta 75:253-274.

Greenway, H., Betty Klepper, and P. G. Hughes. 1968. Effects of low water potential on ion uptake and loss for excised roots. Planta 80:129-141.

Hartt, C. E. 1967. Effect of moisture supply upon translocation and storage of ^{14}C in sugar cane. Plant Physiol. (Lancaster) 42:338-346.

Hiller, R. G., and H. Greenway. 1968. Effects of low water potentials on some aspects of carbohydrate metabolism in Chlorella pyrenoidosa. Planta 78:49-59.

Hopkinson, J. M. 1968. Effects of early drought and transplanting on the subsequent development of the tobacco plant. Aust. J. Agr. Res. 19:47-57.

Humphries, E. C. 1968. CCC and cereals. Field Crop Abstr. 21:91-99.

Iljin, W. S. 1957. Drought resistance in plants and physiological processes. Ann. Rev. Plant Physiol. 8:257-274.

Kemble, A. R., and H. T. Macpherson. 1954. Liberation of amino acids in perennial ryegrass during wilting. Biochem. J. 58:46-50.

Kessler, B. 1961. Nucleic acids as factors in drought resistance of higher plants. Adv. Bot. 2:1153-1159.

King, R. W., I. F. Wardlaw, and L. T. Evans. 1967. Effect of assimilate utilization on photosynthetic rate in wheat. Planta 77:261-276.

Kozlowski, T. 1964. Water metabolism in plants. Harper and Row, New York.

Kramer, P. J. 1963. Water stress and plant growth. Agron. J. 55:31-35.

Lockhart, J. A. 1965. Cell extension, p. 826-849. In J. Bonner and J. E. Varner (eds.) Plant biochemistry. Academic Press, Inc., New York.

McWilliam, J. R. 1968. The nature of the perennial response in Mediterranean grasses. II. Senescence, summer dormancy and survival in Phalaris. Aust. J. Agr. Res. 19:397-409.

Meidner, H. 1961. The minimum intercellular space carbon dioxide concentration in leaves of the palm Phoenix reclinata. J. Exp. Bot. 12:409-413.

Meidner, H. 1962. The minimum intercellular-space CO_2-concentration (Γ) of maize leaves and its influence on stomatal movements. J. Exp. Bot. 13:284-293.

Meidner, H., and T. A. Mansfield. 1965. Stomatal responses to illumination. Biol. Rev. 40:483-509.

Morton, A. G., and D. J. Watson. 1948. A physiological study of leaf growth. Ann. Bot. (N.S.) 12:281-310.

Mothes, K. 1956. Der Einfluss des Wasserzustandes auf Fermentprozesse und Stoffumsatz. In W. Ruhland (ed.) Encyc. of Plant Physiol. 3:656-664.

Newman, E. L. 1966. Relationship between root growth of flax (Linum usitatissimum) and soil water potential. New Phytol. 65:273-283.

Nicholis, P. B., and L. H. May. 1963. Studies on the growth of the barley apex. I. Interrelationships between primordium formation apex length, and spikelet development. Aust. J. Biol. Sci. 16:561-571.

Nösberger, J., and E. C. Humphries. 1965. Influence of removing tubers on dry matter production and net assimilation rate of potato plants. Ann. Bot. (N.S.) 29:580-588.

Novikov, V. P. 1952. The effect of a deficiency of water in the soil at different stages of development in oats. Dokl. Akad. Nauk. SSSR 82:641-643.

Novikov, V. P. 1954. Development of the oat panicle under different conditions of water supply. Bot. Z. 39:17-20.

Osborne, D. J. 1965. Interactions of hormonal substances in the growth and development of plants. J. Sci. Food Agr. 16:1-13.

Plaut, Z., and L. Ordin. 1964. The effect of moisture tension and nitrogen supply on cell wall metabolism of sunflower leaves. Physiol. Plant. 17:279-286.

Plaut, Z., and L. Reinhold. 1965. The effect of water stress on ^{14}C sucrose transport in bean plants. Aust. J. Biol. Sci. 18:1143-1155.

Plaut, Z., and L. Reinhold. 1967. The effect of water stress on the movement of ^{14}C sucrose and of triated water within the supply leaf of young bean plants. Aust. J. Biol. Sci. 20:297-308.

Porter, H. K., N. Pal, and R. V. Martin. 1950. Physiological studies in plant nutrition. XV. Assimilation of carbon by the ear of barley and its relation to the accumulation of dry matter in the grain. Ann. Bot. (N.S.) 14:55-68.

Prusakova, L. D. 1960. Influence of water relations on typtophan synthesis and leaf growth in wheat. Fiziol. Rast. 7:139-48.

Richmond, A. E., and A. Lang. 1957. Effect of kinetin on protein content and survival of detached Xanthium leaves. Science 125:650-51.

Robins, J. S., and C. E. Domingo. 1953. Some effects of severe soil moisture deficits at specific growth stages in corn. Agron. J. 45:612-621.

Russell, R. S., and D. A. Barber. 1960. The relationship between salt uptake and the absorption of water by intact plants. Ann. Rev. Plant Physiol. 11:127-140.

Salim, M.,G. W. Todd, and A. M. Schlehuber. 1965. Root development of wheat, oats, and barley under conditions of soil moisture stress. Agron. J. 57:603-607.

Salter, P. J., and J. E. Goode. 1967. Crop responses to water at different stages of growth. Commonwealth Bureau of Horticulture and Plantation Crops, East Malling, Maidstone, Kent.

Santarius, K. A. 1967. Das Verhalten von CO_2 - Assimilation, NADP-und PGS Reduktion and ATP-Synthese Intakter Blattzellen in Abhängigkeit vom Wassergehalt. Planta 73:228-242.

Santarius, K. A., and R. Ernst. 1967. Das Verhalten von Hill-Reaktion und photophosphorylierung isolierter Chloroplasten in Abhängigkeit vom Wassergehalt. I. Wasserentzug mittels konzentrierter Losungen. Planta 73:91-108.

Santarius, K. A., and U. Heber. 1967. Das Verhalten von Hill-Reaktion und Photophosphorylierung Isolierter Chloroplasten in Abhängigkeit vom Wassergehalt. II. Wasserentzug uber $CaCl_2$. Planta 73:109-137.

Shah, C. B., and R. S. Loomis. 1965. Ribonucleic acid and protein metabolism in sugar beet during drought. Physiol. Plant. 18:240-254.

Single, W. V. 1964. The influence of nitrogen supply on the fertility of the wheat ear. Aust. J. Exp. Agr. Animal Husbandry 4:165-168.

Skazkin, F. D., and R. I. Leiman. 1952. Effects of a deficiency of soil water on vernalized and non-vernalized cereals in different periods of their development. C. R. Acad. Sci. U.S.S.R. 84:627-30.

Skazkin, F. D., and K. A. Lukomskaya. 1962. Characteristics of flowering in cereals in relation to the effects of soil moisture deficiency. Fiziol. Rast 9:703-707.

Skazkin, F. D., and I. G. Zavadskaya. 1957. The effect of soil-moisture deficiency and nitrogen nutrition on microsporogenesis in barley plants. Dokl. Akad. Nauk. SSSR. 117:150-2.

Slatyer, R. O. 1957a. Significance of the permanent wilting percentage in studies of plant and soil water relations. Bot. Rev. 23:585-636.

Slatyer, R. O. 1957b. The influence of progressive increases in total soil moisture stress, on transpiration, growth, and internal water relationships of plants. Aust. J. Biol. Sci. 10:320-336.

Slatyer, R. O. 1965. The physiology of irrigated agricultural plants by N.S. Petinov. An abstract with commentary. Field Crop Abstr. 18:1-8.

Slatyer, R. O. 1957. Plant water relationships. Academic Press, London and New York.

Slatyer, R. O., and J. F. Bierhuizen. 1964. The influence of several transpiration suppressants on transpiration, photosynthesis, and water use efficiency of cotton leaves. Aust. J. Biol. Sci. 17:131-146.

Stutte, C. A., and G. W. Todd. 1967. Effects of water stress on soluble leaf proteins in Triticum aestivum L. Phyton 24:67-75.

Thorne, G. N. 1963. Varietal differences in photosynthesis of ears and leaves of barley. Ann. Bot. (N. S.) 27:155-174.

Troughton, A. 1962. The roots of temperate cereals. Comm. Bur. Pastures and Field Crops. Pub. 2.

Troughton, J. H. 1969. Plant water status and carbon dioxide exchange of cotton leaves. Aust. J. Biol. Sci. 22:289-302.

Troughton, J. H., and R. O. Slatyer. 1969. Plant water status, leaf temperature and the calculated mesophyll resistance to CO_2 of cotton leaves. Aust. J. Biol. Sci. 22: (in press).

Van der Paauw, F. 1949. Water relations of oats with special attention to the influence of periods of drought. Plant and Soil 1:303-341.

Volodarski, N. I. and L. V. Zinevich. 1960. Drought resistance of corn during ontogeny. Fiziol. Rast. 7:176-179.

Wadleigh, C. H., and L. A. Richards. 1951. Soil moisture and the mineral nutrition of plants, p. 411-450. In E. Truog (ed.) Mineral nutrition of plants. Univ. Wisconsin Press, Madison, Wis.

Wardlaw, I. F. 1967. The effect of water stress on translocation in relation to photosynthesis and growth. I. Effect during grain development in wheat. Aust. J. Biol. Sci. 20:25-39.

Wardlaw, I. F. 1969. The effect of water stress on translocation in relation to photosynthesis and growth. II. Effect during leaf development in Lolium temulentum L. Aust. J. Biol. Sci. 22:1-16.

Weaver, J. E. 1926. Root development of field crops. McGraw-Hill, New York.

Wells, S. A., and S. Dubetz. 1966. Reaction of barley varieties to soil water stress. Can. J. Plant Sci. 46:507-512.

West, S. H. 1966. Sub-cellular physiology as affected by drought. 10th Int. Grassland Congr. Helsinki:91-94.

Whiteman, P. C., and G. L. Wilson. 1965. The effects of water stress on the reproductive development of Sorghum vulgare Pers. Queensland Univ. Papers (Dept. of Botany) 4:233-239.

Williams, R. F. 1966. The physiology of growth in the wheat plant. III. Growth of the primary shoot and inflorescence. Aust. J. Biol. Sci. 19:949-966.

Williams, R. F., and A. H. G. C. Rijven. 1965. The physiology of growth in the wheat plant. II. Dynamics of leaf growth. Aust. J. Biol. Sci. 18:721-743.

Williams, R. F., and R. E. Shapter. 1955. A comparative study of growth and nutrition in barley and rye as affected by low-water treatment. Aust. J. Biol. Sci., 8:435-466.

Wilson, A. M., and R. C. Huffaker. 1964. Effects of moisture stress on acid-soluble phosphorus compounds in Trifolium subterraneum. Plant Physiol. (Lancaster) 39:555-560.

Woodhams, D. H., and T. T. Kozlowski. 1954. Effects of soil moisture stress on carbohydrate development and growth in plants. Amer. J. Bot. 41:316-320.

Woodstock, L. W., and F. Skoog. 1960. Relationships between growth rates and nucleic acid contents in the roots of inbred lines of corn. Amer. J. Bot. 47:713-716.

Woodstock, L. W., and F. Skoog. 1962. Distributions of growth, nucleic acids, and nucleic-acid synthesis in seedling roots of Zea mays. Amer. J. Bot. 49:623-633.

Zelitch, I. 1967. Water and CO_2 transport in the photosynthetic process, p. 231-248. In A. San Pietro, F. A. Greer, and T. J. Army (eds.) Harvesting the sun. Academic Press, Inc., New York.

Zholkevich, V. N., and T. F. Koretskaya. 1959. Metabolism of pumpkin roots during drought. Fiziol. Rast. 6:690-700.

Zholkevich, V. N., L. D. Prusakova, and A. A. Lizandr. 1958. Translocation of assimilates and respiration of conductive tissues in relation to soil moisture. Fiziol. Rast. 5:337-344.

4...DISCUSSION

PAUL J. KRAMER

Duke University
Durham, North Carolina

Professor Slatyer's paper emphasizes the fact that in spite of over 50 years of research we do not know enough about the mechanisms by which water stress reduces the growth and yield of crop plants. It is not yet clear how much of the reduction is caused by effects of decreased turgor on cell enlargement and stomatal opening and how much results from direct interference with enzyme-mediated processes brought about by dehydration of the protoplasm. Perhaps modification of "sink" capacity by decreased cell division and enlargement in meristematic regions also is a major factor in the changes in carbohydrate and nitrogen metabolism observed in plants subjected to water stress. Furthermore, we do not know why some kinds of crop plants are more resistant to injury from water stress than others. Is it because they have better stomatal and cuticular control over transpiration, because they have more efficient root systems, or because their protoplasm is more resistant to dehydration? Lack of answers to these and similar questions is particularly embarrassing with respect to plant breeding and crop improvement programs because it is difficult to increase tolerance of drought until we know exactly how drought injures plants.

It is obvious that we need much more research in order to answer these questions. However, we should first ask ourselves why the great amount of research already done on the relationship between water supply and crop yields has not produced more satisfactory answers. I believe that Professor Slatyer has given you the reasons in the last paragraph of his paper and I wish to emphasize them.

The first reason is the common failure to measure plant water stress. The need for such measurements has been mentioned frequently during the past decade and satisfactory methods for measuring water potential and osmotic potential are available, but in too many instances the measurements have not been made. It therefore seems necessary to point out again that the only reliable method of evaluating plant water stress is by direct measurement on the experimental plants. I strongly urge that in all research involving plant water stress, quantitative measurements of plant water potential should be made.

The second reason that we do not have all the information that we should have is that the problem is very complex and our research often is too narrow in scope. We tend to study effects of water stress on only one or two processes at a time. As Professor Slatyer has said, we often study growth or metabolism, but not both simultaneously. Furthermore, we neglect to consider the stage of development, forgetting that a given degree of water stress produces quite different effects at different stages of development. We need more comprehensive studies in which we measure plant growth, metabolism, and water stress, and simultaneously measure environmental factors such as soil water potential and rate of evaporation. In other words, we need to consider the entire soil-plant-atmosphere system.

If we keep these requirements in mind we can make our research much more productive and more useful to agriculture, horticulture, and forestry.

4 ... DISCUSSION

J. J. OERTLI

University of California
Riverside, California

The correlations between water stress and plant responses, discussed by Dr. Slatyer, can be very useful in management practices but they do not—with few exceptions—permit any conclusions on the possible mechanism of operation of water stress since most of the plant responses must be secondary. Furthermore, neither the experiments described today, nor numerous others, give clearcut evidence that the total water potential is really the critical property to which plants respond.

This "critical property" deserves some discussion. Physical chemistry emphasizes the importance of the chemical potential as a criterion for the direction of spontaneous reactions. These concepts are applicable to the living system but one has to be careful to use a correct cell model. Water, in and around a cell, is usually close enough to equilibrium to permit writing the following equation of water potential:

$$\Psi_w = \Psi_{cell} = \Psi_{vac\ P} + \Psi_{vac\ \pi} = \Psi_{prot\ P} + \Psi_{prot\ M(+\pi)} = \Psi_{org\ P} + \Psi_{org\ \pi}$$

where w = cell wall; vac = vacuole; prot = protein, referring to water of hydration on proteins; org = organelle; and P, π, M = pressure, osmotic, and matric components. Suppose, for example, the turgor pressure is critical; in that case, a certain plant response is to be expected for a constant difference $\Psi_{cell} - \Psi_{vac\ \pi}$, but the absolute value of the total and osmotic water potential can still vary widely. Thus, turgor pressure and total water potential do not necessarily change in the same direction. An example: Plants frequently respond to good fertilization by a disproportionate increase of the vacuolar osmotic pressure; because of this overadjustment, the turgor pressure ($\Psi_{vac\ P}$), and with it the water content, increase whereas the total water potential Ψ_{cell} decreases.

<u>Possible direct significance of potentials</u>:

Ψ_{cell} directly: questionable

$\Psi_{vac\ P} \approx \Psi_{prot\ P}$

cell elongation, stomatal openings, structural support, integrity of plasmadesmata, activity of other metabolites, water structure, water content.

$\Psi_{vac\ \pi}$ directly: questionable, perhaps water structure, indirectly: since

$\Psi_{vac\ P} \sim \Psi_{prot\ P}$ also $\Psi_{vac\ \pi} \approx$ $\Psi_{prot\ M}$ but $\Psi_{prot\ M}$ and thus $\Psi_{vac\ \pi}$

is a measure for protein hydration. The importance of protein hydration is really not known. At first sight, it is probably surprising that the degree of protein hydration is more directly related to a potential component than to Ψ_{cell}. (Oertli, 1968b).

$\Psi_{org\ P}$ one of the factors determining the degree of swelling of organelles.

Physiological significance not known.

$\Psi_{org\ \pi}$ directly: questionable.

Direct effects of solutes on metabolism are not considered in this table.

One may perhaps state that vacuolar cell water properties are determined by Ψ_{cell}, the solute content, and cell wall properties; the components $\Psi_{vac\ P}$ and $\Psi_{vac\ \pi}$ adjust to these conditions but these components, especially $\Psi_{vac\ P}$ are physiologically more important.

The problem becomes more complex when we apply some of these concepts to irreversible cell elongation because now the dynamics of solute relations can become critical. Cell elongation requires an excess of internal pressure. The internal pressure can only be maintained at a certain level through continuous solute uptake. The quotient of the rate of solute uptake and the solute requirement is a measure for the rate of cell elongation. It can be shown for a simplified model (Oertli, 1968a) that

$$\text{elongation rate (pressure constant)} = \frac{\text{rate of solute uptake}}{C(\Psi_\sigma + \Delta\Psi - \Psi_{vac}\, P)}$$

where C = constant, Ψ_σ = soil water potential, and $\Delta\Psi = \Psi_{cell} - \Psi_\sigma$. For simplicity, let us restrict the discussion to osmotic moisture stress and to inorganic solute uptake. The rate of solute uptake (numerator) is now a hyperbolic function of the soil water potential. The solute requirement (denominator) increases linearly with soil moisture stress, starting from a finite requirement at $\Psi_\sigma = 0$. As a consequence, cell elongation rates as a function of decreasing soil water potentials are first expected to increase, then to pass through an optimum and at more negative potentials to decrease again. This optimum can be demonstrated by experiments.

Let us now inspect the difference, $\Delta\Psi$, which depends on soil and atmospheric water potentials, on resistances in soils, plants, and atmosphere, and—usually not considered—on solute relations. Solute relations can be included in resistances if one so desires (Oertli, 1966). Here, I shall treat them separately.

1. Effects of atmospheric conditions:

   Day: $\Delta\Psi$ very negative, elongation slow.
   Night: $\Delta\Psi$ near zero, much elongation.

2. Effects of solutes:

   Water in leaf transpires faster than solutes are taken up into leaf vacuoles, hence residual extracellular salt accumulation, hence, $\Delta\Psi$ more negative, hence cell elongation retarded.
   Solute taken into leaf vacuoles faster than water loss through transpiration, hence $\Delta\Psi$ less negative or even positive, hence elongation accelerated.

This last case is interesting because it suggests that water can flow at a steady state against its free energy gradient. Thus, the soil water potential is not the upper limit for the plant water potential. One must realize that, for example, in a well-fertilized lawn, this situation can be observed almost every night.

I shall not discuss effects of resistance changes on $\Delta\Psi$ (wind, stomatal openings, wilting diseases, soil conductivity) nor shall I elaborate on the last term $\Psi_{vac}\, P$, which is really variable and where cell wall properties must be considered. These would add to the difficulty of describing the status of plant water by a single property, such as the total water potential. Another interesting aspect to discuss would have been the effect of increased respiration per unit elongation associated with the increased solute requirement.

My second comment concerns the currently popular view that water deficits (low Ψ_{cell}) generally develop because absorption lags behind transpiration. This statement is not entirely true, because the relation between water content and water potential is not unique, as I have demonstrated in the case of osmotic overadjustment. But even if this relation were unique, exceptions are possible. One example may suffice: Suppose the resistance to flow is increased markedly midway in the plant, e.g., in the petioles because of a wilting disease. If the water capacity effect before this resistance (in root and stem) exceeds the capacity effect after the resistance (leaf), then absorption exceeds transpiration. Nevertheless, leaves will wilt. In this case, the original statement, i.e., absorption lags behind transpiration, would be correct if only entry in and loss from leaves, were considered.

Finally, the terminology "absorption lags behind transpiration" has occasionally led to erroneous interpretations, e.g., that this is an indicator of resistances. The phenomenon is due to capacitance rather than to a prolonged transient state in conductive tissues. After a disturbance of a steady state, e.g., through a change of atmospheric relative humidity, a new steady state is approached rapidly in conduits (in uninterrupted vessels, pressure changes travel at a speed of nearly 1 mile/sec). But cell water is no longer in equilibrium with the nearby transpiration stream and a movement of water is initiated. Thus, there is a multiplicity of sinks and sources, but I suspect that the system between sinks and sources is always close to the steady state. Naturally, as some of these sources become exhausted, new steady states are approached. Taking the viewpoint of cause and effect relations, it is not that water is lost from leaves because absorption lags; rather, absorption lags because water is lost from the leaf cells and the loss is due to an extracellular potential drop.

In summary, I have tried to raise questions as to how one might describe the state of plant water in a physiologically meaningful way; I have questioned generalizations about the direction of flow and free energy gradients, and about the development of plant moisture stress. Always, there are serious exceptions to rules which, at first sight, seem to be generally true. But such complications make the study of water relations more challenging and interesting.

LITERATURE CITED

Oertli. J. J. 1966. The significance of transpiration and various components of the water potential to plant behavior. Advance Front. Plant. Sci. 17:149-172.

Oertli, J. J. 1968a. The significance of the external water potential and of salt transport to water relations in plants. Int. Congr. Soil Sci. Trans. 9th (Adelaide, Australia). 1:95-107.

Oertli, J. J. 1968b. Effects of components of water potential on the water content of plant cells. Zeitschr. Pflanzenphysiol. 59:340-352.

5

Light Interception and Radiative Exchange in Crop Stands

JOHN L. MONTEITH

University of Nottingham
Loughborough, England

I. RADIATION AND CROPS

Crops grow and use water because they intercept radiation from the sun, the sky, and the atmosphere. Diurnal changes of solar radiation dictate the diurnal course of photosynthesis and transpiration, and the vertical gradient of radiant flux in a canopy is a measure of the absorption of energy by foliage at different heights. Without exaggeration, the distribution of radiation within a plant community is the most important single element of microclimate.

Early ecological studies of radiation climate were mainly descriptive and were limited in scope by rather primitive instrumentation. A new quantitative approach to the subject was initiated by Monsi and Saeki (1953) and by Kasanaga and Monsi (1954) whose models of light distribution in plant canopies were a basis for many subsequent studies, both experimental and theoretical. About half the literature published in the last 15 years is concerned with the development of more elaborate models—an indication that it is easier to investigate light distribution at the desk than in the field! About a quarter of the literature describes new measurements, and the balance consists of review articles. Reviews have been so thorough and frequent (Saeki, 1963; Anderson, 1964; Reifsnyder and Lull, 1965; Loomis, Williams and Duncan, 1966) that my contribution to this symposium may appear premature, but I shall try to justify the exercise by being deliberately provocative. As an opening shot, crop ecologists are not concerned with the distribution of radiation per se but with rates of photosynthesis and with yield. The literature reveals a curious reluctance to test models of light penetration in crops by comparing predicted rates of dry matter accumulation with measurements in the field. We have scarcely begun to exploit models for the solution of agronomic problems.

In addition to the primary function of radiation in providing energy for photosynthesis, other less familiar aspects of radiation distribution may influence the pattern of growth and development in a field crop. As sunlight filters through leaves, radiation in the "red" region of the spectrum (ca 0.66 μm) is strongly absorbed, but the absorption is slight in the "far-red" (ca 0.73 μm). In a dense crop, the relative intensity of far red to red radiation increases rapidly between the top of the canopy and the soil surface. Effects of this gradient, mediated by the phyto- chrome system, could determine the growth rates of tillers in cereals and grasses and the germination of weeds. The significance of spectral gradients in the field is still a matter for speculation rather than obser- vation but the distribution of lichens on tree trunks has been related to vertical changes of spectral composition and infrared photography dem- onstrates these changes very vividly (McCree, 1968).

Another neglected aspect of radiation in crops is the gradient of longwave radiation on clear nights. Upper leaves lose radiation more rapidly, cool faster, and collect more dew than lower leaves. Although dew at the top of the crop will evaporate faster after sunrise if the sky stays clear, the number of hours for which leaves are wet may deter- mine their susceptibility to attack by fungal diseases that need a film of water to germinate spores. The net flux of radiation at any level in a crop determines the energy available for the transfer of sensible and latent heat. Measurements of the net radiation gradient are fundamental to the analysis of microclimate (Cowan, 1968) and are needed to esti- mate how the turbulent exchange coefficient increases with height (E.R. Lemon, Chapter 6, this book).

To keep within the topic of our meeting, this review will be con- cerned primarily with the penetration of light in field crops in relation to photosynthesis. Salient features of radiation environment and leaf geometry will be described as an introduction to the measurement and theory of light distribution in the field.

II. SPECIFICATION OF THE SYSTEM

A. Radiation

Features of solar radiation relevant to crop ecology are:

1) The angle of incidence of the sun's rays, usually specified by the solar elevation β;

2) The spectral composition of the radiation. The waveband in which radiant energy is available for photosynthesis is usually defined by the limits 0.4 to 0.7 μm corresponding to the blue and red ends of the visible spectrum. Photosynthetically active radiation in this wave- band will be contracted to PAR;

3) The relative intensity of diffuse radiation from the blue sky, haze and clouds, and of direct radiation from the solar beam. If D is the irradiance of the diffuse component on a horizontal surface and I is the direct irradiance on a surface at right angles to the sun's rays, the total irradiance on a horizontal surface is $D + I \sin \beta$.

In the absence of clouds and haze, scattered radiation is predom- inantly blue and decreases rapidly in strength towards the red end of the spectrum. Analysis of measurements reviewed by Robinson (1956) shows that the fraction of PAR in the spectrum of skylight decreases from about 80% when the sun is near the horizon ($\beta < 10^{\circ}$) to 60% when

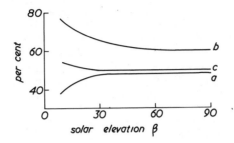

Fig. 5-1—(a) Average ratio of diffuse to total radiation as function of solar elevation from Dogniaux (1954); (b) Direct solar radiation on a horizontal surface; (c) Total (direct and diffuse) radiation on a horizontal surface. (b) and (c) were derived from measurements on a cloudless day (21 August, 1968) at Sutton Bonington and were extrapolated from 50° to 90° by plotting relative irradiance against air mass.

β exceeds 60° (Fig. 5-1). In contrast, the fraction of PAR in the <u>direct</u> beam, measured on summer days at Sutton Bonington (52° N 50' W) increased from 40% when β was less than 10° to 48% when β exceeded 30°.

On cloudless days, radiation at sunrise and sunset is almost entirely diffuse but the fraction of diffuse to total radiation decreases as solar elevation increases and reaches a constant minimum value when $\beta > 50$. Figure 5-2 curve (a) shows the average value of this fraction determined in Belgium by Dogniaux (1954). On overcast days, all radiation is diffuse and the intensity of radiant flux increases towards the zenith. The increase can be described by an empirical formula for a "standard

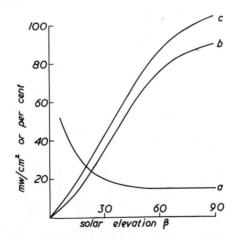

Fig. 5-2—Ratio of PAR (0.4 to 0.7 μm) to total solar radiation (0.35 to 3 μm) on a cloudless day as functions of solar elevation. (a) Direct solar radiation measured at Sutton Bonington; (b) Diffuse radiation from Robinson (1966); (c) Total (direct and diffuse) radiation by calculation.

overcast sky" Anderson (1966) but calculations by Cowan (1968) show only trivial differences in the penetration of light into a stand from "standard" and uniformly bright skies.

Figure 5-2 curve (b) shows how the direct irradiance of a horizontal surface increased with solar elevation on a cloudless day at Sutton Bonington (21 August, 1968). Visibility was average and the atmospheric water content was about 2 cm. Total radiation, curve (c) in Fig. 5-2, was calculated from (a) and (b). Similarly, weighting the direct and diffuse fluxes by coordinates from Fig. 5-1 (a) and (b) gives the fraction of PAR in total radiation as curve (c) in Fig. 5-1. This fraction is surprisingly constant at 50% of total radiation when the sun is more than 20° above the horizon (Fig. 5-1 curve c). The lower figure of 45% often found in the literature is based on Moon's calculations for the direct beam alone and ignores the contribution from scattered radiation, rich in visible light.

The ratio of PAR to total radiation changes slightly with the amount of water vapor and dust in the atmosphere but seems to be relatively insensitive to the presence of cloud. Theoretical estimates of spectral distribution were tabulated by Avaste, Moldau and Shifrin (1962), but as the values of irradiance in Fig. 5-1 and 5-2 are difficult to abstract from the meteorological literature, they are given in Table 5-1.

B. Leaves

Most of the radiation intercepted by a field crop is absorbed by leaves, more specifically, by leaf laminae. Leaf sheaths, stems, and inflorescences also absorb radiation and are capable of photosynthesis in some species. As the relevant dimensions of these organs are seldom recorded—figures quoted by Ross and Nilson (1967a) are almost unique in the literature—discussion will be restricted to the geometry and optics of laminae.

1. Geometry

The area of leaf laminae within any horizontal layer of a canopy is specified by a leaf area index, L, the area of leaves per unit area of ground beneath them. If unit leaf layer (L = 1) occupies a layer of

Table 5-1—Solar irradiances (mW/cm^2)

Solar elevation β	0.3 to 4.0 μm			0.4 to 0.7 μm			Fraction of total in waveband 0.4 to 0.7 μm
	Direct	Diffuse	Total	Direct	Diffuse	Total	
10	8	6	14	3.1	4.5	7.6	54
20	21	7	28	9.5	4.9	14.4	52
30	36	9	45	16.6	5.9	22.5	50
40	51	10	61	24.5	6.3	30.8	50
50	65	11	76	31.3	6.7	38.0	50
60	76	13	89	36.4	7.8	44.2	50
70	83	14	97	39.8	8.4	48.2	50
80	87	15	102	41.7	8.8	50.5	50
90	90	16	105	43.0	9.4	52.4	50

thickness h cm, the density of the foliage is $1/h$ cm^2 leaf area per cm^3 of canopy volume. In crop communities, h can range from about 1 cm in densely sown clover to 50 cm or more in maize at 61,700 plants/ha (25,000 plants/acre).

Leaves or small sections of leaves can be treated as planes making an angle α with the horizontal, referred to as the leaf angle. In theoretical analyses, leaves are usually assumed to be distributed at random with respect to azimuth angle, i.e., they have no preferred compass direction. In maize, however, leaves may tend to grow at right angles to the rows (Ross and Nilson, 1967b) or along the rows (R.S. Loomis and W.A. Williams, Chapter 3, this book); and in heliotropic species such as clover, leaves tend to follow the sun.

The measurement of leaf areas and angles is tedious by any method. Ross and Nilson (1967b) measured the areas of clipped sections of leaves after measuring their angles with a type of protractor, and De Wit (1965) described a method for relating leaf angle to the length of shadow cast by a sphere on a white surface parallel to the leaf. The system of inclined point-quadrats developed by Warren Wilson (1960, 1963) relates the vertical distribution of foliage density and of mean foliage angle to the number of contacts observed between the foliage and a small spear thrust through it at a specified angle. Successful sets of measurements have been obtained in short crops with small leaves but the method is impractical for tall crops such as maize or sorghum or for foliage with large tightly packed leaves such as sugar beet (Beta vulgaris L.). Philip (1965a, b) extended the theory of point-quadrats to derive the distribution of leaf angles and to find the minimum number of measurements needed to achieve a chosen precision. His analysis emphasises the discouragingly large number of observations required, e.g., 100 contacts to determine foliage density to $\pm$ 10% and at least 1,000 contacts to estimate the distribution of leaf angles.

The frequency distribution of leaf angles for a number of species was reported by De Wit (1965) and by Ross and Nilson (1967b). Using terminology introduced by De Wit, species such as clover and beans were "planophile" with a preponderance of leaves at small angles to the horizontal. Sugar beet was "plagiophile" with a fairly uniform distribution of leaf angles from 0 to 90°. Ryegrass was "erectophile" in early growth when more than half the leaf angles exceeded 60°, but as the leaves grew longer and more flaccid, they bent to form a planophile canopy with more than half the leaf angles less than 30°.

Nichiporovich (1961) and Ross and Nilson found (1967b) that the distribution of leaf angles in maize was close to the distribution of surface elements on a sphere. This is a special type of erectophile foliage in which the frequency of leaf angles is proportional to cos α. For the varieties of maize examined by De Wit and by Loomis et al. (1968), there was a significant departure from spherical foliage because of a deficit of leaf angles between 45° and 90°. A photograph of isolated maize plants presented by Williams, Loomis, and Lepley (1965) suggests that the leaves of some varieties may be too short or too stiff to form a complete hemisphere, although individual leaves describe nearly circular arcs.

The way in which direct sunlight penetrates a crop depends on the distribution of gaps in the foliage and this aspect of canopy geometry is fundamental to theoretical analyses of light penetration. There are at least three methods of measuring gap frequency: from inclined point-quadrats; from hemispherical photographs taken with a camera fitted with a fish-eye lens (Evans and Coombe, 1959); from the distribution of sunflecks on a horizontal plane (Horie, 1966). Hemispherical photography has been successfully used in forests but in many crops it would be difficult to operate a camera without disturbing the foliage. Both the point-quadrat and photographic methods of determining gap frequency suffer from the serious disadvantage that they are difficult to adapt for automatic recording and demand considerable manual effort. Though unsuitable for routine work, they provide an absolute method of testing theoretical predictions in specific stands (e.g., Warren Wilson, 1965).

2. Optics

The transmission of radiation by leaves depends strongly on wavelength. In the region 0.4 to 0.7 μm where pigments absorb most strongly, the leaves of many crop plants absorb 80 to 90% of incident radiation. Absorption is much smaller in the infrared (0.7 to 3 μm) often falling to 10 to 20% between 0.7 and 0.8 μm (Gates et al., 1965). The proportions of radiation transmitted and reflected by crop leaves are usually similar at about 5 to 10% in the visible spectrum and 30 to 40% in the infrared. It will be assumed here that leaves transmit 7% of PAR and 25% of total solar radiation.

Because leaves absorb visible radiation preferentially, marked differences of spectral composition are observed in plant communities. Allen, Yocum, and Lemon (1964) and Singh, Peters, and Pendleton (1968), working with portable spectrophotometers, found that radiation in sunflecks was hardly modified spectrally whereas the radiation in shade was severely depleted in visible light. Averaging over sunfleck and shade areas, the attenuation of PAR is much more rapid than the attenuation of infrared or total radiation (Szeicz, Monteith, and Dos Santos, 1964; Szeicz, 1968; Allen and Brown, 1965; Tooming, 1967).

Three independent laboratory experiments are relevant to the study of light regimes in crops. First, Tageeva and Brandt (1961) measured the fraction of radiation reflected and transmitted by leaves exposed to radiation of different wavelengths and at different angles of incidence. In general, as the angle increased, reflection increased at the expense of transmission so that the fraction of radiation absorbed was almost independent of the incident angle. Second, Kriedeman, Neales, and Ashton (1964) found that when leaves were exposed to weak light, rates of photosynthesis were approximately proportional to the cosine of the angle of incidence, a result consistent with a constant absorption coefficient. In strong light, energy will still be absorbed at a rate proportional to the cosine of the angle of incidence but the rate of photosynthesis will no longer be proportional to absorbed energy. Third, Moss (1964) illuminated leaves on both sides simultaneously and showed that rates of photosynthesis were related to the gross absorption of radiant energy irrespective of its distribution on the abaxial and adaxial surfaces. Taken together, these results emphasise the need to determine

the spatial distribution, both of radiation, and of intercepting foliage, in
the canopy of a crop.

III. MEASUREMENT OF RADIATION IN CROPS

One of the most significant features of the radiation regime in a
crop is the extreme variability of radiant fluxes both in the vertical and
and in the horizontal. Many workers have taken the average of a series
of spot measurements with a single photocell or solarimeter thrust
randomly into the canopy at a chosen level. This method is impractical
where the foliage is dense and gives misleading results if the foliage
elements are pushed aside when the sensor is inserted between them.
Better gradients can be obtained with a set of small sensors installed
at different heights on a vertical mast. Hourly profiles of radiation
may be distorted by irregularities in the distribution of foliage round
the mast and by the orientation of rows with respect to solar azimuth,
but a good daily average of the fractional transmission at each height
can be determined by this method.

The problem of spatial integration has been attacked in two ways:
by moving a single sensor backwards and forwards along a fixed path
in the canopy; by exposing fixed sensors with an extended surface.
Allen et al. (1964) made traverses in a dense stand of corn with an integrating photometer described by Miller (1951). Baker and Meyer (1966)
mounted an Eppley solarimeter on a railway system, running at ground
level through four 100-cm (40-inch) rows of cotton and completing the
return journey in 18 min. Such techniques are well suited to measurements in forests and in tall crops with widely spaced plants. In communities with small or slender plants, the use of tube solarimeters is
more attractive. Thermopiles mounted within a long glass tube were
first described by Isobe (1962) and were developed at Rothamsted Experimental Station (Szeicz et al., 1964; Szeicz, 1965). The standard
instruments used at Rothamsted have a sensing surface 90 cm long and
2.5 cm wide and are mounted horizontally on a framework that is placed
on the field as soon after germination as possible so that plants beneath
them are able to grow with minimum interference to the distribution of
foliage. By fitting some of the solarimeters with gelatine filters that
transmit infrared radiation, the attenuation of PAR in the crop can be
estimated. The main defect of tube solarimeters is the dependence of
their sensitivity on solar azimuth and elevation, but by comparing the
output of instruments exposed in the same direction, preferably east-
west across rows running north-south, errors are minimized. Green,
Jones, and Melican (1967) modified Rothamsted solarimeters by measuring total and infrared radiation in the same tube and by exposing three
tubes radially at a separation of 120° to get a good average response
to incident radiation.

Photochemical methods of integrating light energy tend to be unstable and temperature sensitive but for comparisons of light extinction
in crops, several workers have got consistent results from the bleaching of Ozalid paper. Friend (1961) described how the paper is cut into
strips and stapled into small booklets. The number of strips bleached

after exposure to light was uniquely related to the time integral of incident energy in the waveband from 0.35 to 0.45 μm. With this spectral
response, considerable caution is needed in the interpretation of measurements within plant communities.

The virtues and defects of many other instruments and methods
were exhaustively reviewed by Anderson (1964). Gaastra (1968) examined the spectral response of different types of sensor fitted with various filters and concluded that the best estimates of attenuation in plant
communities could be obtained with barrier layer photocells or with
thermopiles measuring total and infrared radiation by separating the
spectrum with an RG 8 filter.

When measurements of the radiant flux at different heights in a
crop are supplemented by measurements of leaf area, it is possible
to calculate an attenuation coefficient, related in principle to the geometry of the system. The theoretical basis of this relation will be discussed in the next section before presenting a summary of field observations.

IV. THEORETICAL PRINCIPLES

A. Random and Nonrandom Foliage

Donald (1961) referred to "the absence in nature of the continuous
profiles of horizontal foliage drawn for symposia." Nevertheless, a
general theory for the transmission of radiation in crops can usefully
be developed from the simplest case of an assembly of horizontal black
leaves of uniform size exposed to vertical radiation. Assuming the leaf
area index for the whole canopy is L, there will be L similar layers
containing unit leaf area, and if the arrangement of leaves within these
layers is purely random, some leaves will appear to overlap their neighbors when viewed from directly overhead. For perfect randomness, the
chance of n leaves overlapping is given by exp-1 n! (Roach, 1968) and
this is the probability of a point quadrat intercepting n leaves within the
layer (Duncan et al., 1967). In the limit, the probability of intercepting
no leaves is exp-1 = 0.368: this is the fraction of radiation transmitted
by the layer. The probability of intercepting an infinite number of leaves
is zero, but an inherent feature of randomness is the chance of intercepting any finite number of leaves, however large.

In real crops, leaves are not arranged at random. Their horizontal
spacing is usually determined by the pattern of drilling or planting;
plants are regularly spaced across rows and often along rows too. In
the vertical, leaves of a single plant form a mosaic determined by phyllotaxy. When leaves from successive nodes emerge from opposite sides
of the stem the chance of two or more leaves overlapping in a unit layer
is significantly less than in random foliage. For example, in a stand of
maize growing at 61,700 plants/ha (25,000 plants/acre), the area per
plant is 1,600 cm^2 and if the average leaf area is 800 cm^2, only two
leaves on each plant are needed to form a unit leaf layer. As adjacent
leaves on the same plant are oriented at 180°, overlapping will be re-

stricted to the leaves of neighboring plants and will be slight if the leaves tend to grow across the rows. In a stand of barley with each plant occupying 10 cm^2 of field area and carrying leaves with an average area of 20 cm^2, unit leaf area is formed by one leaf on every second plant and overlapping will again be restricted to a much smaller range of probabilities than the random model predicts. Moreover, if there is any tendency for leaves to develop where there are gaps in the foliage as Alberda (1966) found in ryegrass, the chances of leaves overlapping within a unit layer may be negligible. In statistical terms, such an arrangement of leaves would be described as regular or very underdispersed. As an extreme contrast, crops such as lettuce (Lactuca sativa L.), drilled in widely spaced rows to allow hoeing, have leaves that are clumped or very over-dispersed and unit leaf layer contains a very large number of overlapping leaves.

Foliage in which the spatial distribution of leaves is effectively random is most likely to be found in communities where the average leaf area is much smaller than the ground area occupied by each plant. The coordinates defining the position of any leaf will then be very weakly correlated with the coordinates of most other leaves in the same layer. This condition may be satisfied in forests and in a few common crops, e.g., lucerne (Medicago sativa) and clover. Warren Wilson (1965) used inclined point-quadrats to show that the foliage of a mature stand of lucerne was effectively random but found significant departures from randomness in other communities. It is no accident that point-quadrat analysis has been applied mainly to foliage with randomly arranged leaves. The large number of contacts which the method needs accumulates most rapidly in stands with a large number of small leaves on each plant.

B. Transmission in Foliage

The theory of light transmission in nonrandom foliage was first presented by Kasanaga and Monsi (1954). They accepted the possibility that leaves within a unit layer might overlap but divided the layer into n sublayers within which they postulated there was no overlapping. In each such sublayer, the leaf area index is $1/n$ and for the special case of black horizontal leaves, the sublayer transmits a fraction $(1 - 1/n)$ of radiation at vertical incidence. The transmission $T(1)$ for unit leaf layer is then given by

$$T(1) = (1 - 1/n)^n. \tag{1}$$

For random foliage, n must be infinite to avoid overlapping in the sublayer. The limit of $(1 - 1/n)^n$ as $1/n \longrightarrow 0$ can be obtained by writing

$$\underset{1/n \to 0}{\mathcal{L}} (1 - 1/n)^n = \mathcal{L} \exp\left[n \ln\left(1 - 1/n\right)\right] = \exp\left(-1\right)$$

a result already stated.

For more general geometry, the fraction of radiation intercepted

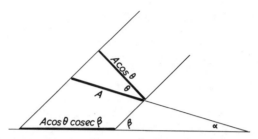

Fig. 5-3—Geometrical relations for the special case of a leaf with its normal in the plane of the sun's rays at angle θ : α is the leaf angle to the horizontal, and β is the solar elevation.

by the leaves in a sublayer will be equal to the area of the shadows they cast on a horizontal surface beneath the layer. For example, if a set of leaves at an angle α faces towards the sun at an elevation β, the shadow area index will be $\cos \theta \; \mathrm{cosec} \; \beta$ where θ is the angle between the sun's rays and the normal to the leaf surface (Fig. 5-3). If the leaves do not face the sun but are arranged uniformly round the compass, $\cos \theta$ is replaced by $\overline{\cos \theta}$, averaging over azimuth angles from 0 to 360°. Then the transmission of unit leaf layer is

$$T(1) = (1 - \overline{\cos \theta} \; \mathrm{cosec} \; \beta /n)^n. \qquad (2)$$

Values of $\overline{\cos \theta}$ originally derived by Reeve (1960) are tabulated as (F'/F) by Duncan et al. (1967). When $\alpha < \beta$ only the upper surfaces of leaves are illuminated so that

$$\overline{\cos \theta} \; \mathrm{cosec} \; \beta = \cos \alpha \sin \beta \; \mathrm{cosec} \; \beta = \cos \alpha$$

i.e., light interception and shadow area are independent of radiation angle. When $\alpha > \beta$, either the upper or the lower surface of a leaf is illuminated depending on its azimuth and $\overline{\cos \theta} \; \mathrm{cosec} \; \beta$ assumes a more complicated form given by Reeve.

Three special cases examined by Cowan (1968) are

1) Horizontal foliage: $\cos \theta \; \mathrm{cosec} \; \beta = 1$ and the expression for transmission reduces to equation (1).

2) Spherical foliage: on a plane normal to the radiation, the area of shadow cast by a sphere is half the area of the illuminated surface $(\pi \; r^2/2\pi \; r^2 = 1/2)$. Projected on a horizontal surface, the shadow area is $(\mathrm{cosec} \; \beta)/2$ so

$$T(1) = [1 - (\mathrm{cosec} \; \beta)/2n]^n. \qquad (2a)$$

3) Vertical foliage: on a plane normal to the radiation the area of shadow cast by a cylinder in $2 \cos \beta/\pi$ times the illuminated area and the transmission is

$$T(1) = [1 - (2 \cot \beta)/n\pi]^n. \qquad (2b)$$

C. Translucent Leaves

When leaves transmit a fraction τ of the radiation falling on them in a specified waveband, the amount of light transmitted by a sub-layer will be $1 - (1 - \tau) \overline{\cos \theta} \ \text{cosec} \ \beta / n$ and the fraction of radiation transmitted by a leaf area index L will be

$$T(L) = \left\{ 1 - (1 - \tau) \cos \theta \ \text{cosec} \ \beta / n \right\}^{nL}. \tag{3}$$

A special form of this expression was derived by Monteith (1965) who assumed that the probability of more than one interception within unit leaf layer was so small that division into sublayers was unnecessary. Then assuming $n = 1$ and setting $1 - s = \overline{\cos \theta} \ \text{cosec} \ \beta$

$$T(L) = \left\{ s + (1 - s) \tau \right\} L \tag{4}$$

a binomial form that can be expanded to find the fraction of radiation reaching a given level after transmission through 0, 1, 2.... leaves higher in the canopy.

Alternatively, equation (3) can be rewritten as

$$T(L) = \exp \left[L \ln \left\{ 1 - (1 - \tau) \overline{\cos \theta} \ \text{cosec} \ \beta / n \right\}^n \right] \tag{5}$$

which tends for random foliage to the limit

$$T(L) = \exp \left[-L (1 - \tau) \overline{\cos \theta} \ \text{cosec} \ \beta \right] \tag{6}$$

$$= \exp (-K'L)$$

where $K' = (1 - \tau) \overline{\cos \theta} \ \text{cosec} \ \beta$ is the form of extinction coefficient most quoted in the literature. To compare coefficients determined by measurements in different spectral ranges, it is convenient to work with a parameter $K = K'/(1 - \tau)$ depending only on the geometry of the system. In principle, the degree of randomness in foliage could be determined by comparing measurements of transmission in a canopy of specified geometry with values predicted from equations (4) and (6). In practice, $\overline{\cos \theta}$ is very difficult to determine accurately and the validity of the two formulae for different crops awaits a critical test.

D. Incident Flux

Equations (4) and (6) describe the transmission of radiation in a canopy in terms of the relative irradiance of a horizontal surface as measured, for example, by a solarimeter or photocell. To estimate the average irradiance of inclined leaf surfaces, two factors must be taken into account. First, the average size of shadow cast by leaves is $K (= \overline{\cos \theta} \ \text{cosec} \ \beta)$ times the leaf area so the irradiance from the downward flux of radiation is K times the flux measured with an instrument facing upwards. Second, because leaves reflect radiation as well as transmitting, they are exposed to an upward flux in the canopy which must be added to the downward flux in order to calculate the total flux available for photosynthesis. The rigorous analytical treatment of upward and downward fluxes given by Cowan (1968) is rather cumbersome and the approximate methods used by Kuriowa (1968) and by Tooming and Ross (1964) (see Tooming, 1967) seem accurate enough in practice. In these methods, the function $\exp[-K(1-\tau)]$ describing the extinction of downward flux is replaced by $\exp[-K(1-\tau-\rho)]$ where ρ is the reflectivity of leaves in a specific waveband. Then if the radiative flux at the top of the canopy is $I(0)$ the total upward and downward flux below leaf area L is given to a good approximation by $I(0)\exp[-K(1-\tau-\rho)L]$. Note that because the values of τ and ρ are similar over the whole spectrum, it is unnecessary to distinguish between the radiation transmitted downward and reflected downwards, or between radiation transmitted and reflected upwards.

The radiation absorbed by leaves can be split into three components:

1) Direct radiation from the sun in the form of sunflecks. For random foliage, this is given by $K I(0) = \overline{\cos\theta}\ \mathrm{cosec}\ \beta\ I(0)$.

2) Diffuse radiation generated within the canopy by the transmission and reflection of sunlit leaves. Below a leaf area L, the total flux of radiation not absorbed by higher leaves is

$$I(0)\exp[-K(1-\tau-\rho)L]$$

but this includes radiation penetrating the foliage without being intercepted, $I(0)\exp(-KL)$. Thus the flux of transmitted and reflected radiation is

$$I(0)\exp(-KL)\left\{\exp\left[-K(\tau+\rho)L\right]-1\right\}.$$

The corresponding irradiance of leaves is found by multiplying this flux by a factor K_d, say, corresponding to the mean value of $\overline{\cos\theta}\ \mathrm{cosec}\ \beta$ for diffuse flux. Cowan's calculations show that the diffuse flux either from a uniform or from a standard overcast sky, penetrates spherical foliage like a beam at 45° giving an extinction coefficient

$$K_d = \overline{\cos\theta}\ \mathrm{cosec}\ 45° = 0.7$$

but for increasingly planophile foliage, K_d will approach unity. Hanau (in Duncan et al., 1967) derives equations for the diffuse flux absorbed by leaves at a fixed angle.

3) Diffuse radiation from the blue sky and clouds. At the top of the canopy, the diffuse flux is assumed to be isotropic, giving an irradiance D. Then at any level specified by L, the total upward and downward flux of diffuse radiation will be approximately

$$D\exp[-K_d(1-\tau-\rho)L]$$

and the corresponding irradiance will be K_d times this flux as in component 2.

The total irradiance of sunlit leaves can now be found by adding components 1, 2, and 3 and the irradiance of shaded leaves is the sum of components 2 and 3. Tooming (1967) gives approximations valid for clear and overcast skies.

For nonrandom foliage with $n = 1$, a much simpler treatment is possible. In the first place, differences in the attenuation of direct and diffuse flux are not distinguished and a single factor $(1 - s)$ describes the fraction of both types of radiation intercepted by unit leaf layer. The irradiance of leaves is therefore $(1 - s)$ times the horizontal irradiance at the same level. If the total flux at the top of the canopy is Q $(= D + I \sin \beta)$, the irradiance of leaves from the downward flux will be

$$(1 - s) \, Q \left\{ s + (1 - s) \, \tau \right\}^{L}.$$

The irradiance from downward and upward fluxes together is

$$(1 - s) \, Q \left\{ s + (1 - s) \, (\tau + \rho) \right\}^{L}.$$

It has not yet been shown whether the lack of rigor in deriving these expressions leads to significant error in subsequent calculations of photosynthesis rate.

E. Sunlit Area

To calculate the contribution to photosynthesis of sunlit and shaded leaves, it is necessary to estimate their respective areas at each height in the canopy. For random foliage, the fractional area of sunlit leaves beneath a layer with leaf area index L is simply e^{-KL} and the area of all sunlit leaves in a canopy with total index L is given by the integral

$$\int_{O}^{L} \exp{-KL} = [1 - (\exp{-KL})/K] \tag{7}$$

tending to $1/K$ at large values of L.

In terms of the nonrandom model ($n = 1$) the area of foliage receiving radiation from sun and sky is 1 in the first leaf layer, s in the second, s^2 in the third, etc. (Monteith, 1965). The total area of foliage exposed to sun and sky is

$$\sum_{o}^{L-1} s^{n} = (1 - s^{n}) / (1 - s). \tag{8}$$

A similar function of s was derived for the area of leaves receiving light transmitted through one higher leaf but this is an unrealistic distinction. It might be better to treat the radiation scattered by foliage as uniformly distributed over the surfaces of leaves in neighboring layers including leaves that are exposed to direct sunlight.

Equation (7) predicts that sunlit area will depend on solar elevation because K is given by $\overline{\cos \theta}$ cosec β. In contrast, when s is assigned the constant value $(1 - \cos \alpha)$ the sunlit area $(1 - s^n)/(1 - s)$ is constant during the day. The difference between the two predicted areas is large when α is taken as 66° to give s = 0.6 as observed in barley (Warren Wilson, 1965). However, measurements of transmission in several crops reveal little diurnal change of s and recent measurements in maize (Horie, 1966) showed that the area of sunflecks was relatively constant during the day.

F. Longwave Radiation

The exchange of longwave radiation in crops depends on the transmission of diffuse fluxes upwards and downwards. In the simplest case when the soil and foliage are at the same radiative temperature $T \, ^OK$, the emission of flux per unit area of foliage will be $\sigma \, T^4$ where σ is Stefan's constant. The downward flux of radiation from the atmosphere can be written $\epsilon \, \sigma \, T^4$ where ϵ is an effective emissivity depending on water vapor content and on cloudiness. (In practice, ϵ will range from from about 0.7 when the air is very dry and the sky is cloudless to 1.0 when the sky is heavily overcast.) The intensity of longwave radiation increases from the zenith to the horizon, so the extinction coefficient for atmospheric radiation will not be exactly the same as the coefficient for longwave radiation emitted by foliage. In practice, the difference will be trivial and it is safe to assume that the extinction coefficient appropriate for longwave fluxes, irrespective of their origin, is the same as the coefficient K_d for diffuse shortwave radiation. Then at any level in the crop specified by a leaf area index L below the top of the canopy, the downward flux of longwave radiation will be $\epsilon \, \sigma \, T^4 \exp(-K_dL)$ from the atmosphere and $\sigma \, T^4 \, [1 - \exp(-K_dL)]$ from higher leaves. The upward flux will be $\sigma \, T^4$ when the foliage and soil are isothermal so the net longwave flux will be $(1 - \epsilon) \, \sigma \, T^4 \exp(-K_dL)$.

Measurements to be reviewed in the next section suggest that profiles of shortwave, longwave, and net radiation are sometimes very similar in shape. This similarity would be expected in planophile foliage with $\alpha < \beta$ for most leaves so that $K_d \simeq K \simeq \overline{\cos \alpha}$. On the other hand, when the temperature of the foliage departs from the soil temperature by more than a few degrees, profiles may be similar in shape near the top of the canopy but may diverge near the soil surface. This behavior can be inferred from measurements reported in bulrush millet by Begg et al. (1964); and in maize by Tanner, Peterson, and Love (1960), and by Denmead, Fritschen, and Shaw (1962). A simple analytical treatment of nonisothermal foliage was given by Saito (1964).

V. MEASUREMENTS

The literature contains numerous measurements of radiation in crop communities but they are difficult to relate because so few workers have used the same instruments in the same way and reported their re-

Table 5-2—Transmission coefficients for crops and leaf areas for 5% light transmission

Crop	K	K_v	s	L_5	Source
Cotton (Gossypium hirsutum L.)	1.13	1.05	0.32	2.9	Ludwig et al. (1965)
Clover (Trifolium repens L.)	1.10 0.91	1.03 0.85	0.33 0.40	2.9 3.5	Wilfong et al. (1967) Brougham (1958) Monteith (1965)
Sunflower (Helianthus annuus L.)	0.97	0.90	0.38	3.3	Hiroi and Monsi (1966)
Beans (Phaseolus vulgaris L.)	0.86	0.80	0.42	3.8	Jones (1968)
Kale (Brassica acephala L.)	0.94	0.87	0.39	3.5	G. Szeicz*
Orchardgrass (Dactylis glomerata L.)	0.72	0.67	0.49	4.5	Pearce et al. (1965)
Maize (Zea mays L.)	0.70	0.65	0.50	4.7	Allen et al. (1964)
Barley (Hordeum distichum)	0.69	0.64	0.50	4.7	G. Szeicz*
Beans (Vicia faba)	0.63	0.58	0.53	4.7	G. Szeicz*
Alfalfa (Medicago sativa L.)	0.83 - 0.66	0.77 - 0.61	0.44 - 0.52	3.9 - 4.9	Wilfong et al. (1967)
Rice (Oryza sativa L.)	0.86 - 0.43	0.80 - 0.40	0.42 - 0.65	3.8 - 7.5	Hayashi and Ito (1962)
Bulrush Millet (Pennisetum typhoides L.)	0.59	0.55	0.55	5.5	Begg et al. (1969)
Sorghum (Sorghum vulgare L.)	0.49	0.46	0.61	6.9	P. R. Goldsworthy (unpublished)
Soybeans (Glycine max L.)	0.45	0.42	0.64	7.2	Sakomoto & Shaw (1967)
Short-rotation ryegrass (Lolium perenne × Lolium multiflorum L.)	0.43	0.40	0.65	7.8	Brougham (1958) Monteith (1965)
Perennial ryegrass (Lolium perenne L.)	0.34 - 0.26	0.32 - 0.24	0.71 - 0.77	8.7 - 11.5	I Rhodes (unpublished)
Wimmera ryegrass (Lolium rigidum L.)	0.29	0.27	0.75	10.4	Stern & Donald (1962) Monteith (1965)

* From unpublished measurements at Rothamsted Experimental Station. The figure underlined in each line is derived directly from measurements and is the basis for calculating the other coefficients.

sults in the same form. For a consistent comparison, measurements from different sources were summarized by three related coefficients:

1) The extinction coefficient for visible radiation K'_V derived from measurements of direct and diffuse flux with a photocell;

2) The general extinction coefficient $K = K'_V/(1 - \tau)$ with τ assumed to be 0.07 for visible radiation;

3) The coefficients derived from equation (4) with $\tau = 0.25$ for total solar radiation or from $s = e^{-K}$.

A parameter of more direct agronomic interest is the leaf area index at which the amount of light transmitted by a canopy becomes trivial. By convention, the limit of transmission is taken as 5% and the corresponding leaf area L_5 is given by

$$0.05 = \exp(-K'_V L_5).$$

Taking logarithms, $L_5 = 3/K'_V$.

Table 5-2 presents estimates of extinction coefficients and of L_5 for 16 species. They are arranged in order of decreasing K and increasing s, i.e., starting with planophile canopies and moving towards erectophile canopies. Some of the measurements on which the table was based will be discussed in more detail, following the same sequence.

1. Cotton

In a growth room experiment, the intensity of light measured with an EEL photometer was a strictly logarithmic function of the cumulative leaf area index implying no change of extinction coefficient with depth in the community (Ludwig, Saeki, and Evans, 1965). In a field crop with 101-cm (40-inch) rows, different diurnal variations of light interception and photosynthesis rate were observed in rows running east-west and north-south (Baker and Meyer, 1966). Daily rates of photosynthesis were indistinguishable, however.

2. Clover

Brougham (1958) found a strong diurnal variation of the fraction of light transmitted by a stand of white clover, e.g., from 1.6% at $\beta = 23^{\circ}$ to 13% at $\beta = 71^{\circ}$. This result is inconsistent with the planophile nature of the foliage and with Brougham's comment that the leaves exhibited phototropism.

3. Kale

From measurements with tube solarimeters, the transmission of total solar radiation decreased logarithmically with the leaf area index as Fig. 5-4 shows but the parameter s was effectively constant within $\pm$ 4 hours of solar noon and was slightly larger on clear than on overcast days.

4. Maize

There are more published measurements of radiation in maize than in any other species. In mature canopies, the diurnal change of K_V was small with ±4 hours of noon (Allen et al., 1964; Allen and Brown, 1965). Loomis et al. (1968) found a preponderance of leaves at $\alpha < 45^0$ when the population density was 48,000 plants/ha or less, but more vertical leaves ($\alpha > 45^0$) predominated at 125,000 plants/ha. This behavior is consistent with the large values of L_5 (7.8 to 9.3) reported in earlier work with dense stands (Williams et al., 1965) and with the observation by Allen and Brown (1965) that K_V may be anomalously small in the upper part of a maize canopy where young leaves tend to be clustered around the stalks. Loomis et al. (1968) were unable to relate K_V closely to the distribution of leaf angles, but for the species of maize studied by Nichiporovich (1961) and by Ross and Nilson (1967b), the distribution was almost spherical implying $K_V = 1/2 \sin \beta$ in good agreement with their measurements of transmission. Duncan, Williams, and Loomis (1967) drew attention to the significant amount of light absorbed by tassels and calculated that the shadow cast on foliage would reduce leaf photosynthesis by about 10% at a population of 50,000 plants/ha.

5. Barley

From unpublished figures supplied by P.V. Biscoe, the percentage transmission did not change systematically within ±5 hours of noon (Fig. 5-5). In a stand growing to 90 cm, the transmission of total solar radiation and of net radiation were almost identical at a height of 10 cm.

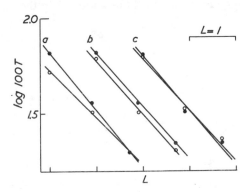

Fig. 5-4—Transmission T of solar radiation in kale, plotted logarithmically as a function of the cumulative leaf area index L with arbitrary origin.

Curve	GMT	β^0	s	
			Overcast	Clear
a	08–10	28–43	0.33	0.41
b	10–14	43–50	0.37	0.37
c	14–16	28–43	0.35	0.40

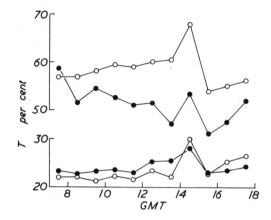

Fig. 5-5—Transmission of solar radiation (open circles) and of net radiation (full circles) in a stand of barley, measured at heights of 45 cm (upper lines) and 10 cm (lower lines).

The difference observed at 45 cm may be a real effect of temperature gradients in the upper part of the foliage or may be the result of small differences in the distribution of leaf area with height over the ground where the two sets of instruments were exposed. Figure 5-6 shows the diurnal change of s in a mature stand of barley at Rothamsted, justifying the assumption that s is constant within ±4 hours of noon (corresponding to $30 < \beta < 60°$ at the time of measurement.)

Pearce, Brown, and Blaser (1968) reported an ingenious experiment in which barley was grown in trays inclined to the horizontal so that the seedlings grew vertically at an angle to the soil surface. The

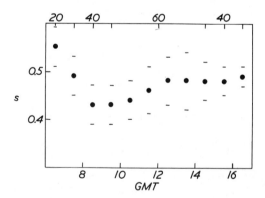

Fig. 5-6—Diurnal variation of s in a stand of barley growing to 53 cm height on 23 June 1963. The standard deviations were calculated from the fit of the relation

$$\ln T = L \left\{ s + (1 - s) \, r \right\}$$

to measurements at three values of L.

trays were then placed horizontally under an extended light source and the transmission was measured with a selenium photocell. The mean angles of leaves to the horizontal were 90, 53, and 18° and corresponding mean values of K_V were 0.32, 0.42, and 0.64. Corresponding differences of photosynthesis rate agreed well with predictions from the theory of Monsi and Saeki (1953).

6. Beans

Measurements with tube solarimeters at Rothamsted confirmed that the diurnal variation of s was negligible. As the canopy expanded to a leaf area index of L = 4, the logarithm of the daily mean light transmission decreased linearly with increasing L (Fig. 5-7). This result implies that the geometry of the foliage was invariant with age. Figure 5-7 also shows the attenuation of infrared radiation, giving the same value of s = 0.53 as the attenuation of total radiation.

7. Rice

Hayashi and Ito (1962) found a wide variation of K_V in varieties of rice with different leaf geometry. In general, the more erectophile varieties developed larger leaf area indices and produced more dry matter at a given leaf area.

8. Ryegrass

Brougham (1958) found that the diurnal change of transmission was even more pronounced in ryegrass than in clover. Kuriowa and Monsi (1963) fitted Brougham's data to a theoretical curve for foliage at a fixed angle $\alpha = 80°$. This value is unrealistically large even for erectophile foliage and the theoretical comparison therefore casts further doubts on the validity of the original measurements.

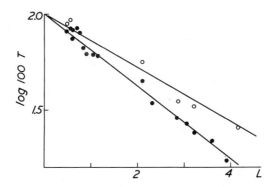

Fig. 5-7—Transmission of solar radiation (full circles) and infrared radiation (open circles) in a stand of beans (<u>Vicia faba</u>) as a function of the leaf area index. Each point represents the average transmission on a day between 25 May and 20 June, 1966.

VI. CONCLUSIONS

1) Several models of light distribution in crops are based on an assumption that the arrangement of foliage is effectively random. In real crops, the spacing of leaves cannot be random because it is determined by the pattern of sowing and by phyllotaxy. A critical study of radiation in relation to leaf geometry is needed to establish whether random or very regular models of canopy structure give the truest description of light distribution and hence the best estimates of photosynthesis.

2) Purists have argued that because the fraction of radiation intercepted by a leaf layer depends in principle on the incident angle of radiation, the diurnal variation of K (or s) must be taken into account in models of light distribution and photosynthesis. Direct measurements of radiation in crops with a wide range of leaf sizes and angles support the opposite view: that the variation of K is usually small enough to neglect, at least over the central 8 hours of the day when most assimilation takes place. This result is consistent with theory provided there is a preponderance of leaf angles less than 30°.

3) Models of photosynthesis reveal that for leaf indices usually met in the field, say 4 to 8 in mature stands, photosynthesis rates are not strongly dependent on leaf angle. At large leaf areas, however, say from 8 to 12, theory predicts that erectophile stands should make more efficient use of light than planophile stands. Critical field experiments are needed to test these predictions as the existing evidence is scanty and inconclusive. In terms of yield at harvest, as distinct from instantaneous rates of photosynthesis, differences of leaf angle are likely to be much less significant than differences in the rate at which the canopy expands to form a complete cover or differences in the rate of respiration per unit leaf area.

4) Progress depends on combining measurements of radiation, properly averaged in time and in space, with corresponding measurements of leaf area distribution determined from an adequate number of samples. In practice, this combination is rare and many studies of light distribution in crops suffer from a disparity in the precision of physical and biological measurements.

5) There is a danger of crop ecologists becoming preoccupied with models at the expense of measurements. This emphasis is irrational because one of the main functions of models is to integrate knowledge derived from measurements in order to predict the response of crops to their environment. Models simulate; but measurements summarize information.

ACKNOWLEDGEMENTS

Several workers kindly provided unpublished measurements for incorporation in Table 5-2. I am grateful to Dr. J. Warren Wilson for discussion of some of the issues raised in this paper and to Dr. J.R.

Philip whose response to a preliminary draft provided a stimulating basis for public and private debate in Lincoln.

LITERATURE CITED

Alberda, T. L. 1966. Responses of grasses to temperature and light. In The growth of cereals and grasses. Ed. Milthorpe and Ivins. Butterworths, London.

Allen, L. H., and K. W. Brown. 1965. Shortwave radiation in a corn crop. Agron. J.57:575-580.

Allen, L. H., C. S. Yocum, and E. R. Lemon. 1964. Photosynthesis under field conditions: VII. Radiant energy exchange. Agron. J. 56:253-259.

Anderson, M. C. 1964. Light relations of terrestrial plant communities. Biol. Rev. 39:425-486.

Anderson, M. C. 1966. Stand structure and light penetration II. J. Appl. Ecol. 3:41-54.

Avaste, O., H. Moldau, and K. S. Shifrin. 1962. Spectral distribution of direct and diffuse radiation. Akad. Nauk. Est. SSR. Inst. Phys. Astron. no. 3.

Baker, D. N., and R. E. Meyer. 1966. Influence of stand geometry on light interception and net photosynthesis in cotton. Crop Sci. 6:15-19.

Begg, J. E., J. F. Bierhuizen, E. R. Lemon, D. K. Misra, R. O. Slatyer, and W. R. Stern. 1964. Diurnal energy and water exchanges in bulrush millet. Agr. Meteorol. 1:294-312.

Brougham, R. W. 1958. Interception of light by the foliage of pure and mixed stands of pasture plants. Aust. J. Agr. Res. 9:35-52.

Cowan, I. R. 1968. The interception and absorption of radiation in plant stands. J. Appl. Ecol. 5:367-379.

Denmead, O. T., L. J. Fritschen, and R. H. Shaw. 1962. Spatial distribution of net radiation in a corn field. Agron. J. 54:505-510.

Dogniaux, R. 1954. Etude du climat de la radiation in Belgique. Inst. Roy. Meteorol. Belgique Contrib. No. 18.

Donald, C. M. 1961. Competition for light in crops and pastures. Symp. Soc. Exp. Biol. XV. 282-313.

Duncan, W. G., R. S. Loomis, W. A. Williams, and R. Hanau. 1967. A model for simulating photosynthesis in plant communities. Hilgardia 38(No. 4):181-205.

Duncan, W. G., W. A. Williams, and R. S. Loomis. 1967. Tassels and the productivity of maize. Crop Sci. 7:37-39.

Evans, G. C., and D. E. Coombe. 1959. Hemispherical and woodland canopy photography. J. Ecol. 47:103-113.

Friend, D. T. C. 1961. A simple method of measuring integrated light values in the field. Ecol. 42:577-580.

Gaastra, P. 1968. Radiation measurements for investigations of photosynthesis under natural conditions. In Eckardt (ed.). Functioning of terrestrial ecosystems. UNESCO, Paris.

Gates, D. M., H. N. Keegan, J. C. Schleter, and V. R. Weidner. 1965. Spectral properties of plants. Appl. Optics 4:11-20.

Green, D. A., L. H. Jones, and N. J. T. Melican. 1967. Radiation measurements. In The measurement of environmental factors in terrestrial ecology. British Ecological Society Symposium no. 8:257.

Hayashi, K., and H. Ito. 1962. Studies on the form of plant in rice varieties. Crop Sci. Soc. Japan 37:329-333.

Hiroi, T., and M. Monsi. 1966. Dry matter economy of Helianthus annuus communities. J. Faculty Sci., Tokyo III, 9:241-285.

Horie, T. 1966. Preliminary report of a method for estimating sunlit leaf area within a corn canopy. J. Agr. Meteorol. Tokyo 22:125.

Isobe, S. 1962. Preliminary studies on physical properties of plant communities. Bull. Nat. Inst. Agr. Sci. A. no. 9, 29–66.

Jones, L. H. 1969. Proceedings of VIIth Eucarpia Congress (In the press)

Kasanaga, H., and M. Monsi. 1954. On the light transmission of leaves. Jap. J. Bot. 14:304–324.

Kriedeman, P. E., T. F. Neales, and D. H. Ashton. 1964. Photosynthesis in relation to leaf orientation and light interception. Aust. J. Biol. Sci. 17:591–600.

Kuriowa, S. 1968. A new calculation method for photosynthesis of a plant community. In Functioning of terrestrial ecosystems. Proc. Copenhagen Symposium UNESCO, Paris.

Kuriowa, S., and M. Monsi. 1963. Theoretical analysis of light factor and photosynthesis in plant communities. J. Agr. Meteorol. 18:143–151.

Loomis, R. S., W. A. Williams, and W. G. Duncan. 1967. Community architecture and the productivity of terrestrial plant communities, p. 291–308. In A. San Pietro, F. A. Greer, and T. J. Army (ed.) Harvesting the sun. Academic Press, New York.

Loomis, R. S., W. A. Williams, W. G. Duncan, A. Dovrat, and F. Nunez. 1968. Quantitative descriptions of foliage display and light absorption of corn plants. Crop Sci. 8:352–356.

Ludwig, L. C., T. Saeki, and L. T. Evans. 1965. Photosynthesis in artificial communities of cotton plants. Aust. J. Biol. Sci. 18:1103–1118.

McCree, K. J. 1968. Infrared sensitive film for spectral measurements under plant canopies. Agr. Meteorol. 5:203–208.

Miller, E. E. 1951. Averaged measurement of optical transmission. Rev. Sci. Inst. 22:56–57.

Monsi, M., and T. Saeki. 1953. Uber den Lichtfaktor in den Pflanzengesellschaften. Jap. J. Bot. 14:22–52.

Monteith, J. L. 1965. Light distribution and photosynthesis in field crops. Ann. Bot. 29:17–37.

Moss, D. N. 1964. Optimum lighting of leaves. Crop Sci. 4:131–136.

Pearce, R. B., R. H. Brown, and R. E. Blaser. 1965. Relationships between leaf area index, light interception and net photosynthesis in orchardgrass. Crop Sci. 5:553–556.

Pearce, R. B., R. H. Brown, and R. E. Blaser. 1967. Photosynthesis in plant communities as influenced by leaf angle. Crop Sci. 7:321–324.

Philip, J. R. 1965a. The use of point-quadrats with special reference to stem-like organs. Aust. J. Bot. 14:105–125.

Philip, J. R. 1965b. The distribution of foliage density with foliage angle estimated from inclined point-quadrat observations. Aust. J. Bot. 13:357–366.

Reeve, J. E. 1960. Appendix on derivation of formulae (In Inclined point quadrats, J. Warren Wilson) New Phytol. 59:1–8.

Reifsnyder, W. E., and H. W. Lull. 1965. Radiant energy in relation to forests. USDA Tech. Bull. no. 1344.

Roach, S. A. 1968. The theory of random clumping. Methuen, London.

Robinson, N. 1966. Solar radiation. Elsevier, Amsterdam.

Ross, Yu. K., and T. Nilson. 1967a. Biometric characteristics of a maize stand. In Nichiporovich (ed.) Photosynthesis of productive systems. Israel Program of Scientific Transl., Jerusalem.

Ross, Yu. K. and T. Nilson. 1967b. The spatial orientation of leaves in crop stands. In Nichiporovich (ed.) Photosynthesis of productive systems. Israel Program of Scientific Transl., Jerusalem.

Saeki, T. 1963. Light relations in plant communities. In L. T. Evans (ed.) En-environmental control of plant growth. Academic Press, New York.

Saito, T. 1964. Method of measurement of transmissivity of atmospheric radiation and of calculation of net longwave radiation within plant communities. J. Agr. Meteorol. Tokyo. 20:7–10.

Sakomoto, C. M., and R. H. Shaw. 1967. Light distribution in field soyabean canopies. Agron. J. 59:7–9.

Singh, M., D. B. Peters, and J. W. Pendleton. 1968. Net and solar radiation in soybean canopies. Agron. J. 60:542-545.

Stern, W. R., and C. M. Donald. 1962. Light relationships in grass-clover swards. Aust. J. Agr. Res. 13:599-614.

Szeicz, G. 1965. A miniature tube solarimeter. J. Appl. Ecol. 2:145-147.

Szeicz, G. 1966. Field measurements of energy in the 0.4-0.7 micron range. In Light as an ecological factor. British Ecol. Soc. Symp. 6.

Szeicz, G., J. L. Monteith, and J. M. Dos Santos. 1964. Tube solarimeter to measure radiation among plants. J. Appl. Ecol. 1:169-174.

Tageeva, S. V., and A. B. Brandt. 1961. Optical properties of leaves depending on the angle of light incidence. In B. C. Christenson et al. (ed.) Progress in photobiology. Elsevier, Amsterdam.

Tanner, C. B., A. E. Peterson, and J. R. Love. 1960. Radiant energy exchange in a corn field. Agron. J. 52:373-379.

Tooming, Kh. 1967. An approximate method for determining the attenuation and reflection of PHAR. In Nichiporovich (ed.) Photosynthesis of productive systems. Israel Program of Scientific Transl. Jerusalem.

Tooming, Kh., and Yu. K. Ross. 1964. Radiatsionnyi rezhim poseva kukuruzy po yarusam. Iss. Fiz. Atmas. 6.

Warren Wilson, J. 1965. Stand structure and light penetration I. J. Appl. Ecol. 2:383-390.

Warren Wilson, J. 1960. Inclined point quadrats. New Phytol. 59:1-8.

Warren Wilson, J. 1963. Estimation of foliage density and foliage angle by inclined point quadrats. Aust. J. Bot. 11:95-105.

Warren Wilson, J. 1967. Stand structure and light penetration III. J. Appl. Ecol. 4:159-165.

Wilfong, R. T., R. H. Brown, and R. E. Blaser. 1967. Relationships between leaf area index and apparent photosynthesis in Alfalfa and Ladino Clover. Crop Sci. 7:27-30.

Williams, W. A., R. S. Loomis, and C. R. Lepley. 1965. Vegetative growth of corn. Crop Sci. 5:211-215.

deWit, C. T. 1965. Photosynthesis of leaf canopies. Agr. Res. Reports 663, I.B.S. Wageningen.

5 ...DISCUSSION

K. L. MCCREE

Texas A & M University
College Station, Texas

I believe we could usefully spend a few minutes defining terms. In this field, it has become customary to use the words "light intensity" for the flux received per unit area. Unfortunately, this leaves us without a term for the more fundamental variable in any light calculation, the flux emanating from the source (or sources). This is what the photometrist calls the intensity. The radiant flux density at a surface is properly called the irradiance, and in the international system of units (S.I.) it is measured in W/m². The luminous flux density is called the illumination, and it is measured in lux (lumens/m²) or in footcandles (lumens/ft²). The International Lighting Vocabulary (C.I.E., 1957), the USA Standard of Nomenclature (USA Standards Institute, 1967), and the I.E.S. Lighting Handbook (Kaufman, 1966) should be consulted for further information on terms, definitions and techniques used in the general field of light measurement.

I have some comments on the proportion of photosynthetically active radiation in natural daylight. According to measurements in New Zealand (McCree, 1966) and in the Netherlands (Gaastra, 1968), in less-than perfect climates the proportion can vary over the range 38 to 65%. Moreover, the variation is systematic, the highest percentages occurring at the lowest irradiances, presumably because of the absorption of the infrared fraction by the water vapor in clouds. Since the leaves of plants are nonlinear integrators, the error resulting from the use of the single figure of 50% may not always be negligible.

I support your plea for more experimental testing of models, but I think we should be quite clear about which models, or parts of models, we are testing. I do not believe that one can "test models of light penetration by comparing predicted rates of dry matter accumulation with measurements in the field." The manner of light penetration is only one of a very large number of parameters which should go into a model of dry matter accumulation, and it is naive to ascribe differences observed in field experiments to any one parameter. Assumptions made about the dependence of light penetration on the geometry of the crop and of the incident light, in models of dry matter accumulation (or grain harvest, or water use, or any other plant response), should be tested by measuring the geometry and the light penetration.

For this purpose, it could be legitimate to average the irradiance measurements in time and space, but this is not what the plant does (McCree, 1965). It integrates CO_2 molecules, not quanta, and any respectable model of crop photosynthesis should do the same. For such a model, the pertinent information on light penetration is not the average irradiance but the area of leaf which is exposed to a given irradiance at a given instant, but this is scarcely amenable to measurement in the field. Hence the need for theories of light penetration.

Are plants perfect time integrators of CO_2 molecules? The results of some experiments made in Davis indicate that they are (McCree and Loomis, 1969). In these experiments, cucumber plants (Cucumis sativa L.) were presented with light which alternated between two levels of irradiance, within the range 16 to 220 W/m² (simulating sunlight and skylight), the bright and dull periods being equal in length, within the range 10^{-2} to 10^3 sec. The mean photosynthetic rate in fluctuating light was within a few percent of the mean of the two photosynthetic rates, obtained in steady light at the two levels of irradiance which were alternated. Deviations of up to 20% were obtained when a high irradiance was alternated with complete darkness, an unnatural condition similar to those used in early experiments on flashing light.

LITERATURE CITED

C.I.E. (Commission Internationale de l.Eclairage). 1957. International lighting vocabulary, 2nd ed. (3rd ed. is in press). Vol. 1. Bureau Central de la C.I.E., 57 Rue Cuvier, Paris 5, France. (obtainable in the USA from the Secretary, U.S. National Committee for the C.I.E., National Bureau of Standards, Washington, D.C. 20234).

USA Standards Institute. 1967. USA Standard RP-16 (USAS Z7.1-1967): Nomenclature and definitions for illuminating engineering. (obtainable from the Illuminating Engineering Society. 345 East 47th Street, New York, N.Y. 10017).

Kaufman, John E. (ed.) 1966. I.E.S. Lighting handbook. 4th ed. Illuminating Engineering Society, 345 East 47th Street, New York, N.Y. 10017.

Gaastra, P. 1968. Radiation measurements for investigations of photosynthesis under natural conditions. In Eckardt (ed.). Functioning of terrestrial ecosystems at the primary production level. Proc. Copenhagen Symp., Paris, UNESCO.

McCree, K. J. 1966. A solarimeter for measuring photosynthetically active radiation. Agr. Meteorol. 3:353-366.

McCree, K. J., and R. S. Loomis. 1969. Photosynthesis in fluctuating light. Ecology: in press.

McCree, K. J. 1965. Light measurements in plant growth investigations. Nature 206:527-528, and 210:753 (1966).

5... DISCUSSION

JOHN R. PHILIP

CSIRO Division of Plant Industry
Canberra, Australia

I. NONRANDOMNESS OF FOLIAGE DISTRIBUTION

A proper analysis of nonrandomness in foliage distribution has not yet been developed, in my opinion. To take n in Monteith's paper as infinite seems to overlook some important points:

1) The case n = finite implies a very special form of nonrandom structure, involving exact and rigid geometrical constraints which do not apply to vegetation. It must be understood that the value n = 0 <u>does not forbid nonrandomness</u> and seems appropriate to foliage.

2) Used as described in Monteith's paper, a finite n cannot represent underdispersion.

II. DISTRIBUTION OF RADIANT FLUX DENSITY
ON FOLIAGE SURFACES

Many authors have emphasized that it is not enough to know the mean irradiance received at foliage surfaces. Because of the usual nonlinearity of the photosynthetic response to radiation, we need to understand the distribution of irradiance. The remainder of this discussion considers certain influences on this distribution. Progress seems best served if we can assess the relative importance of various influences and concentrate our attention on the important ones. I discuss three influences: (i) foliage inclination to incident radiation; (ii) the finiteness of the sun's disc; and (iii) transmission through leaves. I shall treat all three with reference to direct radiation at the top of the canopy. Extensions (where relevant) to diffuse radiation will be obvious.

III. FOLIAGE INCLINATION TO INCIDENT RADIATION

The flux density of incident radiation increases from zero to its maximum as the angle of incidence increases from 0° to 90°. In general all angles of incidence will occur and thus the full scale of densities will be received. This seems to be the major (though, of course, not the only) cause of the distribution of incident densities.

IV. FINITE RADIUS OF THE SOLAR DISC

As Minnaert (1954) explains, "sun-pictures" occur because the sun's disc subtends a definite nonzero angle at the earth's surface, ζ. $\zeta = 0.093$ rad $= 0.53^o$. For the same reason shadows cast in direct sunlight are contained, not by a cylindrical surface with axis in the sun's direction, but by a tapering surface everywhere inclined at angle $\zeta/2$ to this axis. (We use "shadow" in the sense of umbra, the region which receives no direct illumination.) With increasing distance from the object, shadows [on planes in any fixed orientation] get progressively smaller; all such shadows except circular ones become more elongated; and all shadows disappear at distance $d/(2 \sin \zeta/2)$ [$\approx d/\zeta$], where d is the "minimum diameter" of the projection of the obstacle on a plane normal to the direction of the sun.

The fact of the finiteness of the sun's disc was recognized in passing by Warren Wilson (1967), but, so far as I know, it has been ignored to date in all calculations of distribution of irradiance in canopies.

A leaf presenting a minimum diameter of 1 cm casts no shadow beyond 107 cm; and a sunlit hole of 0.1 cm diameter illuminates 100 times its area [at roughly 1/100 intensity] at a level 100 cm below it. Figures such as these point up the fact that the finiteness of the sun's disc should be taken into account in investigations of the radiation climate in tall vegetation. Studies of plant structure concerned with optimum morphology for photosynthesis should not ignore it either.

V. TRANSMISSION THROUGH LEAVES

Direct radiation, of density I_0 on a plane normal to ray, arrives at top of canopy. Direct radiation incident on foliage is supposed to be absorbed, except for a fraction τ transmitted from lower surfaces as diffuse radiation, D. If $\bar{I}$ is mean direct irradiance

$$\frac{d\bar{I}}{d\ell} = - \bar{I} \text{ so that } \bar{I} = I_0 \exp(-\ell) \tag{1}$$

where ℓ is cumulative LAI projected on plane normal to ray.

Also

$$\frac{dD}{d\ell} = - (1-\tau) D - \tau \frac{d\bar{I}}{d\ell}, \tag{2}$$

where, for simplicity, we treat the absorption and transmission of diffuse radiation as similar to that of direct. Combining (1) and (2) and solving, we get

$$D = I_0 \left[\exp[-(1-\tau) \ell] - \exp(-\ell) \right] \tag{3}$$

Whence at position ℓ, the distribution of irradiances (on planes normal to direct radiation) is as follows:
Over "sunlit area" $\exp(-\ell)$,

$$\text{irradiance} = I_0 + D = I_0 \left\{ 1 + \exp[-(1-\tau) \ell] - \exp(-\ell) \right\}.$$

Over "shaded area" $1 - \exp(-\ell)$,

$$\text{irradiance} = D = I_0 \left\{ \exp[-(1-\tau) \ell] - \exp(-\ell) \right\}.$$

$\tau = 0.07$ for wavelengths of interest. D has maximum value approx. $0.027 I_0$ at $\ell = $ approx. 1.

This analysis avoids difficulties of Monteith (1965) of (i) taking n = finite, and (ii) treating transmitted light as direct, which it is not. Note that D/I_0 is usually trivially small.

ADDITIONAL LITERATURE REFERENCE

Minnaert, M. 1954. The nature of light and color in the open air. Dover, New York.

6

Gaseous Exchange in Crop Stands[1]

EDGAR LEMON

Agricultural Research Service, USDA
Ithaca, New York

I. PROBLEMS OF MEASUREMENT AND UNDERSTANDING

Man through the ages has evolved a strategy, albeit empirical, of manipulating the environment and the plant to his advantage. Practices such as fertilizing the soil, irrigation, weed control, and plant breeding and selection are common. Nonetheless, concentrated and coordinated efforts to understand the mechanisms controlling the whole soil-plant-atmosphere continuum is a new approach to finding new ways to favorably manipulate the whole system as well as predict response.

Conceptually and experimentally it has proven advantageous to view the total system in terms of energy, momentum, and mass exchange. This makes sense because in the first instance the foundations of crop production and water use are based upon two solar energy conversion processes—photosynthesis and evaporation. In the second instance, the momentum exchange of the wind creates the necessary turbulent ventilation to diffuse heat, water vapor, carbon dioxide, and oxygen. Of course, all of these exchange processes are driven by a common energy source—the sun.

My subject in this paper focuses on the ventilation of crop stands. We shall be mainly concerned with the turbulent diffusion of the physical properties of the air. The movement of air in crop stands has relevance to photosynthesis and respiration through the exchange of carbon dioxide and oxygen with the atmosphere. It has relevance also to transpiration through the exchange of water vapor and heat. Over the past 5 years we have taken advantage of the physics of turbulent diffusion to measure the rates of gaseous exchange layer-by-layer within the cano-

[1]Contribution from the Northeast Branch of the Soil and Water Conservation Research Division, ARS, USDA, in cooperation with the New York State Agricultural Experiment Station at Cornell University, Ithaca, N.Y., and the Atmospheric Sciences Research Division, US Army Electronics Command, Fort Huachuca, Ariz. Cornell University Department of Agronomy Series Paper no. 841.

117

pies of some crops (Begg, et al., 1964; Brown and Covey, 1966; Denmead, 1964, 1966; Inoue, et al., 1968; Lemon, 1967; Lemon and Wright, 1969; Wright and Lemon, 1966; Uchijima, 1962a, 1962b). Our primary purpose has been to relate environmental factors to plant response. From such studies we have hopes of improving the architecture of crop stands not only for light capture but for optimum ventilation as well. The latter is needed for optimizing plant temperature, and supply of CO_2 and minimizing water vapor loss. Ultimately the ideal crop structure will be a compromise for all of these attributes and will be specific for the crop product and the climate under which it is grown.

How well do we understand the physics of gaseous exchange and what are the chief problems of measuring it in the field? It seems appropriate after 5 years of progress to explore the answers to these questions at this symposium. I will focus only on the major weak points still needing attention. As a beginning I will briefly take up the methods of measurement. Since the methods are based upon the natural physical processes at work in the field much can be gained by understanding their principles. Later we will speculate about some relevant facets of the aerodynamic processes important to crop production.

A. Brief Review of Energy and Momentum Balance Methods of Measuring Gaseous Exchange in Crop Stands

To date most of our studies have dealt with large uniform fields of agricultural crops where we measure the energy and gaseous exchange in a vertical direction. This exchange is usually expressed in units of flux intensity, i.e., calories or grams per square centimeter of land surface per minute. During this talk I will concentrate on the exchange of CO_2 and momentum but the principles apply equally as well to exchange of the other physical properties of the air such as heat and water vapor.

Figure 6-1 is intended to picture the energy balance method or model to determine CO_2 exchange. In the upper left-hand corner the little box represents a layer or slab of a crop which is photosynthesizing, taking out of the air the amount of $CO_2 = QP$. The flux intensity at the top diffusing downward is $P + \Delta P$ and the flux intensity at the bottom diffusing downwards is P. Thus the difference between $P + \Delta P$ and $P = QP$. Expressed in another way, the sink strength, QP is equal to the derivative of the flux intensity on height, dP/dz. The name of the game is determining the flux intensity, P, at several levels of z in a crop canopy. In the lower left-hand corner of the figure you will find the treatment for one level z. Here the CO_2 flux intensity P is equal to the diffusivity coefficient of CO_2 in the air, K_C, and the CO_2 concentration gradient on height, dc/dz. Getting dc/dz is not too difficult; it is the slope of the CO_2 profile at z pictured in the insert. Today we are fairly confident in obtaining good CO_2 profiles. The major problem comes in evaluating K_C in order to solve the equation for P. Here one has to assume that in a turbulent wind regime, such as commonly occurs out-of-doors, the diffusivity coefficients for other physical properties of the air are the same as they are for CO_2. We have not learned how to de-

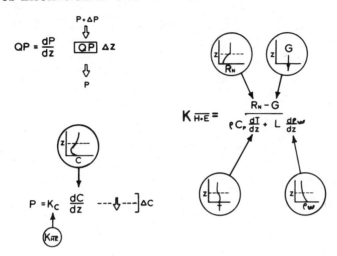

ENERGY BALANCE MODEL

Fig. 6-1—The energy balance model used to measure CO_2 exchange in plant communities (see text and Lemon, 1967).

termine K_C independently of P or dc/dz. By assuming the diffusivities are equal, however, one can turn to either the momentum or energy budget for a fair approximation of K_C. The right-hand side of Fig. 6-1 gives the energy balance method of determining a diffusivity coefficient which is the mean for heat and water vapor. The inserts depict the field measurements needed. These measurements have to be taken simultaneously with the CO_2 profile. These are: profiles of net radiation, RN; temperature, T; and water vapor, ρw, as well as soil heat flux, G. The slopes of these profiles at z give the derivatives desired. The other symbols in the equation are known constants. Once $K_{H \& E}$ is evaluated it is substituted for K_C, then CO_2 flux intensity, P, is calculated.

Figure 6-2 gives the momentum balance method of approximating K_C. Here the diffusivity coefficient for momentum, K_m, is substituted in the CO_2 flux equation. Now turn directly to the right side of the figure. In the upper right-hand corner is an insert containing a wind speed profile. It is obvious that the wind speed, u, decreases with decreasing height, z. Since air has mass, a decrease in velocity is indicative of friction or "drag" on the crop surfaces. The loss of momentum is "transferred" to the crop. This downward flux intensity of momentum, τ, "diffuses" in a manner similar to the other physical properties of the air, thus the process can be defined by an equation similar to the diffusion equation for CO_2. The equation on the upper right side is the diffusion equation for momentum rearranged so that the diffusivity coefficient K_m is equal to the momentum flux intensity, τ, divided by the wind speed gradient, du/dz, and the air density, ρ. The wind speed gradient,

MOMENTUM BALANCE MODEL

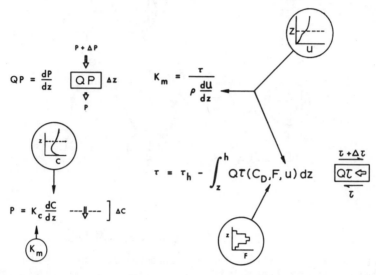

Fig. 6-2—The momentum balance model used to measure CO_2 exchange in plant communities (see text and Lemon, 1967).

du/dz, is the slope of the wind profile at z. Good wind speed profiles can be obtained with care.

The evaluation of the momentum flux intensity, τ, at a given level in the crop presents difficulties. In effect one determines the "drag" of the whole crop by evaluating the total momentum flux intensity at the top of the crop, τ_h, then partitions the momentum exchange with depth below the top of the stand as a function of foliage surface density F and and wind speed, u. This scheme is found in the lower right of Fig. 6-2. First, look at the little box representing a slab or layer of crop. The momentum flux intensity at the top is $\tau + \Delta\tau$ and at the bottom τ. The difference between the top and bottom gives the sink for momentum in the layer, $Q\tau$. This force per unit volume of crop stand is related to the foliage area density, the wind speed and a "drag coefficient," (C_D) characteristic of the surfaces in the crop. Integrating this drag force, $Q\tau$, from a height z to the top of the stand, h, is given by the equation. The inserts indicate the field measurements needed, the distribution of wind speed, u, and foliage area density, F. These measurements are not too difficult. The total shear at the top of the stand, τ_h, is determined from classical analysis of the log wind profile above the crop. As in the energy balance, wind speed and CO_2 profiles have to be made simultaneously. Once knowing τ_h and the integral of $Q\tau$ from z to h, one can solve for τ, then for K_m, and finally for P by substituting K_m for K_c.

However, two critical assumptions have to be made about C_D, the "drag coefficient" characteristic of the crop surfaces: (i) that it is a constant for all surfaces in the crop, and (ii) that it is independent of wind speed. Neither assumption is correct. This will be the subject of further comments later.

B. Some Weak Points in the Methods

1. The Heat Budget

Perhaps the most serious problem in using the energy balance to study gaseous exchange within the stand is the satisfactory measurement of net radiation. This is a sampling problem and has much in common to properly sampling for light distribution within the stand. Spatial variation is extremely great and special pains have to be taken to obtain an adequate sample. This subject has been adequately aired in Dr. J. L. Monteith's earlier discussion (Chapter 5, this book) and I will not dwell on it further here.

2. The Momentum Budget

I would like now to spend considerable time discussing the "aerodynamics" of crops because of its importance not only in the use of the momentum balance for measuring exchange but its importance to crop climate, exchange processes in the bulk air of the canopy as well as at foliage surfaces, and its application to prediction models. We have already demonstrated the usefulness of knowing the bulk air diffusivity coefficient for measuring flux intensities in stands. This parameter is an especially sensitive aerodynamic term defining the transport characteristics of the turbulent air. Knowledge of its correct quantitative value is indispensable to the correct measurement of canopy fluxes and the correct operation of prediction models for crop climate or crop processes. Figure 6-3 presents some relationships intended to demonstrate why this is so. Here are plotted various profiles for two crops quite distinctly different in geometric structure. The corn crop (Zea mays L.) example was 225 cm high with an LAI (leaf area index) of 4.3 while the contrasting orchardgrass (Dactylis glomerata L.) was 40 cm high with an LAI of 6.0. The foliage area density more appropriately defines the difference. In corn $F \simeq 0.02$ cm^2/cm^3 and in orchardgrass $F \simeq 0.2$ cm^2/cm^3. The profiles were selected for a given time period near midday when the wind speed at the top of both crops was nearly the same. Insulation and soil moisture conditions were not sufficiently different to play a role. By normalizing both crops as to height, it is easier to demonstrate the absolute differences in profile characteristics. Notice first, that despite the fact that wind speed profiles are quite similar, there is an order of magnitude difference in the diffusivity values for the two crops; $K \simeq 2000$ cm^2/sec in corn and 200 cm^2/sec in orchardgrass. The drag coefficients for the two crops also differed by an order of magnitude, $C_D = 0.08$ for corn and 0.009 for orchardgrass. Thus there is a strong correlation between foliage area density, drag coefficient and the diffusivity.

As a result of the differences in aerodynamic properties of the two

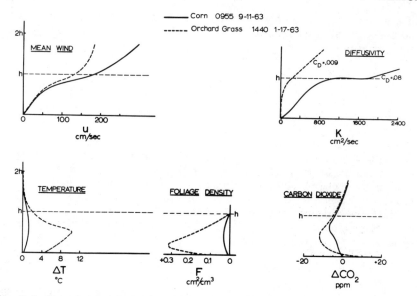

Fig. 6-3—Some comparisons between two crops differing widely in structure but under similar midday wind and radiation regimes on clear days. All comparisons made on a relative height basis where h is the height of the crop.

crops there will be a marked difference in the climate in the two stands. Profiles of temperature and CO_2 are the examples chosen. The trends are as one would anticipate but the magnitude is somewhat surprising. The maximum temperature of the air in the orchardgrass was almost $10°C$ greater than that of the air over the crop while in the corn the difference was of the order of $1-2°C$. The CO_2 profile differences are not as marked, however. One can correctly conclude that a crop's structure definitely plays a role in controlling its own climate. Indirectly, structure effects can alter plant processes. For example, the temperature influences respiration.

It is rather difficult to demonstrate a coupling of stand structure on exchange rates, however, because of the multiplicity of feedback mechanisms involved. For example, with an increase in diffusivity, the CO_2 differentials will decrease but other indirect effects will also take place, such as the lowering of leaf temperature and, maybe, an increase in evaporation rate. Still further, the conditions close to the leaf surface will undergo considerable change affecting the stomates or the exchange of gases through them. The complexity of these feedback mechanisms will always be the burr under the model-builder's saddle.

The site where interaction between the wind and leaf takes place is at the leaf surface. Figure 6-4 pictures the local situation at a leaf where the drag force is defined by the equation. The total force is related to the square of the wind speed, the area, the drag coefficient, and the density of the air. We will focus on the drag coefficient here. This parameter defines the ability of the surface to extract momentum from the wind stream thus creating turbulence to enhance mass diffusion. One can easily imagine that shape and size of the surface will play a

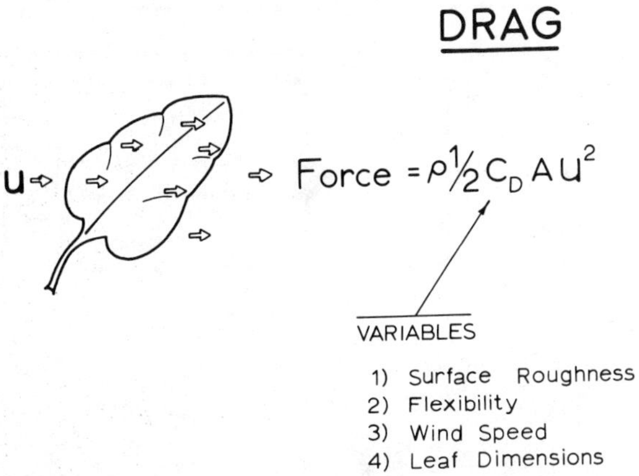

DRAG

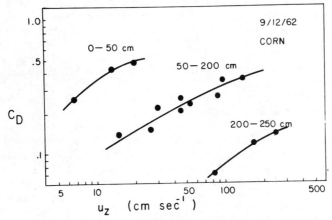

$$\Rightarrow \text{Force} = \rho \tfrac{1}{2} C_D A u^2$$

u ⇨

VARIABLES

1) Surface Roughness
2) Flexibility
3) Wind Speed
4) Leaf Dimensions

Fig. 6-4—Drag force at a leaf surface due to the wind, where ρ is the density of the air, C_D is the drag coefficient, A is the leaf surface area, and u is the wind speed. Variables affecting C_D are listed.

role, as well as roughness and flexibility. In rigid bodies the drag coefficient will be independent of wind speed but in elastic bodies that bend, such as stems and leaves, the drag coefficient increases with increasing wind speed until streamlining occurs. To make matters even more complex, the interaction between the turbulence generated at one leaf surface on another nearby leaf surface, affects still further the drag coefficient. The complexity of distribution, shapes and size, roughness and flexibility of surfaces, and their interaction through and by the wind, precludes any simple understanding or model at present. A challenge is there!

Wright and Brown (1967) have evaluated the effect of wind and canopy structure on the drag coefficient in a corn crop. Figure 6-5 gives their

Fig. 6-5—Logarithmic plot of the local drag coefficient, C_D as a function of wind speed for 50-cm increments of height within a corn crop. From Wright and Brown (1967).

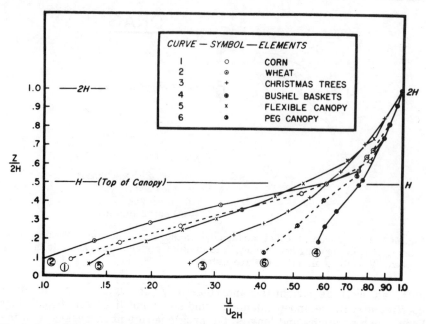

Fig. 6-6—Relative mean wind profiles for various "canopies" of relative height H. From Cionco (1967).

results. It is obvious that there is a coupling between wind speed and drag coefficient. They speculate that the depth effect in the canopy can be attributed to incorrectly judging the surface area of the tassel in the top layer and ignoring the soil surface influence in the bottom layer. All the points for the three midlayers of the stand fall on a common curve, however. This should be expected in corn because it is relatively uniform in the midstructure.

A manifestation of the coupling between wind and drag coefficient is found in the attenuation characteristics of the mean wind speed into flexible crops. Figure 6-6 gives normalized wind profiles as summarized by Cionco (1967). The shapes of the profiles in the stands are similar to light attenuation profiles and can be treated mathematically in the same way. One can characterize a profile shape by an attenuation or extinction coefficient. Cionco (1969) has done this for the same systems given in Fig. 6-6. Figure 6-7 shows Cionco's calculated attenuation coefficients as a function of wind speed for the several "crops." Notice that rigid, open systems, have low "a" or attenuation coefficient values that do not change with wind speed. On the other hand, more compact, flexible systems have higher "a" values that are sensitive to changes in wind velocity. All of these complexities associated with the coupling of wind and vegetation surfaces serve as a caution to those using the momentum balance approach to measure gaseous exchange in crop stands. This approach is not recommended for indiscriminate use, but it can be successfully used in uniform stands under steady winds, Lemon and Wright (1969).

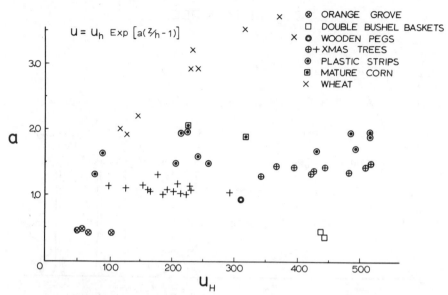

Fig. 6-7—Mean wind profile attenuation coefficient, a, plotted against mean wind speed u_H at the top of various "canopies." From Cionco (1969).

People who have studied wind flow in forest canopies are now cautioning us about a common phenomenon, that we have not recognized too clearly in crop stands. This is wind "blowthrough" below the crown canopy. This is an acceleration in wind speed, creating "horizontal divergence" of momentum. Necessarily this also creates "horizontal divergence" of other atmospheric properties, too. How widespread this phenomenon is in agricultural crops is uncertain but open row crops and crops with distinct top canopies may be suspect. If this is a feature of a plant stand, then our present models cannot be used without considerable modification. Even the use of the classical log profile method for exchange calculation above the stand has to be treated with caution.

Figure 6-8 schematically presents an extreme case found in a tropical rain forest in Costa Rica by Lemon et al. (1969). One can see that there is a distinct "blowthrough" of wind under the crown canopy and a distinct "advection of CO_2" or horizontal divergence in the midlayer of the forest.

Special assumptions and unique applications of the momentum budget had to be used to evaluate the CO_2 flux intensities through the various layers of the forest. Nonetheless, the end results of the calculations are reasonable. We shall discuss them later. Returning to Fig. 6-8, it is of interest to point out that the momentum "diffusing downward" from the top of the forest goes to zero where du/dz goes to zero in the midpoint of the upper canopy. Therefore, log profile characteristics above the forest have relevance only to the top half of the upper canopy. Below this, the "blowthrough" phenomenon dominates the exchange processes.

Where do we stand today on simple mean wind velocity models for

CO_2 FLUX MODEL

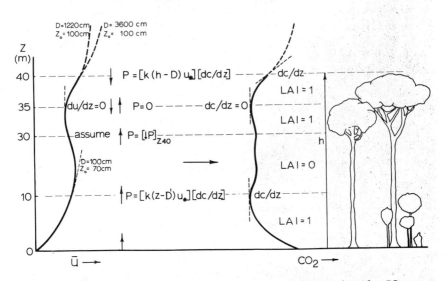

Fig. 6-8—Representative daytime wind speed, u, and carbon dioxide, CO_2, profiles in a tropical rain forest. From Lemon et al. (1969).

well-behaved uniform agricultural crops ? Figure 6-9 points up some striking results recently reported by Ordway (1969) and Ordway and Groom (1969). Using computer techniques they tested more than 150 cases over a wide variation of input to evaluate two flow models, a Viscosity Model and Mixing Length Model. The test results for a corn stand are presented here. In the Viscosity Model test the momentum flux intensity τ, or so-called Reynolds shearing stress, was assumed to be proportional to the wind speed gradient, du/dz, while F and K_m were adjusted. In the Mixing Length Model test, however, τ was assumed to be proportional to $(du/dz)^2$, while F and L were adjusted. L is the Prandtl mixing length. The assumed distributions of F, K_m, and L to obtain the best fit of the models to actual cornfield data are presented. These assumed distributions are representative of the real world, however. In the Viscosity Model the best fit was obtained when the foliage area density, F, was assumed to be constant up to $z/h = 0.73$ and then decreased linearly to zero at h, the height of the stand, along with assuming a linear increase of K_m from 0 at $z = 0$. The goodness of fit between model points and experimental profile is perfect. Unfortunately an equally perfect goodness of fit was obtained with the Mixing Length Model when a constant distribution of F was assumed and L was assumed to be linear from 0 at $z = 0$ to $z/h = 0.25$ and then constant to h. Amazingly both models give equally good results despite the fact that they are quite different physically. As Ordway understates, "This lack of discrimination, or uniqueness, leaves our understanding somewhat shaky."

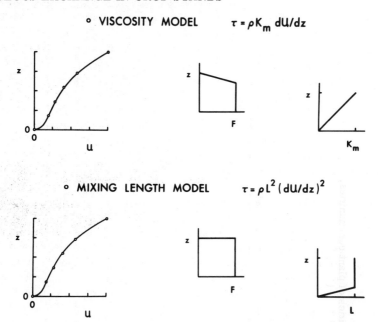

Fig. 6-9—Mathematical experiment for two theoretical wind profile models (see text). From Ordway (1969) and Ordway and Groom (1969).

II. AGRONOMIC USEFULNESS OF MICROMETEOROLOGICAL STUDIES

A. As a Measuring Tool and the Pursuit of Understanding

1. Plant Growth

In spite of the absence of sound physical models for predicting mean wind flow in crop stands, of the difficulty in measuring net radiation distribution in crop stands, and the need to assume constant drag coefficients in crop stands, progress has been made. In fact, 5 years ago we knew almost nothing about meteorological processes below the top of the crop. Today many of the physical processes and their coupling to plant characteristics are sufficiently well known that the model-builders are having a heyday. Progress on all fronts will pick up.

Viewed simply as a tool to measure the CO_2 balance in several different kinds of plant communities, meteorological methods reveal quantitative likenesses and differences of interest. Attention is directed to Table 6-1 where relevant data are presented for a few forests and agricultural crops. These data are representative CO_2 flux intensity values for clear days during the growing season. The values are for near mid-day and after darkness. The meteorological method used in each case is indicated, as is date and researcher.

Table 6-1—Representative CO_2 flux intensities of plant communities, $g/cm^2/sec \times 10^{-9}$

	Forests			Agricultural crops			
	70 yr. spruce, Germany (Picea abies, L.)	40 yr. jungle, Costa Rica (mixed)	7 yr. pine, Australia (Pinus radiata)	Corn, Japan (Zea mays)	Corn, USA (Zea mays)	Wheat, Australia (Triticum vulgare)	Sugar beet, England (Beta vulgaris L.)
Photosynthesis							
Upper story↓	150	32.5	}200	}300	}225	}125	}84
Lower story↑	50	2.5					
Respiration							
Upper story↑	20	1.9	} 25	} 20	} 50	} 20	} 14
Lower story↑	10	0.7		20	5	20	
Ground↑	50	3.1					
Midday Solar radiation (cal/cm²/min)	1.1	1.3	1.2	1.3	1.1	0.9	0.7
Date	12/VII/66	15/XI/67	1/XI/64	22/VIII/64	11/IX/63	21/X/64	15/VIII/58
Method	HB MB	MB	HB	HB	MB	HB	MB
Author	Baumgartner	Lemon, et al.	Denmead	Inoue, et al.	Lemon and Wright	Denmead	Monteith

With study of Table 6-1 several points of interest emerge. Firstly, the photosynthesis rates of crops and forests are not uniquely different during the favorable part of the growing season when full canopy leaf development has been established. Secondly, the respiration rates of the canopies of crops and forests are not too different either. Thirdly, the respired CO_2 evolved from the ground surface is quite variable. It is highest from the temperate region spruce forest and lowest in the tropical region rainforest. In our own studies in corn we have observed wide variation in the apparent evolution of CO_2 from the ground. Two variables seem operative, time of growing season and wetness of soil. The time of the season effect is not related to soil temperature.

Monteith and Szeicz (1960) mention similar seasonal fluctuations in a field of sugar beets. Values for our corn in Table 6-1 and those for sugar beets were taken in times of evident low ebb.

While it may be questionable to make an efficiency ranking of the different systems, based on the figures given in Table 6-1, such a ranking may in fact be realistic. The method of ranking was this: First, all the photosynthesis gains in Table 6-1 were adjusted to a common radiation base (1.0 $cal/cm^2/min$) assuming proportional response, then the total respiration losses of both ground and canopy were deducted. The highest net value is considered associated with the most efficient plant community. Their ranking from high to low is: corn (Japan), corn (USA), 7-year Pinus radiata forest (Australia), sugar beet (England), wheat (Australia), 70-year spruce forest (Germany), and 40-year tropical rain forest (Costa Rica). This ranking only holds for the conditions of midgrowing season after full leaf development. While a highly selected tropical grass leads the listing, the other cultivated agricultural crops show no evident superiority to the forests. The tropical jungle however is definitely the lowest.

No doubt, on a yearly basis the difference between the tropical forest productivity and the temperate forest productivity would equalize somewhat because the jungle never rests. Of more profound importance to this symposium emerges the realization that highly selected agricultural crops may be no more efficient in their photosynthesis and respiration processes than less highly selected plant communities such as forests. Man's manipulation of plant materials for production has not resulted in increasing the efficiency of the photosynthesis or respiration processes per se but rather has further channeled the products of photosynthesis into harvestable items.

2. Used as a Tool to Pinpoint Critical Plant-Environmental Interactions

Because plants are so "plastic" and so beautifully integrate the variables of the environment into smooth growth curves over days, or weeks, or seasons, classical growth analysis over days, or weeks, or seasons can hope at best to evaluate only the most pronounced features of the environment affecting plants, such as sunlight or extremes of temperature and moisture. Plant-to-plant variation in the field also presents a tremendous sampling problem.

Thus there would appear to be advantages to using gas exchange methods to measure plant growth and environmental interaction on a short-time basis. Indeed use of the methods discussed here have pinpointed interesting interactions; for example, the short-time intermittent cloud and sunshine influence on sunlight utilization in corn discovered by Denmead (1966). Because of the response time characteristics of stomates closing and opening and the time scale of sunshine and intermittent cloud passage, a cornfield in Iowa used sunlight less efficiently on the day with intermittent sun than on a clear day. Another example, less clearly defined, is the apparent influence of wind on the utilization of sunlight by corn in the field on bright days. Lemon (1963) and Wright and Lemon (1966) and Denmead (1966) have reported an increase in CO_2 exchange rate with increasing wind. They speculate that this is due to increased CO_2 concentration at the immediate leaf surface through the influence of increasing wind turbulence favorably altering the immediate leaf boundary layer. This has to be speculation, however, because increasing wind alters temperature and humidity relationships as well as the frequency distribution of light in a flexible canopy. Perhaps the simple mechanical movement of the leaves influence the stomates ?

In any event the number of interlocking relationships between plants and the environment in time and space are infinite if one recognizes the dynamics involved. Take on the one hand, as an example, the whole hierarchy of temperature fluctuations in the environment from a seasonal scale to the scale of fractions of a second. Now consider on the other hand, the lag time, the feedback, the hysteresis in the multiple control systems sensitive to temperature in the plant. On top of all this, remember the wide variation in plants and the potential for manipulation. It seems that the future will always bring us a new array of plant environment interactions requiring study and understanding. We'll never run out. This applies to temperature, soil nutrition, sunlight capture, or what have you.

Where do we stand today facing these complexities ? Of one thing we are sure, the physiologist and his growth chambers has to be linked, with leg irons if necessary, to the meteorologist and his outdoor studies. The latter has to define causes and frequency of environmental variation and the former has to interpret response in the plants.

People talk of "climatic noise" for the relatively short time variation in the climatic elements, perhaps on the scale of day-to-day, hour-to-hour, maybe even second-to-second. The title "noise" may be appropriate, if these variations are just minor background to the big events. We simply don't know. There is a challenge !

I'd like now to briefly discuss some of our recent studies at Ithaca defining some of the very short-time environmental variation attributable to local turbulence. First, we have to give a qualitative description of turbulence and an "eddy." Figure 6-10 borrowed from Ordway (1969) is very helpful. In the lower left is depicted a section of a large forest with the wind blowing from left to right. The mean wind, u, above the stand is indicated by the large horizontal arrow. The profile of the mean horizontal flow of wind in the stand is sketched in part on the right. Far from the edges of the forest with adequate fetch this mean wind profile will be the same everywhere. Superimposed on this mean

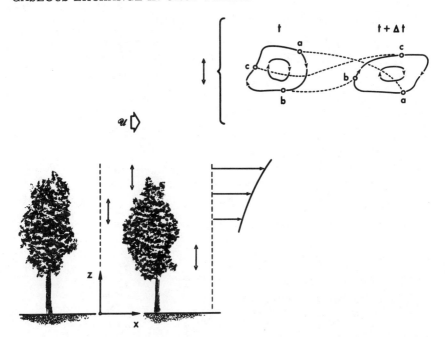

Fig. 6-10—Idealized wind flow characteristics in a forest stand. Horizontal arrows indicate mean horizontal wind flow. Vertical arrows indicate vertical wind flow due to turbulent motion of "eddies" between time t and t $+\Delta$t (see text).

windflow will be a variation in velocity associated with turbulence. Turbulence is a fluid dynamic instability caused by two mechanisms:

1) Thermal effects causing density variation in the air, thereby creating additional fluid motion. This is common where surfaces are heated by sunlight and then adjacent air is heated in turn. This less dense air will rise in globs we call eddies, being replaced by sinking cooler, denser globs or eddies. Such "buoyancy" effects will impart vertical motion to the mean flow, diffusing physical properties of the air down vertical gradients.

2) Frictional effects caused by wind flow over rough surfaces together with the excessive Reynolds Number that must be sustained. The Reynolds Number is defined as the ratio of inertial forces to the viscous forces of flow. For typical wind speeds and roughness elements in our crop stands, the Reynolds Number will be of the order of 10^6 or greater, sufficiently large to classify such a system as a turbulent regime. Paraphrasing Schlichting (1955), "The most striking feature of turbulent motion is the fact that the velocity and pressure at a fixed point in space do not remain constant with time but perform very irregular fluctuations of high frequency. The lumps of fluid which perform such fluctuations in the direction of flow and at right angles to it do not consist of single molecules as assumed in the kinetic theory of gases. Instead they are macroscopic fluid balls of varying size, superimposing their own intrinsic motion on the mean flow. The size of the balls which

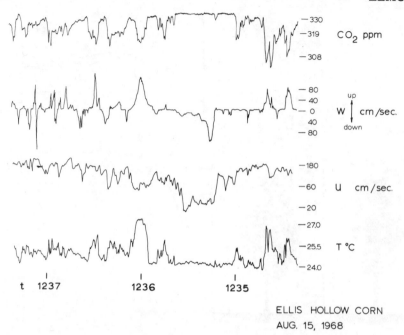

Fig. 6-11—Short-time variation of some climatic properties of the air flowing 2 m above an actively-growing cornfield during the midday period 1234 to 1237 EST. Air properties indicated are: carbon dioxide, C; vertical wind speed, w; horizontal wind speed, u; and temperature, T. From Desjardins (personal communication).

continually agglomerate and disintegrate is determined by the scale of the associated geometric boundaries, whatever they may be."

In Ordway's figure (Fig. 6-10) the turbulent fluctuations in the forest are the double-pointed arrows at right angles to the mean wind flow. The upper right corner diagram amplifies the significance of the vertical arrows. This pictures an eddy as it moves from left to right in the period, t to t + Δt and in the same period rotates in the direction of the arrows. By tracing the trajectories of the three particles in the fluid ball, a, b, and c over the period, it is apparent that the criss-crossing of the paths produce the characteristic upward and downward motion that is responsible for vertical diffusion in a horizontal flow.

One eddy to the next will also have different physical properties. One may be hotter or colder than another, one may be wetter or drier than another and/or richer or poorer in CO_2. Figure 6-11 taken from Raymond Desjardins' thesis research demonstrates this beautifully. (To be submitted in partial fulfillment of the requirements of the Ph.D. degree at Cornell University.) The continuous traces over a short-time period give the wind stream variation in CO_2, C, vertical wind speed, w, horizontal wind speed, u, and temperature T. These were obtained on a clear day about 2m above our Ellis Hollow cornfield when the corn was growing rapidly.

Casual inspection reveals a correlation between all elements, but less so for the horizontal wind. Further study reveals that "up drafts" are associated with an increase in temperature and a fall in CO_2. Evidently eddies coming up from the crop are hotter, indicative of warmer surfaces. Their lower CO_2 content is indicative of photosynthesis sinks in the stand. "Down drafts" are associated with cooler eddies which are also richer in CO_2. Up drafts appear to be "stronger" and associated with a decrease in mean wind flow. Up drafts may be stronger too because they were measured relatively near the surface and appear less frequently yet persist for shorter periods of time. Major variations appear to be of the frequency of 2 to 4 cycles/min. Amplitude is 3-5°C in air temperature and 10-20 ppm in CO_2. The wind component amplitudes are about ± 80 cm/sec for vertical wind and 50-100 cm/sec horizontal wind speed.

Without further analysis not much can be said about the mechanisms creating the eddies in the cornfield. Both thermal and frictional effects are undoubtedly at work. An analysis of the frequency distribution of the eddies will eventually throw light on their origins. Allen (1968) has made such an analysis for another plant stand.

Figure 6-12 from Allen's work gives the relative contribution to the total variance of horizontal wind speed as a function of frequency at which the variation occurs. Six levels are shown for a 30-year-old Japanese larch forest (Laris leptolepis L.).

The spectrum of wind speed variations is expressed on a cycle per

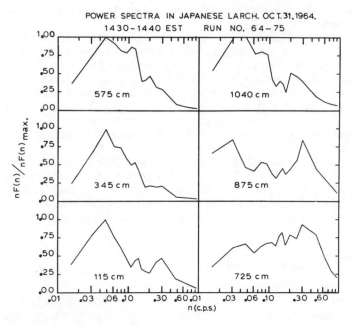

Fig. 6-12—Composite, normalized power spectra of the wind at the indicated heights in a Japanese larch forest near Ithaca, N. Y. From Allen (1968).

second basis and the relative energy distribution of the variation at each frequency is expressed as a fraction of the maximum energy at some frequency. The forest was 1,040 cm high. The top one-third of the forest consisted of conical tree tops and was fairly open in contrast to the middle one-third which was quite dense. The lower one-third was somewhat more open, consisting of many needle-less dead branches. In each of the six power spectra presented there is a pronounced low frequency peak at about 0.04 cycles/sec corresponding to a period of 20 to 25 sec. With a wind speed about 350 to 375 cm/sec at 1,569 cm above the ground, the low frequency peak is associated with gusts or eddies of about 70-100 m wavelength. Near the forest floor at a height of 115 cm there appears to be very little high frequency variance. This can be interpreted to mean that there is less turbulence on a small scale and most of the variation is due to large eddies. A scale of 70-100 m for these large eddies might be associated with topographic features of the landscape but definitely not the local vegetation. On the other hand, further up into the vegetation more high frequency peaks develop in the spectra. Peaks in the 3-7 sec period range, with wind velocities at about 100 cm/sec, are indicative of eddies on the scale of the individual trees which were planted on a 3-4 m grid. At height 725 cm the vegetation was densest. Fluctuation periods in the high frequency range here had a period of 3 sec. With an average wind of 60 cm/sec at this level, the eddy scale becomes 180 cm. Unfortunately, response time characteristics of the measuring system filtered out the very high frequency components, so we have no idea of their relative contributions. Nonetheless there is reason to believe that Allen's spectra cover much of the eddy scale that significantly contributes to climatic variation up to 10-min periods.

What can we deduce out of all this? For one thing the meteorologists have made a beginning to understand the sources of climate variation due to local turbulence. But, in addition, we need to know which physiological processes have a response time comparable to these short-time variations in climatic elements. Perhaps there are none. We do know that stomates respond to variation in the environment on the scale of 1-30 min. Variations due to local eddies of the scale discussed here are too short-lived to be of significance to stomates, or it would seem so.

In the study of exchange rates, people like Desjardins are taking advantage of the eddy structure and its vertical transport properties to measure, on a very short-time scale, the flux intensity of CO_2. Once these tools are developed and the tremendous data-handling problems solved, short-time crop response in the order of minutes will be measurable in the field.

3. Model Building and Testing

One of the ultimate objectives of making measurements in the pursuit of understanding is the development of prediction models. Models may be used to predict crop response, to predict crop climate and water use. Inherent in these models will come the ability to optimize architectural design or crop geometry, to predict new crop performance in

a given climate regime and further suggest favorable management practices. Naturally models have to be crude at first, representing the level
of understanding at the time. They evolve into more complex (or simpler) ones as understanding increases, coming closer and closer to
representing reality. While I have stressed, in this presentation, some
of the weak spots in our understanding of the aerodynamic exchange
processes, it would be wrong to leave a pessimistic impression.

As a note of optimism, I would like to emphasize the progress we
have made in understanding the meteorology involved in CO_2 exchange
in crops. This is best illustrated by Fig. 6-13 from Lemon and Wright
(1969). In this figure we have light response curves, presented on a
leaf area basis, determined by the momentum balance method of measuring CO_2 exchange in a cornfield. Each experimental point is a "mean
value" for a unit leaf area in a given 25-cm leaf layer in the crop at the
indicated time of day. The highest points are for the top 25-cm layer,
the next highest point for the second 25-cm layer from the top, and so
on downwards. Encouraging is the fact that the light response curves
approach and look very similar to those determined by my colleague,
Dr. Musgrave, using a plastic chamber gas exchange technique in the
field. However, they are not quite alike. They should not be on two
counts at least. First of all, the crop structure-light interaction would
have to be correctly taken into account. For example, randomness of
leaf angle distribution in each layer as well as frequency distribution of
light intensity in each layer would have to be evaluated in a "correct"

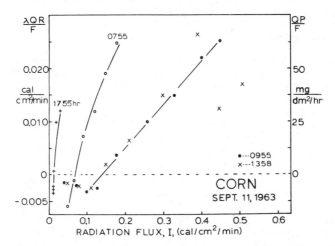

Fig. 6-13—Light response curves for corn plant community as indicated by hour.
Radiation flux is incident intensity $(0.3-0.7 \mu$ wavelength). Photosynthesis and
respiration expressed on a leaf area basis as CO_2 exchange or energy equiva-
lence. Each point at a given hour represents a given leaf level in the canopy
beginning with the top leaves at 225 cm at the highest radiation intensity and
progressing downwards into the canopy in 25-cm increments with decreasing
radiation. Not all 1755 and 0755 points near the bottom of the canopy are plotted. Each point is the "mean" response of all leaves at a given level. Ellis
Hollow, N. Y. Sept. 11, 1963.

light response model for plant communities. Second, other community structure effects would have to be evaluated as well. For example, supply of CO_2 at each layer, in addition to temperature effects at each layer. This all could be tested provided we accepted in the very beginning that the original measurements and assumptions in the momentum budget were all correct. So this brings us to the conclusion that we have made progress in view of the "reasonable" results given in Fig. 6-13, yet proof of correctness presents very real complexities. We can turn the coin over and say, too, that testing of light models will prove equally complex by the same line of reasoning. Models, however, are very useful tools, as Dr. Waggoner demonstrates in this symposium (Chapter 15, this book). His modeling is an excellent step forward, yet our work on the physics of the environment and the physiology of plants is not finished.

LITERATURE CITED

Allen, L. H., Jr. 1968. Turbulence and wind speed spectra within a Japanese larch plantation. J. Appl. Meteorol. 7:73-78.

Baumgartner, A. 1969. Meteorological approach to the exchange of CO_2 between the atmosphere and vegetation, particularly forest stands. Photosynthetica (Czechoslovakia) 3:127-149.

Begg, J. E., J. F. Bierhuizen, E. R. Lemon, D. K. Misra, R. O. Slatyer and W. R. Stern. 1964. Diurnal energy and water exchanges in bulrush millet in an area of high solar radiation. Agr. Meteorol. 1:294-312.

Brown, Kirk W., and Winton Covey. 1966. The energy-budget evaluation of the micrometeorological transfer processes within a cornfield. Agr. Meteorol. 3:73-96.

Cionco, R. 1967. Flow characteristics and mathematical modeling of canopy regimes. Proc. Tech. Exch. Confer. AWS Tech. Report 196, p. 260-1. Published by Air Weather Service (MAC), U. S. Air Force.

Cionco, R. 1969. Some aspects of airflow characteristics of simple canopies. J. Appl. Meteor. (In preparation).

Denmead, O. T. 1964. Evaporation sources and apparent diffusivities in a forest canopy. J. Appl. Meteorol. 3:383-389.

Denmead, O. T. 1966. Carbon dioxide exchange in the field; its measurement and interpretation. Proc. WMO Seminar on Agricultural Meteorology, Australia, p. 445-482.

Denmead, O. T. 1969. Comparative micro-meteorology of a wheat field and a forest of Pinus radiata. Agr. Meteorol. (in press)

Inoue, E., Z. Uchijima, T. Udagawa, T. Horie, and K. Kobayashi. 1968. Studies of energy and gas exchange in crop canopies (2) CO_2 flux within and above a corn plant canopy. J. Agr. Meteorol. (Japan) 23:165-176. [In Japanese with English Summary]

Lemon, Edgar. 1963. Energy and water balance of plant communities, p. 55-78. In L. T. Evans (ed.) Environmental control of plant growth. Academic Press Inc., New York.

Lemon, Edgar. 1967. Aerodynamic studies of CO_2 exchange between the atmosphere and the plant, p. 263-290. In A. San Petro, F.A. Greer, and T.J. Army (ed.) Harvesting the sun: Photosynthesis in plant life. Academic Press, New York.

Lemon, E. R., and J. L. Wright. 1969. Photosynthesis under field conditions. XA. Assessing sources and sinks of carbon dioxide in a corn crop using a momentum balance approach. Agron. J. 61:405-411.

Lemon, Edgar, L. H. Allen, Jr., and Ludwig Muller. 1969. Photosynthesis in a tropical rain forest. II. Vertical carbon dioxide fluxes. Science (in preparation).

Monteith, J. L., and G. Szeicz. 1960. The carbon dioxide flux over a field of sugar beets. Quart. J. Royal Meteorol. Soc. 86:204-214.

Ordway, D. E. 1969. An aerodynamicist's analysis of the Odum cylinder approach to net CO_2 exchange. Photosynthetica (Czechoslovakia) 3:199-209.

Ordway, D. E. and M. A. Groom. 1969. Wind Profile Prediction: Basic formulation and mathematical experiment. J. Appl. Meteorol. (In preparation).

Schlichting, H. 1955. Boundary layer theory. Pergamon Press, N. Y. p. 370-384.

Wright, J. L. and K. W. Brown. 1967. Comparison of momentum and energy balance methods of computing vertical transfer within a crop. Agron. J. 59: 427-432.

Wright, J. L. and E. R. Lemon. 1966. Photosynthesis under field conditions. IX. Vertical distribution of photosynthesis within a corn crop. Agron. J. 58:265-268.

Uchijima, Z. 1962a. Studies on the microclimate within plant communities. (1) On the turbulent transfer coefficient within plant layers. J. Agr. Meteorol. (Japan) 18:1-9.

Uchijima, Z. 1962b. Studies on the microclimate within plant communities. (2) The scale of turbulence and the momentum transfer within plant layers. J. Agr. Meteorol. (Japan) 13:58-65.

6... DISCUSSION

O. T. DENMEAD

CSIRO Division of Plant Industry
Canberra, Australia

I will confine my remarks to two points of methodology.

The first concerns the relationships between the eddy diffusivities for heat, water vapor, CO_2 and momentum and some practical consequences for field measurements of CO_2 exchange. Dr. Lemon has indicated that the eddy diffusivity for CO_2 is commonly assumed equal to that for heat and water vapor, or momentum. Similarity between the diffusivities can be tested in the following way:

Consider the vertical flux of any transported entity whose concentration at height z_i is s_i. It can be shown that above the crop, where the fluxes that interest us are constant with height,

$$\frac{S_1 - S_2}{S_1 - S_3} = \frac{\int_{Z_1}^{Z_2} K^{-1} \, dz}{\int_{Z_1}^{Z_3} K^{-1} \, dz},$$

in which K is the appropriate eddy diffusivity. By comparing ratios of concentration differences for the various entities, we can make some assertions about their diffusivities.

Figure 6D-1 presents comparisons of this type for the transport of heat, water vapor, momentum and CO_2 above a sward of turf. The observations were made over a wide range of stabilities as indicated by the Richardson Numbers shown in the figure. There is some scatter in the observations but this is within the expected errors in measurement, and the data generally conform to the hypothesis that the eddy diffusivities are the same for all entities, or at least in some constant ratio to each other.

It should be pointed out that the measurements shown in Fig. 6D-1 were made very close to the surface. There is evidence, e.g., Swinbank

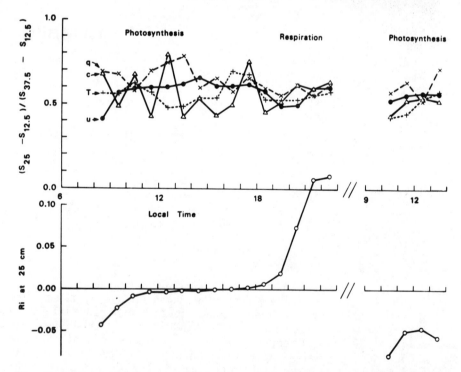

Fig. 6D-1—<u>Top</u>: Comparison of difference ratios for specific humidity q, CO_2 concentration c, temperature T and horizontal wind speed u over grass. <u>Bottom</u>: Richardson Number at 25 cm.

and Dyer (1967), that at larger distances from the surface there is still similarity between the diffusivities for heat and matter, but not between them and the diffusivity for momentum.

These possible differences in transport mechanisms, combined with height limitations due to insufficient fetch [for which it appears from many investigations (e.g., Bradley, 1968) that a suitable fetch to height-above-surface ratio might be as much as 200:1], mean that in both heat budget and momentum budget approaches, measurements above the canopy will usually have to be restricted to a region close to the surface. In these circumstances, accurate measurements of the small differences in CO_2, temperature, humidity, and wind velocity which exist, test the capabilities of most instruments, particularly those now used for CO_2 measurement. Thus, instrumental errors alone will often limit the accuracy of gas exchange measurements above the canopy to 5% to 10%.

Within the canopy, quite apart from any considerations of similarity between the diffusivities, procedures for estimating fluxes require estimates of the gradients of the various entities. I don't share Dr. Lemon's belief that forming the gradients "is not too difficult." Differentiating experimental data usually is. Our experience is that computational and instrumental errors can easily introduce uncertainties in these within-canopy flux estimates of 20%.

My purpose in making these remarks is to point out that although micrometeorological measurements of CO_2 exchange provide us with a valuable tool for studying photosynthesis in the field and for rationalizing plant-environment interactions, we should not expect too much of them. They may not be able to detect a difference of 10% or less in CO_2 exchange, which the practical agronomist would consider of significant economic value.

My second point concerns the use of the heat budget method. Dr. Lemon has pointed out the difficulty in obtaining suitable spatial and time averages of net radiation. We have been tackling this problem by the use of strip net radiometers (Denmead, 1967) to obtain line averages of the net radiation at appropriate levels in the canopy. The instrument can be expected to have an azimuthal error but tests which we have made indicate that for most times of day, this is within acceptable limits.

Following Dr. Lemon's development of the energy balance equation (contained in his Fig. 6-1), and defining the equivalent temperature θ as $T + L\rho_w/\rho c_p$, we have that

$$K = \frac{R_N - G}{\rho c_p \, d\theta/dz}.$$

θ is normally a slowly varying, monotonic function of z so that $d\theta/dz$ can be calculated with small error. This method of arriving at K seems to me to have a number of advantages over the momentum balance approach. First, the calculation of K is less prone to computational errors. Second, insofar as steady-state conditions prevail and there is similarity between the diffusivities, the formulation of K is exact; no assumptions are needed about the relation between drag coefficients, foliage geometry, and wind speed. Third, the method does not require specification of the foliage distribution. Finally, the method has a bonus since the measurements needed for the calculation of K also yield the evaporation profile within the canopy, and in most investigations of plant growth processes in the field, we are not only interested in the distribution of the sources and sinks for CO_2, but also in the corresponding distributions for water vapor and heat.

This is not to discount the importance of understanding the "aerodynamics" of crops, to which Dr. Lemon and his colleagues have contributed so substantially. I believe, however, that further progress in this field will require both controlled studies in properly constructed wind tunnels in which the structure of turbulence within plant canopies can be modelled successfully, and elaborate studies in the field with appropriate fast-response sensors small enough not to disturb the canopy and cheap enough to sample at many points.

LITERATURE CITED

Bradley, E. F. 1968. A micrometeorological study of velocity profiles and surface drag in the region modified by a change in surface roughness. Quart. J. Roy. Meteorol. Soc. 94:361–379.

Denmead, O. T. 1967. A strip net radiometer. Aust. J. Instr. Control 23:61.

Swinbank, W. C., and Dyer, A. J. 1967. An experimental study in micrometeorology. Quart. J. Roy. Meteorol. Soc. 93:494–500.

6...DISCUSSION

PIETER GAASTRA

Centre for Plantphysiological Research
Wageningen, The Netherlands

Dr. Lemon has presented an excellent review of aerodynamic principles governing gaseous exchange in crop stands. As an agronomist-plant physiologist I would like to present some of my conclusions about some aspects of CO_2-exchange in crop canopies.

1) Table 6-1 in Lemon's paper shows that the CO_2-flux from the soil can be of similar magnitude as the CO_2-uptake by the crop. This is a complicating factor for the aerodynamic methods of measuring crop canopy photosynthesis. It does not mean, however, that soil respiration can appreciably enhance crop photosynthesis. This is shown by the data in Fig. 6-3 of Lemon's paper. Canopies with very different geometric canopy structures (corn and orchardgrass) show distinct differences in diffusivity values and drag coefficients, but for both crops the CO_2-

gradients are similar and small. This suggests that the CO_2-transport resistance in the air between the plants is small as compared with the boundary layer resistances and internal resistances of the leaves. Another conclusion is that CO_2-fertilization usually cannot be profitably applied in the field.

2) Although differences in crop structure probably have a small effect upon photosynthesis through CO_2-concentration, crop structure can strongly affect plant temperature and transpiration rate. In this way, photosynthesis can be correlated with stand structure, and Lemon has rightly stated that the multiplicity of feedback mechanisms involved make it difficult to demonstrate a coupling of structure on exchange rates. Certainly, for the model builder, insight in principles governing exchange rates is extremely important. Equally important and perhaps even more difficult are the evaluation of the meaning of transpiration and plant temperature not only for photosynthesis, but also for the way in which photosynthates are utilized by the plant in, for example, leaf initiation and leaf expansion. In the classical methods of growth analysis, the importance of photosynthesis for plant performance tended to be underestimated, that of growth phenomena to be overestimated. At present there is a tendency for the reverse to be true.

3) Climate rooms can be a useful tool for getting information about the relation between photosynthetic rate and utilization of photosynthates by the plant. Prerequisite is that through manipulation of the environment, processes directly affected can be varied as independently as possible over ranges to be expected in nature. The processes are photosynthesis, transpiration rate, and all temperature-dependent processes (through effects of the environment upon plant temperature). For this purpose, high irradiances in the photosynthetically active part of the spectrum are required. Independent variation of photosynthesis, transpiration, and plant temperature then becomes a problem, in particular because the wind speeds applied usually are very low, between for example 10 to 40 cm sec^{-1}, resulting in high boundary layer resistances. Our experiments with model leaves have shown that the boundary layer resistance then is in the order of $0.5 - 1.5$ sec cm^{-1}, whereas for an acceptable coupling between for example leaf temperature and transpiration rate, its size should be 0.25 sec cm^{-1} or less, see Table 6D-1.

The problem of getting low r_a-values is closely related with the effect of various factors upon the drag force at a leaf surface, as presented in Fig. 6-4 of Lemon's paper. The situation for a model leaf could differ from that of a real leaf through effects of surface roughness, flexibility, and local convections at the leaf surface. It would be extremely important if micrometeorologists could provide the users of growth rooms with an evaluation of the effects of these factors as compared with those of wind speed, leaf area, and leaf shape. If wind speed would be the dominant factor, this speed should be increased for those experiments in which transpiration rate and leaf temperature should be uncoupled as much as possible.

If windspeeds have to be increased up to 1 or 2 m sec^{-1}, this certainly gives technical problems which can be solved, but it is unlikely that this also would be unfavorable for plant growth, as sometimes is stated. Table 6D-1 shows that lowering of r_a can result in considerably

Table 6D-1—Transpiration rate and difference between leaf and air temperature $(t_1 - t_a)$ as affected by boundary layer resistance (r_a) and vapor pressure deficit of the air. Leaf resistance $r_1 = 1$ sec cm^{-1}; absorbed radiation = 0.3 cal cm^{-2} min^{-1}; $t_a = 20C$.

| | r_a (sec cm^{-1}) | Vapor deficit air, mm Hg | | | | |
		0	2.5	5	7.5	10
Transpiration rate	2.0	0.80	1.01	1.22	1.43	1.64
(g dm^{-2} h^{-1})	1.0	0.80	1.12	1.44	1.76	2.08
	0.25	0.48	1.16	1.65	2.23	2.82
$t_1 - t_a$ (° C)	2.0	6.47	5.85	5.22	4.60	3.97
	1.0	4.28	3.66	3.04	2.42	1.80
	0.25	1.62	1.25	0.87	0.50	0.12

increased transpiration rate at large vapor pressure deficits. However, good control of air humidity would prevent excessive transpiration rates to occur. These relations are demonstrated in Table 6D-1.

Higher wind speeds also induce movements of plant parts. It seems unlikely that the moderate movements to be expected at windspeeds between 1 and 2 m sec^{-1} would have an unfavorable mechanical effect upon plant performance. Nevertheless, it would be worthwhile to investigate the nature of such effects more closely.

4) Micrometeorological methods of measuring gaseous exchange are not likely to become a tool for routine measurements. A team of highly skilled personnel and sophisticated equipment is needed to make measurements and for the handling and interpretation of measured items. Large assimilation chambers used outside during short periods in the order of minutes, could give useful information about instantaneous photosynthetic rates of crop canopies. The proper use of such chambers depends upon the insight we get into the effects of air movement upon boundary layer resistance and, consequently, upon photosynthesis. It might well be that changes of transpiration rate and leaf temperature in many cases do not have a large influence upon photosynthesis in short-time experiments.

7

Mechanisms of Translocation of Plant Metabolites

ORLIN BIDDULPH

Washington State University
Pullman, Washington

I. INTRODUCTION

The mechanism of translocation has been discussed since the latter part of the 19th Century, when DeVries, in 1885, proposed protoplasmic streaming as the mechanism. Since that time O. F. Curtis, beginning about 1920, and more recently Thaine (1961) and Canny and Phillips (1963) have become interested in this approach to the problem. In the meantime Münch, in 1930, proposed a pressure flow mechanism based on a turgor pressure gradient in the phloem between metabolite supplying and metabolite consuming areas. These two mechanisms, and others, are fully discussed in Swanson (1959), so the present paper will deal with a compilation of the factors upon which a sound view of mechanisms must rest. It does not seem possible to arrive at a decision as to mechanisms on the basis of any narrow approach to the subject. The distribution system itself is complex in its cellular make-up, ramifies to all parts of the plant body, and lacks a centralized pumping mechanism. For these reasons it is considered, by most workers in the area, that a very broad knowledge of the plant and its processes is necessary if one is to evaluate the phenomenon of translocation fruitfully.

The most recent comprehensive treatment of the broad considerations of translocation is that of Kursanov (1963). Proceeding backwards there are the reviews of Crafts (1961), Swanson (1959), and Biddulph (1959). The most comprehensive mathematical treatment is that of Horwitz (1958), but specialized applications to particular aspects of translocation can be found in Preston (1963) and Canny and Phillips (1963).

Because of limitations of space and other reasons the work on translocation of herbicides is not included (see Crafts, 1961 for this) nor is much attention given to two, as yet, anomalies in the literature. These are the very rapid translocation rates reported by Nelson et al. (1958), and the "transcellular strand" view of Thaine (1961). In regard to the first, our early experiences with $^{14}CO_2$ and THO led us to the adoption of triple seals between application and target organs in order to avoid

143

artifacts due to external convection. The work of Nelson et al. needs
verification using equal precautions, but it should be emphasized that
neither the profiles, (Horwitz, 1958) nor the amount moved (Nelson et al.,
1958) are right for this to be the main stream of translocation.

Regarding Thaine's transcellular strands--I think more positive
evidence for their existence is necessary before a mechanism of translocation is based upon them. The translocation profiles worked out by
Canny and Phillips (1963) for Thaine's model are not sufficiently different from Horwitz's treatments of pressure flow and cyclosis-diffusion,
to expect that acceptance or rejection can be reasonably based on profiles. Also the calculated rate of movement by transcellular streaming
is too slow to fit the known rates of movement.

II. ANATOMY OF THE PHLOEM

One of the important points bearing on the hypotheses concerned
with translocation mechanisms is the condition (size) of the openings in
the sieve plate, and the degree of continuity of movement that is possible
between successive members of the sieve tubes. It should be emphasized
that the volume and velocity of flow is known to be sufficient to require
that the anatomical features of the conduits do not deter this flow in a
serious manner. The work on the sieve-tube members with conventional
histological procedures has therefore caused much confusion because it
has consistently shown the pores in the sieve plates to be closed. It is
now reassuring that newer work with the electron microscope shows that
the pores, in those plants that have been so examined, are indeed open.

Duloy et al. (1961) using Cucurbita pepo (Duchesne) described a
parietal layer of cytoplasm as lining the sieve plate and extending as a
lining to the open sieve pores. There was no closing layer or membrane
across the sieve pores. Individual elements are continuous with each
other—via the open sieve pores, forming a conduit, the sieve tube. The
absence of a typically organized cytoplasm with organelles suggested to
these authors that the sieve tubes were metabolically inert, and that it
was the companion cells that possessed the cytoplasmic organization and
components capable of a high metabolism. Kollmann (1963) has compared the structural features of dormant and reactivated sieve cells of
Metasequoia and has shown the presence of plastids, mitochondria, endoplasmic reticulum, and nucleus. The changes observed in the transformation from dormant to active include a change from regular tubules of
endoplasmic reticulum to dilated tubules with "cisternae" and local
swellings which apparently disintegrate into numerous separate vesicles.
In addition to these vesicles, well-differentiated lamellar bodies derived
from either form of the endoplasmic reticulum appear, and what is most
significant, were found to traverse the pores in the sieve plates. After
this comparison with his earlier work on Passiflora caerulea (1960),
Kollmann expressed the conclusion that these tubules arose from the
endoplasmic reticulum. Arrigoni and Rossi (1965) using Avena coleoptile
for studies of fine structure of sieve tubes found that the strands con-

necting the sieve-tube members with each other (through the sieve plate) were produced by a double membrane system very similar to the endoplasmic reticulum. This constituted cytoplasmic continuity between cells.

Cronshaw and Esau's (1967) observations are also compatible with the view that the contents of contiguous mature sieve elements are continuous through the sieve-plate pores, and Esau et al. (1966) have reported the movement of virus particles through the pores. This step in bringing anatomical observations into closer alignment with physiological observations is helpful in that it materially reduces the calculated energy expenditure necessary to account for passage of solute through the sieve plate.

III. LOADING OF THE PHLOEM

The movement of photosynthate, or metabolites from the surrounding mesophyll cells of the leaf into the conducting tissues of the phloem is known as "loading" and has been investigated to some extent. The transfer is known to be rapid, requiring only a few minutes (2 to 3 min in rhubarb [Kussanov et al., 1959] and less than 10 min in maize [Pristupa, 1964]) from $^{14}CO_2$ to labeled metabolite in the conducting phloem. The process of loading is selective, as shown by the failure of certain sugars and organic acids to be transferred while others moved in readily (Kursanov et al., 1959). As a further example the amino acids threonine and to a lesser extent serine and alanine were shown to move into the sieve tubes rapidly whereas others including aspartic acid and proline moved in more slowly (Kursanov and Brovchenko, 1961).

Entrance into the sieve tubes is apparently independent of concentration differences between mesophyll and sieve tubes in the case of sucrose (Canny, 1961), amino and organic acids (Kursanov and Brovchenko, 1961), and phosphorylated sugars (Ziegler, 1956). It is apparently quite consistent with these data to view the movement of sugars to the sieve tubes as occurring in the phosphorylated form with synthesis of sucrose occurring as a last step before or during entrance into the sieve tubes (Pavlinova, 1955).

Both the process of transport to the sieve tubes and the terminal step of passage into the sieve tubes may require ATP (adenosine triphosphate) (Kursanov and Brovchenko, 1961; and Shiroya, 1968). A separation of the two processes, i.e., movement to and secretion into the sieve tubes, has not been satisfactorily attained, but Kursanov and Brovchenko's results strongly suggest a final loading via the energy source of ATP. This loading also appears to be sensitive to O_2 shortage and to metabolic inhibitors (Leonard and Glenn, 1968).

Age may also be a factor in loading of the phloem both as to the time course of loading (Kursanov and Brovchenko, 1961; Nelson, 1962; Ursino et al., 1968) and as to the types of materials loaded (Biddulph and Cory, 1965), but data on the latter point are limited.

Table 7-1—Sugars in sieve-tube exudate of some American trees
(from Crafts, 1961)

Family	Name of tree	Sucrose, %	Raffinose, %	Stachyose, %	Verbascose, %
Salicaceae	Aspen (Populus tremuloides)	10-25	< 0.5	< 0.5	0.5-0
Fagaceae	Beech (Fagus grandifolia)	10-25	< 0.5	0.5-0	0.5-0
	Chestnut (Castanea dentata)	10-25	< 0.5	0.5-0	0.5-0
	White oak (Quercus alba)	10-25	0.5-0	0.5-0	0.5-0
	Chestnut oak (Q. prinus)	10-25	0.5-0	0.5-0	0.5-0
	Red oak (Q. rubra)	10-25	0.5-0	0.5-0	0.5-0
Ulmaceae	Elm (Ulmus americana)	2-10	2-10	2-10	0.5-0
Magnoliaceae	Tulip tree (Liriodendron tulipfera)	10-25	< 0.5	< 0.5	0.5-0
Rosaceae	Black cherry (Prunus serotina)	10-25	< 0.5	0.5-0	0.5-0
Leguminoseae	Black locust (Robinia pseudo-acacia)	10-25	0.5-0	0.5-0	0.5-0
Aceraceae	Striped maple (Acer pennsylvanicum)	10-25	< 0.5	0.5-0	0.5-0
	Sugar maple (Acer saccharinum)	10-25	0.5-0	0.5-0	0.5-0
Rhamnaceae	Buckthorn (Rhamnus cathartica)	10-25	< 0.5	< 0.5	0.5-0
Tiliaceae	Basswood (Tilia americana)	10-25	< 0.5	< 0.5	0.5-0
Nyssaceae	Blackgum (Nyssa sylvatica)	10-25	< 0.5	0.5-0	0.5-0
Oleaceae	White ash (Fraxinus americana)	2-10	2-10	10-25	< 0.5

IV. MATERIALS TRANSLOCATED

The principal carbohydrate translocated in the sieve tubes appears to be sucrose, but in trees and some other plants this molecule may have condensed with it one or more molecules of galactose, to give raffinose, stachyose, or verbascose in order of decreasing concentrations (Table 7-1).

Sucrose is also the principal carbohydrate translocated in herbaceous plants. Amino and organic acids, minerals, viruses, hormones and steroids are also known to be translocated. As sucrose moves through the sieve tubes it may be withdrawn into surrounding cells and hydrolyzed there so that whole-phloem analysis may give misleading results. One of the most convincing demonstrations that sucrose is the translocatory substance with glucose and fructose the products of its breakdown in surrounding tissue is that of Biddulph and Cory (1965). Here $^{14}CO_2$ and ^{32}P were given to a leaf simultaneously. The labeled sugar, sucrose, and the sugar phosphates, glucose-6, PO_4 and fructose 1-6, diPO_4, were isolated from whole phloem of the stem below the leaf, but whereas the P^{32} (as phosphate) moved with the sucrose in the sieve tubes none of the glucose-6, PO_2 or fructose 1-6, diPO_4 isolated from whole phloem contained the P^{32} label. This led to the conclusion that they had been phosphorylated outside the sieve tubes with indigenous (not translocatory) phosphate. Swanson and El-Shishiny (1958) have also supplied convincing evidence that sucrose is the translocatory substance and that the presence of glucose and fructose represent hydrolytic products outside of the sieve tubes.

Studies of enzymes associated with phloem tissues are still largely descriptive and until more refined methods are devised that permit in situ studies, or studies of organelles isolated from specific cell types it is doubtful that much additional useful information on mechanisms of transport will be obtained. Kursanov (1963) has included a summary of this topic, so no further review will be made here.

V. LINEAR RATE OF MOVEMENT

There are sufficient studies on the rate of movement in the phloem to establish some minimal values. For sucrose this rate is often in excess of 100 cm/hr. Some representative values are presented below:

Plant	Rate, cm/hr	
Metasequoia	48-60	Willenbrink & Killman, 1966
Potato (Solanum tuberosum L.)	20-80	Mokronosov & Bubenschikova, 1962
Sugar beet (Beta vulgaris L.)	50-135	Mortimer, 1965
Bean (Phaseolus vulgaris)	107	Biddulph & Cory, 1957
Cucurbita	250-300	Webb & Gorham, 1965
Wheat (Triticum aestivum L.)	100	Wardlaw, 1965
Sugarcane (Saccharum officinarum L.)	240-360	Hatch & Glasziou, 1964

There are technical reasons why the velocities (or rates) must be given in minimal values when determined by the movement of tracer assimilates. There is always attenuation at the front of the tracer stream by a lateral loss of the tracer from the sieve tubes which causes the marker to fall further and further behind the theoretical rate of movement (Biddulph and Cory, 1957; Horwitz, 1958; Spanner, 1963). The technical mathematical treatment of attenuation and loss will not be considered here, for both would appear to alter rates by relatively small amounts (except, perhaps, for a diffusible substance like water), and velocities are not completely accurate in most cases, for they include a photosynthetic incorporation of $^{14}CO_2$ and movement of the photosynthate to the sieve tubes.

VI. DISTRIBUTION

The destination of metabolites exported from a given leaf depends upon the leaf's position. In the bean plant, lower leaves export primarily to the root with a small fraction ascending to the apex. From the uppermost exporting leaves the flow is chiefly to the apex. Intermediate leaves may export in both directions. Similar patterns of distribution have been reported for soybean (Clycine max L.) (Thrower, 1962), grape (Vitis vinifera) (Hale and Weaver, 1962), cotton (Gossypium hirsutum L.) (Tuichibaev and Kruzhilin, 1965), and tea (Thea sinensis L.) (Sanderson and Sivapalan, 1966).

It cannot be emphasized too strongly that a knowledge of the anatomy of the phloem of the plant under study is prerequisite to understanding distribution phenomenon. It is known that there is a relatively strict or direct functional channel between a particular part of a root system and a corresponding part of an aerial organ. The best data are for minerals locally absorbed by selected regions of the root (Biddulph, 1959). There is also a similar strict relationship between metabolite-supplying and metabolite-using parts, as assimilates from mature leaves move only to immature ones of the same orthostichy (Jones et al., 1959 and Kursanov, 1963).

Joy (1964) has shown that in sugar beet plants an older leaf will translocate to younger ones directly above it (on the same side of the stem) but not to leaves located on the far side of the stem. However, movement into young leaves on the opposite side of the stem could be forced by removing the intervening leaves—leaving the young leaves dependent on a supplying leaf on the opposite side of the stem. Shiroya et al. (1961) have shown a similar phyllotaxic relationship between the supplying leaf and the receiving leaves on tobacco (Nicotinana tabacum L.). Some tangential movement occurred, but leaves on the opposite side of the stem from the supplying leaf failed to acquire the tracer. Partial girdles made in phloem to interrupt the normal flow of metabolite between a particular source and sink have been shown to result in the development of new phloem (from parenchyma cells) around the girdle. Most experimentalists consider that the distribution of metabolite between source and sink is controlled by the gradient between the two areas. The rapidity of flow toward a given sink is determined by the steepness of the gradient, and the gradient is made steeper by the unloading, or removal, process at the sink. Experimental control over gradients by direct means has, however, not been satisfactorily attained.

VII. RADIAL LOSS FROM THE PHLOEM

During the course of movement of metabolite in the phloem some withdrawal for storage in or nutrition of adjacent tissues occurs, and if there is sufficient radial movement some may even ascend in the xylem. If a distinct cambium is present a radial loss of tracer from the phloem bundles can be determined by the separation of xylem from phloem and the determination of the amount of tracer in adjacent sections. This type of study has shown the radial loss to be some function of the amount of tracer moving in the phloem. This relationship is, in turn, responsible for the development of the generalized logarithmic pattern of tracer as it moves through the phloem (Biddulph and Cory, 1957). Stated simply, there is a linear relationship between the logarithm of the concentration present and the distance of movement. These losses can be significant, i.e., up to 49% of the total labeled metabolite at the position just below the node of a newly exporting leaf, diminishing progressively to 4% in the internode below the primary leaves (Biddulph and Cory, 1965). Losses to the xylem of approximately 24% of the ^{14}C metabolites and ^{32}P during a 60-min migration period in the internode below the first trifoliate leaf of a bean plant (and 25% for a comparable position in a cotton plant) have also been reported (Biddulph and Cory, 1965 and Biddulph and Markle, 1944). When the loss was high, i.e., 49%, the metabolite was rich in steroid and contained 12 other labeled substances besides sucrose; but which substances left the phloem was not determined.

Tritiated water moving in the phloem also crosses to the xylem in amounts up to 31% during a 20-min migration period. Such a significant loss, in this case probably representing a continuous exchange with indigenous water, may explain why labeled water movement in the phloem presents some patterns different from that of sucrose and other tracers (Biddulph and Cory, 1957; Gage and Aronoff, 1960; Choi and Aronoff, 1966; and Trip and Gorham, 1968). Actually the plasmalemma of sieve-tube members should be permeable to water even though they are quite impermeable to sucrose.

Webb and Gorham (1965) have measured the velocity of the radial movement in squash plants and have found that there was variation with age of the tissues. Young petioles displayed maxima of 6 cm/hr while older ones showed 1 cm/hr. The principal sugar in lateral movement was sucrose, whereas for longitudinal movement it was stachyose, illustrating differences in lateral loss of the two sugars from the phloem. Radial movement to the central pith of the potato plant was also shown by Mokronosov and Bubenschikova (1962).

Horwitz (1958) and Spanner (1963) have presented a mathematical treatment of tracer distribution in the stem during its course of movement. Both studies show that there will be a deviation from the logarithmic pattern if any of the following conditions do not remain constant during the experimental period: the rate of entrance of tracer into the phloem; the cross-sectional area of the conduits; the lateral loss at different levels; the velocity of flow at different levels. To the present time, satisfactory mathematical studies with these factors as variables have not been made. One of the reasons why a more refined analysis has not been attempted is that the anatomy of the phloem system itself, and consequently the flow pattern, may contribute a variable of greater magnitude than any of the above factors. The types of irregularities in phloem movement will become apparent under the following treatment of tangential movement.

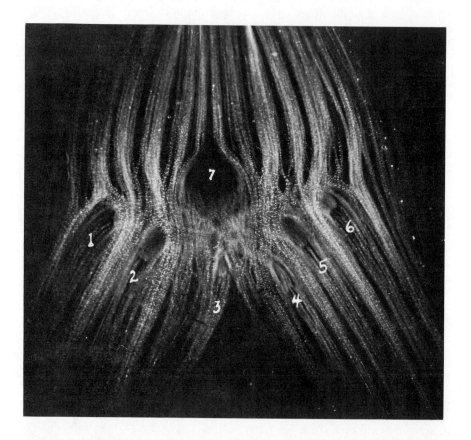

Fig. 7-1—The fluoresced phloem at the first trifoliate leaf node of a bean plant. Numbers 1 through 6 identify the leaf traces by the broken stubs of the xylem components. The branch gap is identified by the number 7. A longitudinal slit along leaf trace number 3 was necessary to flatten the section for photography. In the following figures the slit was made into the branch gap from above for the same reason. The figure represents the phloem as viewed from the inner face. The sheathing cylinder of "bark" has been slit, peeled off, fluoresced, and laid open for viewing (see Biddulph and Cory, 1965). For callose fluorescence see Currier and Strugger, 1956.

VIII. TANGENTIAL MOVEMENT

Tangential movement from a particular phloem bundle to an adjacent one would result in a more or less direct intercontamination of the two streams. This would mean that only a generalized rather than a strict nutritional interrelationship would exist between exporting and importing parts. We have ample evidence that the relationship is a rather strict

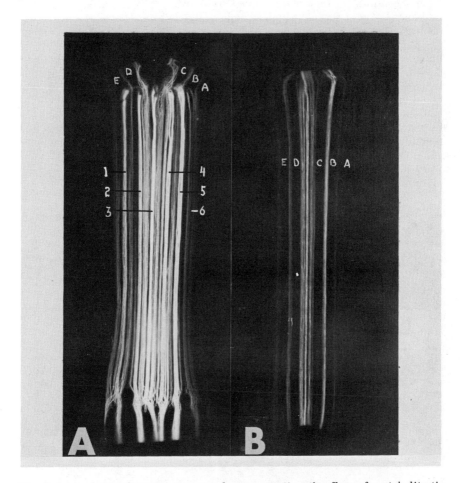

Fig. 7-2—An autoradiogram (reversed) representing the flow of metabolite (in the phloem) from the first trifoliate leaf. Metabolite entered in leaf traces 1 through 6 at the node in upper figure A. It descended to the primary leaf node at lower figure A. A fraction of the metabolite then ascended in bundles alternating with the leaf traces back past the node of entrance and on up past the second trifoliate leaf node in upper figure B. The descending leaf traces from the second trifoliate leaf are lettered A through E (Fig. 7-2B) and can be followed downward to the first trifoliate leaf node. They do not conduct labeled metabolite into the second trifoliate leaf: From Biddulph and Cory, 1965.

one, both for the xylem system (Roach, 1939) and for the phloem system (Biddulph and Cory, 1965; Kursanov, 1963).

Fig. 7-1 shows the phloem pattern at the node of the beam stem and 7-2 shows how strictly the labeled photosynthate follows the phloem channels. The leaf traces carry the labeled metabolite to the first node below the point of entrance into the stem, and from here, by means of anastomoses, the metabolite may move tangentially into adjacent phloem bundles where a portion of it may ascend the stem back up past the node of entry and into the internode above (Fig. 7-2B). The metabolite stream then ascends past the next higher node without delivering metabolite into the leaf.

Fig. 7-3 shows what happens to the ascending metabolite as it approaches a young leaf that is just changing from an importing to an exporting organ. By comparing the vascular anatomy shown by fluorescence in A) with the autoradiogram (B) it can be seen that there is only the slightest indication of import into this leaf.

Finally, when the destination of the initial export from a newly matured leaf is examined it is evident that most of the metabolite ascends in the phloem to the immature leaves and bud at the stem tip, Fig.

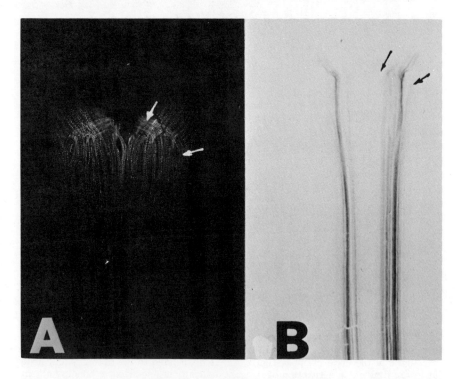

Fig. 7-3—The fluoresced phloem A and the corresponding autoradiogram B at the node of a young leaf that is just changing from an importing to an exporting leaf. The metabolite in Fig. 7-3B is ascending in the phloem from a lower leaf. There is only a very slight indication that metabolite is entering this leaf. The arrows indicate a possible importing phloem bundle.

7-4. A downward flow in the leaf traces from this newly exporting leaf extended for only approximately 25mm during the experimental period. A chromatographic examination of the composition of the labeled metabolite from similar newly exporting bean leaves showed fourteen ^{14}C labeled compounds to be present, but of these fourteen steroid was initially the preponderant one. A time sequence study of the labeling of the first exported metabolite showed (i) that upward export always preceded downward export; (ii) that upward export consisted of labeled metabolite rich in steroid; (iii) that approximately 2 hours were required for $^{14}CO_2$ to be incorporated into steroid and for the labeled steroid to appear in

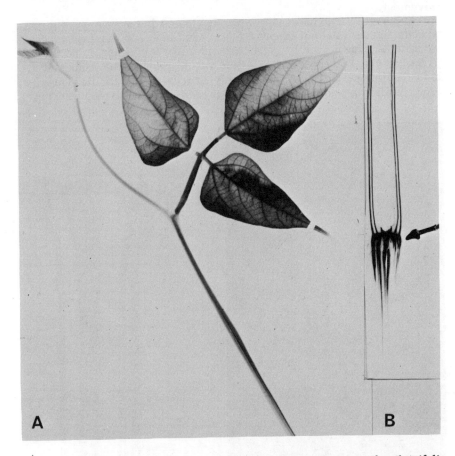

Fig. 7-4—(A) A gross autoradiogram (life size) of the very young fourth trifoliate leaf and stem apex showing the path of labeled metabolite originating from the third trifoliate leaf as it first began to export. The position of the exporting leaf, the third trifoliate leaf, is shown by the arrow in Fig. 7-4B. (B) An autoradiogram (considerably enlarged) of the frozen-dried stripped bark above and below the third trifoliate leaf node. A and B are contiguous sections; upper B joining lower A. The principal export from the young third trifoliate leaf was upward (from Biddulph and Cory, 1965).

the exported metabolite; (iv) that after sufficient maturity the labeled export was preponderantly sucrose, and that it moved downward a full node before ascending to the stem tip; and (v) that the labeling time from $^{14}CO_2$ to ^{14}C sucrose, when it finally appeared in the stem in large quantity, was less than 15 min.

The direct upward movement of steroid from the node of the newly exporting leaf took place in the phloem. This means that at the node, where the cauline phloem bundles pass under (on the cambial side) the phloem bundles in the leaf trace girdle, there was a direct transfer of this lipid-soluble fraction into the cauline bundles. The detailed autoradiogram in Fig. 7-5 contains a representation of this type of direct movement.

Related to the topic of tangential movement is the subject of simultaneous import into and export from a given leaf. Of five papers dealing with this subject all agree that older leaves either do not import (Biddulph and Cory, 1965; Sanderson and Sivapalan, 1966; Jones et al., 1959; Williams, 1964) or import only traces of metabolite (Thrower, 1962. Williams and Thrower claim there is a short period wherein a

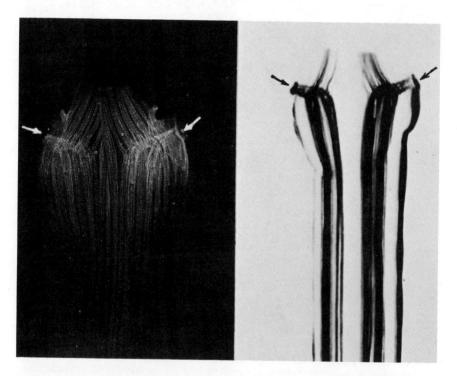

Fig. 7-5—The fluoresced phloem and the corresponding autoradiogram showing the export of C-labeled metabolite from a young but well established exporting leaf. The entrance of metabolite from the leaf is through the two halves of the slit petiole base indicated by the arrows. Most of the metabolite descends in the leaf traces, but a small amount is shown crossing directly into cauline bundles and ascending toward the apex.

newly maturing leaf may import as well as export. Two points need be made from these data. First, import of metabolites into mature leaves appears to be limited to that fraction that moves rapidly from the phloem during its course of descent and on entering the xylem may ascend into a mature leaf. Second, if a leaf both imports and exports simultaneously there occurs what is designated as bidirectional movement in the petiole. This may be possible for a short time since growth of a leaf may not be uniform throughout so that while one portion is still importing another may have matured sufficiently to have begun exporting. This would mean that adjacent phloem traces may be supplying and delivering metabolite at the same time. The duration of such a condition, however, must be relatively short. The phenomenon will be referred to again under bi-directional movement.

The origin of nonuniformities in the distribution pattern along the stem can easily be understood when the general pattern of movement of metabolite from a single leaf is considered in relation to the pattern of phloem bundles through which it moves. In many instances the flow becomes divided in a rather complex way, some of it ascending from various nodes and some of it continuing on toward the root. Within a given internode, then, there may be descending and ascending streams—the ascending stream having been withdrawn from an originally descending stream and on ascending it increases the total mobile metabolite in the internode above while it decreases the amount that continues downward by a like amount. If radial loss also occurs, and is some variable function of the amount moving in the sieve tubes, it is to be anticipated that still greater irregularities in the distribution profile will be found. Such irregularities have been observed by many experimentalists and they illustrate the reason why a mathematical treatment of distribution in the stem must be viewed with caution when such a treatment is used as a guide to discriminate between mechanisms of translocation. The specific reason for the inclusion of the autoradiograms in Fig. 7-1 to 7-5 is to illustrate distribution patterns and some of their complexities, and to show the integrity of the phloem system as a conduit for metabolite flow.

IX. REMOVAL FROM THE PHLOEM

The withdrawal into surrounding tissues of substances (largely sucrose) from the phloem appears to be regulated as completely and in much the same fashion as their entrance into it. The process has been studied more indirectly than directly, but to date the studies show the uptake into the surrounding tissues to consist of a two-phase system with a non-metabolic and a metabolic phase (Bieleski, 1962). Absorption into the nontranslocating tissue proceeds at different rates for different sugars (Glasziou, 1960), and the internal concentration of a given sugar with respect to another, e.g., sucrose, to fructose, remains the same even when the relative external concentration is varied greatly.

In sucrose storing tissue, such as paranchuma, the sucrose will be equally labeled in the two hexose moieties regardless of which of the externally fed hexose precursors, fructose or glucose, carries the label (Glasziou, 1960; Pavlinova, 1955). The synthesis of the sucrose stored in the "inner" space therefore involves isomerization and polymerization at or within the boundary separating the two spaces, inner and outer. The absorption into the storage cells is selective, in that there is competition between sugars for carrier (Bieleski, 1960a; Glasziou, 1960), and absorption can be inhibited by KCN, Na-azide, monoiodoacetate and chloramphenicol (Bieleski, 1960b).

The topics of "loading" and "unloading" are not intended to be presented as exhaustive surveys as this subject is covered elsewhere in this book. The important relationship to translocation phenomenon is simply that the loading and removal from the translocation stream, both active processes, help to maintain the gradients essential to movement of substances in the sieve tubes. The capacity for an isolated section of phloem to accumulate sucrose (Bieleski, 1966) and to build up a pressure sufficient to maintain a flow of solution through aphid stylets penetrating the sieve tubes (Weatherly et al., 1959) should be considered as being particularly revealing and of great importance in understanding the overall mechanics of translocation.

X. MECHANICS OF TRANSLOCATION

There are so many aspects of the translocation phenomenon, each related to some vital part of the whole, that it still seems impossible to formulate a clear statement of the mechanics of the process. The heart of the matter is, of course, the mechanism that propels the materials—metabolite, minerals, regulatory substances, virus particles etc.—across the sieve plates, for if it were not for this resistance to movement the Munch hypothesis would appear adequate. Actually there exists in the phloem all of the requisites of an osmotic system; a sucrose injection process, a system of tubular conduits in which longitudinal flow usually far exceeds lateral losses, and a sucrose removal system that is particularly strong at the extremities of the conduit system. It just seems unrealistic not to recognize in this at least the rudiments of the Munch system—yet there exists the hard facts of the high theoretical resistance that should be offered by the sieve plates, if they are structurally as pictured by anatomists. For the sieve tubes to function in the Munch manner the resistance offered to flow through each sieve plate must somehow be substantially reduced or some other compensating factors must be disclosed.

It is generally agreed that the rate of assimilate flow in the phloem is slow enough that laminar flow through the sieve plate may occur—if the pores are open and they collectively constitute a reasonable percentage of the cross-sectional area of the sieve tube.

Horwitz (1958) has shown that if a solution flow were to take place through the submicroscopic openings of the sieve plate (opening diameter 150-45A) rather than through the sieve pores, the pressure drop across one sieve plate would be about 0.5 atm, and Weatherly (1963) has has calculated that the pressure drop for flow through sieve tubes with sieve pores 0.1μ in diameter would be about 300 atm/meter of sieve tube. Observations by several investigators show a concentration gradient, which is equivalent to a pressure gradient if expressed in the same units (atm/meter), in the sieve tube contents of approximately 0.5 atm/meter.

Concentration Gradients—Zimmerman, 1960.

Pfeiffer	0.11 to 1.04	atm/meter	var. tree species
Huber et al.	0.312	atm/meter	Red oak
Zimmerman	0.026	atm/meter	White ash

The Poiseuille equation, in its simple form, can be used to calculate the pressure drop (in atm/meter) for the flow of solution in an open tube

$$p = \frac{8\eta vl}{\pi r^4}$$

where p = the pressure difference at the two ends of the tubes in dynes per cm^2, η = the viscosity in dyne seconds per cm^2 (poises), v = the volume in cm^3 of solution escaping per second, l = the length of the tube in cm, and r = the radius of the tube in cm (1 atm corresponds to approximately 10^6 dynes/cm^2).

If we assume, as Weatherly has (1963), that a flow of $1mm^3$/hr of a 10% sugar solution (Mittler, 1958) takes place in an unobstructed tube of 12μ radius, then the pressure drop should be near the observed values given above, i.e., 0.51 atm/meter. Using a 20% sugar solution a value of 0.66 atm/meter is obtained. This would suggest that the resistance of the sieve plate to flow is either very low or that the above comparison is unreal in some way. Actually the values in the above comparison are derived from different species of plants and when one remembers that there is a fourth power of the radius in the denominator of the Poiseuille equation it would appear wise to await better data before proceeding very far in this direction. The deficient points for a better understanding of pressure gradients are: pore size, tube diameter, and flow rate. The first two are usually derived from conventional measurements on "fixed" tissue: The third is derived from solution flow from a sieve tube through an aphid stylet.

It seems proper to consider the possibility of an infinite number of pumping stations, i.e., perhaps one for each sieve plate, or companion cell, along the phloem channels. This is a significant departure from the Munch system since additional forces are required—even though they may be multiple miniature forces each of sufficient magnitude to maintain the partial pressure gradient within each segment of the system. Spanner (1958) has proposed an electro-osmotic potassium pump at each sieve plate. This proposal has led to an interest in an examination of the potassium relations of the phloem, but sufficient data is not yet available to permit a decision as to whether or not this idea has merit.

Canny (1960) has measured the CO_2 evolution of the phloem and has shown a metabolic rate equivalent to the consumption of 0.5 mg of sucrose per ml of phloem per hour, or 0.012 g/day. This appears to be insufficient to operate a streaming or cyclosis mechanism (Spanner, 1962), which would appear to require 2.5 g of sucrose per ml of sieve tube sap per day. The 0.012 g may be sufficient to operate the K pumps, or some active loading system, but this is entirely speculative since the details of such systems are lacking. The conditions of the openings in the sieve plates are, of course, the important factor controlling the amount of energy that must be expended at each plate. Spanner (1962) has discussed this matter and until some additional progress is made it seems that the selection of a mechanism for translocation on the basis of a quantitative energy requirement is improbable. One cannot even dismiss the pressure flow mechanism on the basis of energy consumption, for even the maintenance of the semipermeable membranes in the sieve-tube system is an energy-requiring process. In addition the pressure developed in a plant cell is due to an active metabolic process, the process of accumulation against a gradient.

There are a number of phenomena as yet undiscussed that are normally considered to be of importance in helping to focus on the translocation mechanism. These are: temperature, inhibitors, the log pattern, water movement, and bidirectional movement. The pressure gradient has been discussed above: Each of the others will now be surveyed in relation to mechanisms of transport.

A. Temperature

The effects of low temperature on translocation recently have been considerably clarified, in part by Ford and Peel (1966) and in part by Swanson and Geiger (1967). Both studies showed that translocation can proceed at low temperatures, i.e., -1.5C to 2C. An understanding of the situations controlling movement under various temperature regimes was considerably advanced by the latter authors. They found that recovery from translocation stoppage by low temperatures occurred spontaneously (without a temperature rise), and that the stoppage, in certain plants, was only a temporary condition with a predictable half life (or duration). This means that it is probably not valid to discriminate against a pressure flow mechanism on the basis of a temperature response.

B. Inhibitors

The way in which metabolic inhibitors exert their effects in controlling translocation is still in limbo. When such inhibitors are used in simple purified systems of enzyme and substrate, as in a test tube— it is possible to know their role more or less specifically. When inhibitors are applied to whole tissue their mode of producing a given effect is much more in doubt. Nevertheless, there is evidence to indicate a suppressing effect on translocation by a number of inhibitors. From this work we can state that living cells in a normal functional condition are involved in translocation, but we have known this since the earliest days of translocation research. What must be known to be relevant to a given theory of translocation is how and where the metabolic forces are applied. We can hope for more definitive data in this area as a consequence of the ever increasing knowledge of the specific roles of individual inhibitors on specific processes.

C. Log Pattern

The consequences of the log pattern of distribution of tracer in a section of phloem to the various hypotheses of translocation have been examined by Horwitz (1958) and Canny and Phillips (1963). Horwitz shows that with reasonable assumptions, both en mass flow by an osmotic pressure flow model, and certain cases of cyclosis-diffusion, can be expected to produce a log pattern of tracer distribution in the conduction system. Canny and Phillips (1963) have also shown the streaming model of Thaine to produce curves not unlike the cyclosis-diffusion curves of Horwitz. Because of the general similarity of the curves and the relatively large number of assumed parameters that are necessary in order to apply a mathematical treatment it is questionable that an interpretation in favor of a particular mechanism is possible by this means. However, this need not detract from the value of mathematical treatments, for they frequently show the possible from the impossible and they systematize and guide the creative effort.

D. Water Movement

Water movement in the phloem has been conclusively demonstrated (Biddulph and Cory, 1957; Gage and Aronoff, 1960). In dealing with this subject one must be aware of the fact that water is freely permeable through cell membranes and therefore cannot be expected to be as rigorously retained in the conduit system as is sucrose. Due to its constant exchange with indigenous water along the path of movement its front would be, and is, quickly dissipated (Gage and Aronoff, 1960). This is why very high efficiency counters such as those used by Biddulph and Cory (1957) are necessary in order to detect the front for any appreciable distance. The actual flow of the substance "water" must be considerably stronger than the measured flow of tracer water, so a demonstrated flow offers support for a general en mass flow in the sieve tubes.

E. Bidirectional Movement

The most critical single phenomenon remaining for discussion is that of bidirectional movement in the same sieve tube. This, of course, is the only sense in which bidirectional movement has significance—and it is still doubtful that it has ever been successfully demonstrated with materials normally found in plants. The experiment that appears most convincing is that of Trip and Gorham (1968) wherein tritiated sugar (glucose-6-T) was induced to move into a young leaf that had just begun to export ^{14}C-labeled sugar (from $^{14}CO_2$). The questionable aspect of this work is with the state of maturity of the leaf in whose petiole the bidirectional movement was supposed to occur. The leaf in question was apparently at the age where it could be both importing and exporting by virtue of its growth state: i.e., it was in the process of changing over from an importing to an exporting organ, and while one portion of the leaf was still importing, another may have been exporting. This means that in closely adjacent sieve tubes there may have been mono-directional movement rather than bidirectional movement in the same sieve tube. It may also be possible that each tracer had merely distributed itself according to its own diffusion gradient (Canny and Askham, 1967). There are, however, merits to this experiment and further refinement of it using older leaves would lead to more convincing results. In our own experiments (Biddulph and Cory, 1965) we could never find the import of labeled metabolite into a leaf that was strongly exporting unlabeled metabolite—an experiment that would have disclosed bidirectional movement had it occurred. Only in the newly exporting leaf was there any suggestion of such a movement (Fig. 7-3). This indecisive period during which import continues while export begins is apparently of short duration (see above), and we have decided that during this changeover period bidirectional movement is not good evidence upon which to make or break any theory of translocation.

Kursanov (1963) has shown that the metabolite-supplying areas, the leaves, are capable of delivering sucrose into the translocation system faster than the absorbing system in the roots or fruits can remove it. The consequence is that some of it may be removed from the channel at various levels to be held in abeyance until equilibrium conditions favor its re-entry and further transport. The deposition of "half soluble" starch in cells surrounding the conducting channels has been known for many years, as has the observation that in the apple (Malus sylvestris) much of the reserves for flower and fruit development are stored, from the previous years photosynthate, in the twigs not many inches from the site of flower and fruit development.

It seems highly probable that the localized tissues surrounding the sieve tubes may act as a buffer system by absorbing or releasing materials—depending on their concentration in the sieve tubes and the needs of the surrounding tissues. Active absorption at any "sink" could then set in motion a flow of materials extending back along the phloem channel to the supplying leaves themselves, and if the supplying power of the leaves were insufficient to maintain normal concentrations of sucrose within the channels the reduced concentration would stimulate reloading from the temporary reserves. Weatherly et al. (1959) have shown that a pressure of sufficient magnitude to cause the exudation of phloem sap from aphid stylets can be generated in an isolated section of willow stem only 16 cm (or 800-1,000 sieve elements) in length. This indicates an internally developed pressure caused by the loading of sucrose into the sieve tubes by either the companion or parenchyma cells. The loading represents an active process that appears to be able to work against a high concentration gradient.

With an infinite number of loading stations along the channel the demands for generating large pressure differences between the two ends of the system might be circumvented, particularly if Hammel's (1968) suggestion applies—that an assimilate fluid under high pressure can move longitudinally and with less pressure drop in an inflated system, as in the phloem, than would be so if the sieve tubes were rigid.

XI. SUMMARY

In summary it should be stressed that there is, in reality, only one understandable mechanism of propulsion for translocation: This is the Münch system. All other systems (activated diffusion, streaming-cyclosis and surface active movement) are based on unknown or inadequate mechanisms as we know them and therefore require a belief that future undisclosed evidence will support them. This could occur, but for the present the pragmatic person must favor the workable hypothesis.

Yet the Münch system in its rigid form appears not to suffice. Logical modifications include a pumping system interposed along much of the conduit pathway. The pumping stations may be the potassium pumps, but anatomical evidence does not favor this. For such a system one

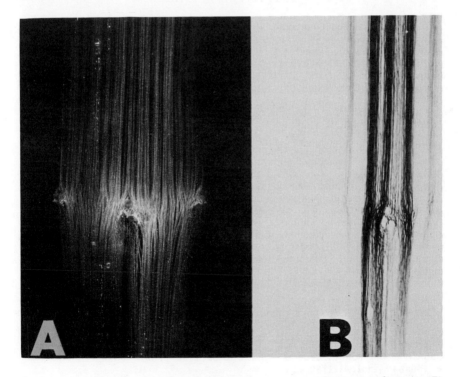

Fig. 7-6—The fluoresced phloem (A) and the corresponding autoradiogram (B) showing the downward component of the ^{14}C-labeled metabolite originating from the terminal leaflet of the first trifoliate leaf. The labeled metabolite is passing the cotylendonary node but the "front" of the stream is already to the root system. The movement of metabolite shows more of the characteristics of a flow pattern than a diffusion pattern.

would expect a regularity in the anatomical pattern of companion cells and sieve plates, which, in so far as I know, does not exist. The relationship appears random more than ordered. As a contributing factor for overcoming some of the resistance to passage of solute through the sieve tubes the evidence favors the loading capacities of the companion or parenchyma cells and their ability to maintain positive pressures within the sieve tubes. A further study of the Münch system to bring it into line with the additional energy required to make a workable system seems desirable. The alternate directions of attack seem toward metabolic processes, or toward a new appraisal of flow characteristics as they are related to the structural features in the living functional plant.

The most convincing visual evidence that translocation of sucrose in the plant displays a flow pattern is that of Fig. 7-6. This autoradiogram gives the distinct impression that the flow is "lead" through a specific group of sieve tubes toward a specific sink.

LITERATURE CITED

Arrigoni, Oreste and Gianfranca Rossi. 1965. Research on ultrastructure of Avena coleoptile. 3. The sieve elements. G. Bot. Ital. 81:96–112.

Biddulph, O. 1959. Translocation of inorganic solutes. In F. C. Steward (ed). Plant Physiol. 2:553–603. Academic Press, New York and London.

Biddulph, O., and R. Cory. 1965. Translocation of ^{14}C metabolites in the phloem of the bean plant. Plant Physiol. 40:119–129.

Biddulph, O., and R. Cory. 1957. An analysis of translocation in the phloem of the bean plant using THO, ^{32}P, and ^{14}C. Plant Physiol. 32:608–619.

Biddulph, O., and J. Markle. 1944. Translocation of Radiophosphorus in the phloem of the cotton plant. Amer. J. Bot. 31:65–70.

Bieleski, R. L. 1960a. The physiology of sugar cane. III. Characteristics of sugar uptake in slices of mature and immature storage tissue. Aust. J. Biol. Sci. 13:203–220.

Bieleski, R. L. 1960b. The physiology of sugar cane. IV. Effects of inhibitors on sugar accumulation in storage tissue slices. Aust. J. Biol. Sci. 13:221–231.

Bieleski, R. L. 1962. The physiology of sugar cane. V. Kinetics of sugar accumulation. Aust. J. Biol. Sci. 15:429–444.

Bieleski, R. L. 1966. Accumulation of phosphate sulfate and sucrose by excised phloem tissues. Plant Physiol. 41:447–454.

Canny, M. J. 1960. The breakdown of sucrose during translocation. Ann. Bot. n.s. 24:330–344.

Canny, M. J. 1961. Measurements of the velocity of translocation. Ann. Bot. n.s. 25:152–167.

Canny, M. J., and M. J. Askham. 1967. Physiological inferences from the evidence of translocated tracer; a caution. Ann. Bot. n.s. 31:409–416.

Canny, M. J., and O. M. Phillips. 1963. Quantitative aspects of a theory of a translocation. Ann. Bot. n.s. 27:379–402.

Choi, Ivan C., and S. Aronoff. 1966. A petiolar photosynthate translocation. Plant Physiol. 41:1130–1134.

Crafts, A. S. 1961. Translocation in plants. Holt, Rinehart and Winston, New York. 182 p.

Cronshaw, James, and Katherine Esau. 1967. Tubular and fibrillar components of mature differentiating sieve elements. J. Cell Biol. 34:801–816.

Currier, H. B., and S. Strugger. 1956. Aniline blue and fluorescence microscopy of callose in bulb scales of Allium cepa L. Protoplasma 45:552–559.

Duloy, Margaret, F. V. Mercher, and N. Rathgeber. 1961. Studies in translocation. II. Submicroscopic anatomy of the phloem. Aust. J. Biol. 14:506–518.

Esau, K., J. Cronshaw, and L. L. Hoefert. 1966. Occurrence of virus particles in sieve tubes and its relation to virus movement in the plant. Science 154: 418.

Ford, J., and A. J. Peel. 1966. The contributory length of sieve tubes in isolated segments of willow and the effect on it of low temperature. J. Exp. Bot. 17:522-533.

Gage, R., and S. Aronoff. 1960. Radioautography of tritiated photosynthate arising from THO. Plant Physiol. 35:65-68.

Glasziou, K. T. 1960. Accumulation and transformation of sugars in sugar cane stalks. Plant Physiol. 35:895-901.

Hale, Charles R., and Robert J. Weaver. 1962. The effect of developmental stage on direction of translotation of photosynthate in Vitis vinifera. Hilgardia 33:89-131.

Hammel, H. T. 1968. Measurement of turgor pressure and its gradient in the phloem of oak. Plant Physiol. 43:1042-1048.

Hatch, M. D., and K. T. Glasziou. 1964. Direct evidence for translocation of sucrose in sugar cane leaves and stems. Plant Physiol. 39:180-184.

Horwitz, L. 1958. Some simplified mathematical treatments of translocation in plants. Plant Physiol. 33:81-93.

Jones, H., R. V. Martin, and H. K. Porter. 1959. Translocation of carbon in tobacco following assimilation of carbon dioxide by single leaf. Ann. Bot. n.s. 23:493-510.

Joy, K. W. 1964. Translocation in sugar beet. I. Assimilation of $C^{14}O_2$ and distribution of materials from leaves. J. Exp. Bot. 15:485-494.

Kollmann, R. 1960. Untersuchungen Uber Das Protoplasma Der Siebrohren von Passiflora coerulea. II. Electronenoptische Untersuchungen. Planta 55:67-107.

Kollmann, R. 1963. Fine structure in sieve tubes. Progress in biophysics and molecular biology 13:244-246. Macmillan Co., New York.

Kursanov, A. L. 1963. Metabolism and the transport of organic substances in the phloem. Adv. Bot. Res. 1:209-278. Academic Press, London and New York.

Kursanov, A. L., and M. I. Brovchenko. 1961. Effect of ATP on the entry of assimilates into the conducting system of sugar beets. Fiziol. Rastenii 8:211-217 (Eng. Transl.).

Kursanov, A. L., M. I. Provchenko, and A. N. Pariiskaya. 1959. Flow of assimilates to the conducting tissue in rhubarb (Rheum rhaponticum L.) leaves. Fiziol. Rastenii 6:544-552 (Eng. Transl.).

Leonard, O. A., and R. K. Glenn. 1968. Translocation of assimilates and phosphate in detached bean leaves. Plant Physiol. 43:1380-1388.

Mittler, Tom E. 1958. Sieve-tube sap via aphid stylets. In K. V. Thimann (ed.). The physiology of forest trees. Ronald Press, New York.

Mokronosov, A. T. and N. B. Bubenschikova. 1962. Translocation of assimilates in potato plants. Fiziol. Rastenii 8:447-454.

Mortimer, D. C. 1965. Translocation of the products of photosynthesis in sugar geet petioles. Can J. Bot. 43:269-280.

Nelson, C. D. 1962. The translocation of organic compounds in plants. Can. J. Bot. 40:757-770.

Nelson, C. D., H. J. Perkins, and P. R. Gorham. 1958. Note on a rapid translocation of photosynthetically assimilated C^{14} out of the primary leaf of a young of a young soybean plant. Can. J. Bot. 36:1277-1279.

Pavlinova, O. A. 1955. Conversion of sugars in the vascular tissue of sugar beets. Fiziol. Rastenii 2:378-386. (Seen only in B. A. 24803. 1958.)

Preston, R. D. 1963. Ultrastructure and kinetic aspects of solute translocation in the stems of plants. Progress in biophysics and molecular biology. 13: 242-260.

Pristupa, N. A. 1964. Redistribution of radioactive assimilates in the leaf tissues of cereals. Fiziol. Rastenii 11:31-36.

Roach, W. A.   1939.   Plant injection as a physiological method.   Ann. Bot. n.s. 3:155-226.

Sanderson, G. W., and K. Sivapalan.   1966.   Translocation of photosynthetically assimilated carbon in tea plants.   Tea Quart 37 (Pt. 3):140-153.

Shiroya, M.   1968.   Comparison of upward and downward translocation of ^{14}C from a single leaf of sunflower.   Plant Physiol. 43:1605-1610.

Shiroya, M., C. D. Nelson, and G. Krotkov.   1961.   Translocation of ^{14}C in tobacco at different stages of development following assimilation of [14]CO_2 by a single leaf.   Can. J. Bot. 39:855-864.

Spanner, D. C.   1958.   The translocation of sugar in sieve tubes.   J. Exp. Bot. 9:332-342.

Spanner, D. C.   1962.   A note on the velocity and the energy requirement of translocation.   Ann. Bot. 26:511-516.

Spanner, D. C.   1963.   The mathematical pattern of tracer movement.   Progress in biophysics and molecular biology.   13:246-251.   Macmillan Co., New York.

Swanson, C. A.   1959.   Translocation of organic solutes.   In F. C. Steward (ed.) Plant Physiol. 2:481-551.   Academic Press, New York and London.

Swanson, C. A., and E. D. H. El-Shishiny.   1958.   Translocation of sugars in the concord grape.   Plant Physiol. 33:33-37.

Swanson, C. A., and D. R. Geiger.   1967.   Time course of low temperature inhibition of sucrose translocation in sugar beets.   Plant Physiol. 42:751-756.

Thaine, R.   1961.   Transcellular strands and particle movement in mature sieve tubes.   Nature 192:772-773.

Thrower, Stella L.   1962.   Translocation of labelled assimilates in the soybean. II. The pattern of translocation in intact and defoliated plants.   Aust. J. Biol. Sci. 15:629-649.

Trip, P., and P. R. Gorham.   1968.   Bidirectional translocation of sugars in sieve tubes of squash plants.   Plant Physiol. 43:877-882.

Tuichibaev, M., and A. S. Kruzhilin.   1965.   Translocation of labeled assimilates from cotton leaves.   Fiziol. Rastenii 12:1045-1050.

Ursino, D. J., C. D. Nelson, and G. Krotkov.   1968.   Seasonal changes in the distribution of photo-assimilated ^{14}C in young pine plants.   Plant Physiol. 43:845-852.

Wardlaw, I. F.   1965.   The velocity and pattern and assimilate translocation in wheat plants during grain development.   Aust. J. Biol. Sci. 18:269-281.

Weatherly, P. E.   1963.   Mass flow in phloem transport.   Progress in biophysics and molecular biology.   13:251-255.   Macmillan Co., New York.

Weatherly, P. E., A. J. Peel, and G. P. Hill.   1959.   The physiology of the sieve tube. Preliminary experiments using aphid mouth parts.   J. Exp. Bot. 10:1-16.

Webb, J. A., and P. R. Gorham.   1965.   Radial movement of ^{14}C-translocates from squash (Cucurbita melopepo torticollis) phloem.   Can. J. Bot. 43:97-103.

Willinbrink, Johannes, and Rainer Killmann.   1966.   Uber den assimilattransport im phloem von metasequoia.   Zeitschrift fur Pflanzenphysiologie 55:42-53.

Williams, R. Dorrington.   1964.   Assimilation and translocation in perennial grasses.   Ann. Bot. 28:419-426.

Zeigler, H.   1956.   Untersuchengen uber Die Leitung und Sekretion Der Assimilate.   Planta 47:447-500.

Zimmermann, M. H.   1960.   Transport in the phloem.   Ann. Rev. Plant Physiol. 11:167-190.

7 ... DISCUSSION

ALDEN S. CRAFTS

University of California
Davis, California

Two possible mechanisms: (i) Mass flow, and (ii) diffusion analogue. Mass flow in the phloem seems to be as well substantiated as the cohesion mechanism in the xylem. The following facts seem to be well established.

A. Anatomy

Sieve tubes make up an open system of conduits. Pores through the sieve plates are 0.5 to 5.0 μ in diameter. The nucleus and most organelles are lost upon maturity. The parietal layer of cytoplasm occupies only 5% or less of the lumen.

B. Phloem Exudation

Sieve tubes comprise an inflated, elastic, open osmotic system. Initial exudation from a cut may take place at 1,000 cm/hr-10 times the normal velocity of assimilate flow. Sugar is the principal translocate. Exudation may take place for 48 hours or more from aphid stylets and the stylets tap a single sieve tube.

C. Tracer Movement

Velocities of assimilate movement have been recorded up to 360 cm/hour. Distribution follows a source-to-sink pattern. Mature leaves are bypassed. Toxic and nontoxic compounds assume similar patterns and they go where the sugar goes.

D. Calculations

Using the Poiseuille equation the following resistances to flow through sieve tubes and sieve plate pores have been calculated. They indicate that the mass flow mechanism may very well account for assimilate translocation in plants.

Calculations*	Cucurbits	Willow	Pine
Sieve pores	0.38	0.32	0.48
Open tubes	0.05	0.23	0.07
Total	0.43	0.55	0.55

* Resistances thru sieve pores in atmospheres per meter.

Cucurbits (Cucumis sp.; Citrullus sp.; Cucurbita sp.)—For a 15% sucrose solution having 12 atm osmotic pressure (OP) flow could occur through 28 or 92 feet.

Ash (Fraxinus sp.)—For ash gravity would account for 0.1 atm per meter, and with an OP of 12 atm, would transport against a resistance of 0.33 atm/meter and would allow for a flow through 37 or 122 feet.

Willow (Salix sp.)—For a 12.5% sucrose solution having 10 atm OP, flow could take place against a resistance of 0.45 atm/meter through 22 m = 74 feet.

Pine (Pinus sp.)—For a 25% sucrose solution having 25 atm OP, flow could take place through 56 m equivalent to 185 feet.

In all cases cited for trees the lower branches could well be below the above heights.

E. Alternatives

1) There are no pistons, no valves, no impellors in the sieve tubes. What sort of pumps could possibly serve to move the assimilate stream?

2) Volume relationships—the cytoplasm occupies 5% or less of the total lumen volume of the sieve tube whereas sugar may occupy 10 to 15% more. If cytoplasm provides the surface or makes up the pumps they would have to move 2 to 3 times their own volume at 100 cm/hour.

3) The pumping mechanism would have to handle 2,4-D, amitrole, 2,3,6 TBA, picloram, MH, endothall, fenac, amiben, dalapon and other toxic materials. It is difficult to visualize metabolic pumps that would do this.

4) The pattern of distribution of these toxic substances is not random, as by diffusion. They all go where sugars go as along in a stream, accumulating in meristematic regions (shoot and root tips) and bypassing mature, exporting leaves.

7...DISCUSSION

C. A. SWANSON

Ohio State University
Columbus, Ohio

Although the weight of evidence continues for the most part to favor the pressure-flow hypothesis, I will speak briefly on recent unpublished observations made in my laboratory which are not readily compatible with this view.

Earlier we showed in sugar beet (Plant Physiol. 42:751-756, 1967) that the rate of sucrose translocation from a mature leaf to a rapidly expanding leaf is only temporarily inhibited by chilling a 2-cm zone of the donor-leaf petiole to 1-2C. These studies have since been repeated at 0C with essentially the same results. After about 2 hours, the rate of translocation across the chilled zone is restored to the pretreatment rate, even though the petiole zone is maintained at 0C.

Assuming that the chilled zone imposes an increased resistance in the translocation system (as a result of radial contraction of the sieve tubes, increased viscosity of water, callose formation, decreased rates of oxido-reduction processes which presumably maintain electrical gradients across sieve plats and membranes, etc.), it may be postulated that the observed homeostasis in translocation rates is effected through corresponding adjustments in pressure gradients across the 0°-zone.

This hypothesis predicts that the equilibrium pressure gradient across an 8-cm 0°-zone should be four times the pressure gradient across a 2-cm 0°-zone. It may be anticipated, therefore, that the kinetics of the homeostatic process under these two conditions would be different. However, a careful comparison of the recovery times for translocation rates across the 2-cm and 8-cm 0°-zones revealed no sensible differences. Similarly, measurements of the sucrose concentration gradient in the petioles under these two conditions were not significantly different. These data suggest that higher pressure gradients are not required to maintain a constant rate of translocation across zones of higher flow resistance, and hence are in violation of the simple Poiseuille relationships required by the pressure-flow hypothesis.

The required experiment to make this conclusion more convincing is to measure simultaneously changes in the hydraulic pressure drop across the chilled zone and changes in the translocation rate. Conceivably this can be done by measuring the relative exudation rates from aphid stylets implanted above and below the chilled zone and relating the time course in relative rates of exudation at these two sites to the time course in translocation rates. Independent variations in these parameters would invalidate the pressure-flow hypothesis. We plan to continue further studies along these lines.

I am indebted to John W. Sij, Jr. and Dr. David E. Bayer for assistance in these experiments.

8

Metabolic Sinks[1]

HARRY BEEVERS

Purdue University
Lafayette, Indiana

The continued growth of higher green plants well supplied with water and inorganic nutrients depends primarily on (i) the accomplishment of photosynthesis in the leaves and (ii) the transport of organic compounds from the leaves to heterotrophic cells which constitute metabolic sinks.

I. THE KINDS OF METABOLIC SINKS

Underground parts—roots and a variety of storage organs—are obvious examples of plant parts leading a heterotrophic existence and developing tubers have come to be regarded as the classical sink for products of photosynthesis. Nongreen aerial plant parts—buds, flowers and fruits—and most of the cells in stems and petioles also constitute a drain on photosynthetic products. Even within leaves there are many cells without chloroplasts, and the autotrophic cells themselves consume photosynthate in their own growth and respiration.

In the literature on translocation to sinks much emphasis has been placed on the storage aspect because massive amounts of photosynthate, more or less unchanged, accumulate. It is emphasized here that wherever in the plant the products of photosynthesis are utilized, we have by definition a sink. Another source, sink relationship, which has not been fully exploited in work on translocation, is the germinating seedling. Here the sink is the rapidly growing embryo and this is supplied by mobile organic materials produced during hydrolytic activity in the source storage organ-cotyledon or endosperm.

The establishment of new sinks during plant growth depends on specific developmental process whose onset may be controlled by environmental influences such as temperature, photoperiod, and light quality; these in turn depend for their expression on internal regulatory compounds. Two further aspects should be mentioned. Most plants are ex-

---

[1]Our own (limited) work on this topic was supported by AEC Contract AT(11-1) 330.

posed to the activities of microorganisms. Whether the type of relationship established is a tenuous and fleeting one as when organisms in the
rhizosphere grow on root exudates, or develops into symbiosis or para-
sitism, the extra burden constitutes an additional sink which, indeed,
can prove to be of lethal consequence. Finally the production of the
whole gamut of secondary products—defined here as those compounds
having no structural function or readily discernible role in metabolism—
represents a metabolic sink. In most plants only a small fraction of the
photosynthate is diverted to these compounds but in some, e.g., those
extruding resins and latex, the drain is a considerable one.

The extensive literature on translocation (see reviews by Swanson,
1959; Crafts, 1961; Leopold, 1964; Wardlaw, 1968) provides important
information on the changing demands of sinks during development. In a
vegetative plant the developing green leaves are a sink not only for their
own photosynthate but also for that produced in older leaves with appropriate vascular connections, which also support apical growth. The
oldest leaves near the base of the plant, provided they receive adequate
illumination, export sugars to the roots. Several authors have concluded
(see Wardlaw, 1968 for a summary) that once a leaf is mature it is no
longer capable of importing photosynthate even when it is made heterotrophic by natural or experimental shading. This conclusion is based
largely on autoradiography after exposing upper leaves to $^{14}CO_2$. The
successful models of Duncan (Loomis, Williams, and Duncan, 1967) also
suggest that shaded leaves (those below light compensation) do not represent a major sink. However, it follows that if these leaves are not
importing sugars they must be consuming their own substance and are
therefore incipiently senescent. Presumably a limited importation of
sugars, adequate for maintenance but insufficient to survive drying prior
to autoradiography, may occur before senescence and loss in dry weight
ensues.

The concept has grown that developing buds and meristematic
regions in roots place demands on the available assimilate and compete
successfully as sinks with developing leaves. The onset of flowering
and subsequent fruit development have a marked effect on the redistribution of assimilate; fruits develop at the expense of vegetative growth,
and at this time the growth of roots may be restricted.

II. CONCENTRATION GRADIENTS AND SINKS

Most of the metabolic sinks in plants are connected with the source
by phloem elements in the vascular strands. In considering the fate of
photosynthate at the sinks it is important to take into account what has
been established about the material moving in the phloem and the direction of its movement. From the time of the important work of Mason,
Maskell, and Phillips (Mason and Phillis, 1937) the idea of sugars moving from source to sink down concentration gradients has become en-
trenched. Refined experiments with $^{14}CO_2$, augmented with analyses of
phloem contents have more recently provided much detailed information

(Swanson, 1959). For our present purposes the following are the most important findings.

Translocation occurs in the sieve tubes of the phloem and although other sugars and derivatives and also nitrogenous compounds may be found in the phloem exudates, by far the most important and general constituent in the disaccharide sucrose (Kursanov, 1963). At a time when it was thought that sugar movement into plant cells was strictly a downhill diffusion process, concentration gradients between leaves and sinks were given strong emphasis. The concentration of sugars in leaves where they were produced was higher than that in the sinks; the consumption of sugars in roots, meristems, etc., was considered to give direction, if not the driving force, for the movement observed.

Of course the rates of movement—computed from information on cross-sectional area of the phloem connection and the increasing weight of tubers and fruits (see Crafts, 1961)—showed that these were enormously greater than could be expected from simple diffusion, and direct measurements of rate of movement have shown that rates of 50 cm/hr or greater are commonly achieved. Whatever the final solution of this accelerated movement of sugars in the phloem, a further question was raised against the concept of simple diffusion gradients when it was found that the actual concentration of sucrose in the phloem was very high (10-15% or $> 0.3\underline{M}$) and therefore considerably higher than in the leaf cells generally.

It thus seems clear that the introduction of sucrose (or its component hexoses) into the phloem cells of leaves is an active loading process, one requiring an expenditure of cellular energy (see Kursanov, 1963; Wardlaw, 1968). Although the mechanism of the process is not established, it should be stressed that this is, after all, only a special aspect of the now well-established ability of plant cells to absorb and concentrate sugars (e.g., Bieleski, 1960; Grant and Beevers, 1964). Glucose and fructose have been shown to be taken up from dilute solutions and concentrated within cells and some cells accumulate sucrose directly (Kriedemann and Beevers, 1966a,b).

The concentration gradient between source and sink is therefore not a simple one, but the representation below is probably close to reality (Fig. 8-1). It is emphasized that detailed information is not available about sugar concentrations in cells adjacent to sieve elements in the loading areas, but the important fact is that, in the confined channels through which it moves out of the leaf and over long distances, the sucrose concentration remains high, and it thus seems that the receiving cells immediately adjacent to sieve elements in the sink may be exposed to solutions of roughly $0.2\underline{M}$ sucrose.

At the terminus of a transport pathway, efficiency would seem to be achieved most readily by some finishing reaction which drastically lowered the concentration of the moving component. The reactions described in the next section do indeed have high affinity for sucrose and are thus capable of reducing its concentration far below that of $0.2\underline{M}$. But if the receiving cells are indeed exposed to a continuous supply of $0.2\underline{M}$ sucrose its concentration may not be significantly reduced by these reactions.

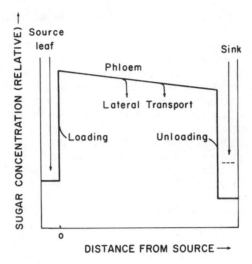

Fig. 8-1—Concentration gradients between source and sink - schematic.

III. METABOLIC REACTIONS IN SINKS

One of the first reactions to which sucrose moving out of phloem cells is frequently subject is hydrolysis by invertase. This applies both to sucrose moving radially from phloem during transport and that arriving at the termini of transport chains.

A. Absorption of Sugars

As indicated earlier, there is now good evidence that sugar absorption by plant cells is itself a metabolic event. The evidence for this is summarized briefly as follows:
  a) Selectivity among sugars and competitive effects.
  b) O_2-requirement.
  c) Uptake rates maintained for long periods.
  d) Accumulation against concentration gradients.
  e) Inhibition by respiratory inhibitors and uncouplers.
  f) Saturation of rate at relatively low concentrations (c $0.01\underline{M}$)
  g) High Q_{10} in 5^0-30^0 range.
Not all of the tissues examined show the same selectivity in uptake. Frequently it is observed that the hexoses, glucose and fructose, are absorbed at the highest rates and when sucrose is supplied, hydrolysis by surface invertases precedes uptake, even though sucrose may be rapidly reformed upon crossing the plasmalemma. However, in some tissues, e.g., castor bean cotyledons, sucrose is absorbed intact as shown by the maintenance of assymetry of labeling when sucrose-(fructose-^{14}C) is supplied, and in this tissue sucrose is absorbed more rapidly than the hexoses (Kriedemann and Beevers, 1966a,b).

Utilization of the absorbed sugar in any metabolic event might be expected to prolong uptake or maintain it at a higher rate, but direct measurements have shown that uptake can continue long after the average internal concentration equals that outside the cells. Sugars can accumulate until the outside solution is virtually depleted. Thus regardless of the fate of the sugar absorbed, the intrinsic capacity for metabolic uptake is emphasized as an important general phenomenon which allows cells in metabolic sinks to deplete the sucrose or hydrolysis products arriving in their vicinity during translocation. Although the mechanism of this process is not understood it is clear that some expenditure of cellular energy is involved; in most theories adenosine triphosphate (ATP) or its equivalent is invoked as an activator or as a maintainer of a hypothetical carrier molecule. The elucidation of cellular accumulation is necessary too for an understanding of the loading process at the source and it may well have a bearing on the mechanism of long distance transport in the phloem.

B. Fate of the Entering Sugar

The fate of the entering sugar in cells of different kinds of sinks may now be examined. In rapidly growing cells at meristems, whether these are in vegetative apices, cambial regions, storage organs, floral parts or embryos, the major fate of the sugar is conversion to new cell material. Figure 8-2 summarizes a few of the reactions leading from sugar to important intermediates. It is meant to emphasize that the breakdown sequence comprising familiar respiratory pathways is at the same time the source of carbon for the monomeric units—amino acids, fatty acids, uridine diphosphate (UDP) hexoses and pentoses—which are, respectively, the precursors of proteins, fats, and cell wall components. In actively growing cells more than half of the sugar may be diverted to these constituents.

The rest of the sugar introduced into the sequence is oxidized to CO_2 and water in providing the ATP and reduced nucleotides required to drive the synthetic events, to allow the cell to accumulate ions, and to reduce NO_3 and SO_4 to forms appropriate for introduction into the metabolic sequence. It follows that the pace of the synthetic events, by draining off intermediates and regenerating the acceptors adenosine diphosphate (ADP) and nicotinamide adenine dinucleotide (NAD) and nicotinamide adenine dinucleotide phosphate (NADP), determines the pace of sugar breakdown. Superimposed upon this general regulation are various other controls such as end-product inhibition and allosteric effects which apparently ensure the harmonious coupling of degradative and synthetic processes in cell growth. These latter controls have not, as yet, been searchingly examined in plant tissue.

The onset of cell division which initially defines the various sinks, and its subsequent regulation are, of course, other problems. However, insofar as this continues at growing points, the sink for photosynthate is maintained. In expanding and fully mature cells the demand for sugars is less, but even here respiration continues. It is not suggested that the gearing between respiration rate and useful deployment of the

174   BEEVERS

DIVERSION OF RESPIRATORY INTERMEDIATES

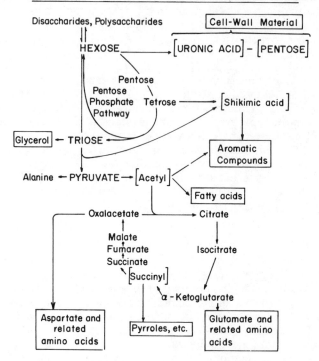

Fig. 8-2—Diversion of respiratory intermediates in synthetic events (Beevers, 1951).

respiratory products is absolute—there is probably a low idling rate—and even in mature cells there is turnover of protein and other constituents whose resynthesis and maintenance consume ATP.

C. Accumulation of Sugars and Starch at Sinks

Major sinks for photosynthate occur at a variety of storage sites. After cell division and expansion some parenchymatous cells (e.g., of tubers, internodes, seeds, fruit, and roots) become repositories for organic compounds which are mobilized subsequently when other sinks appear during development. Two aspects of this accumulation will be considered.

1. Absorption of Sugars at an Accumulating Sink

In an important series of papers, Australian investigators have studied sugar accumulation in the internodes of sugarcane (Saccharum officinarum L.). (Bieleski 1960, 1962; Hatch et al., 1963; Hatch and Glasziou, 1963; Sacher et al., 1963). For our purposes the major findings are as follows.

In the mature internode the sugar concentration (almost exclusively sucrose) is roughly 20%, in the young internode it is 4-10%, and in the leaf 2-3%. No starch appears in the storage tissue. In this example it should be noted that there is no apparent downward gradient between source and sink, and although the concentration of sucrose in the phloem supplying the storage cells is not given, it seems that sugars are more concentrated in the receptor cells. Sections of internode of the appropriate age retain the remarkable capacity for sugar accumulation even when removed from the intact plant. Glucose and fructose are actively absorbed and sucrose accumulates as a result. When sucrose is supplied it too is absorbed but apparently only after hydrolysis at the cell surface or in the outer (free) space. Sugar uptake continues from dilute solutions until the concentration inside the cells exceeds that outside by a factor of 50-200. It was calculated that in the accumulation process itself less than 10% of the sugar was consumed in energy yielding reactions, and it was shown that, regardless of which sugar was supplied, sucrose accumulated in the vacuole. Invertases, one of which was deduced to be associated with the wall, were shown to be concerned with sucrose absorption, and the various enzymes bringing about sugar transformations and sucrose synthesis from hexose were shown to be present in the tissue. It was deduced, as shown in Fig. 8-3, that synthesis of sucrose or a derivative occurred in the metabolic or protoplasmic compartment and that free sucrose accumulated.

The major difference observed in absorption by castor bean (Ricinus communis L.) cotyledon (Fig. 8-4) was that sucrose was absorbed intact; virtually no free hexose exists in this material, or in the exudate obtained on excising the radicle. (Kriedemann and Beevers, 1966a,b).

2. Starch Formation

In many storage sinks the entering sugar is converted to starch. The effect of this change is to keep the sugar concentration low and to maintain a higher (less negative) water potential. The biochemistry of

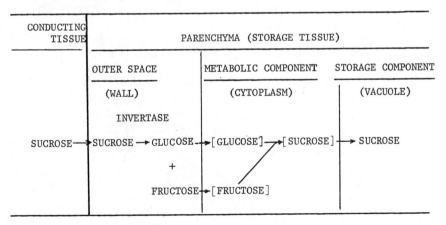

Fig. 8-3—Sucrose accumulation in sugar cane storage tissue (see text).

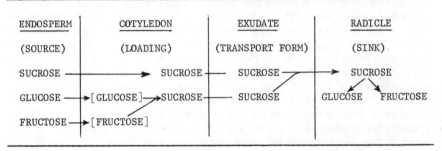

Fig. 8-4—Sutar absorption in cotyledons of castor bean seedling (see text).

starch formation is not yet fully understood. Several enzyme systems are known which could conceivably contribute, including several phosphorylases, starch synthetases bound to starch granules and soluble synthetases (see review by Akazawa, 1965). A good deal of current emphasis is on the synthetases, which utilize nucleotide sugar derivatives; this aspect of starch formation will be considered, and the relation to its origin from sucrose, the transport sugar.

The starch synthetases are able to add glucose units to pre-existing starch or smaller primer molecules when this is provided as uridine diphosphate-glucose (UDPG) or adenosine diphosphate-glucose (ADPG). UDPG, an important glucose donor in the synthesis of sucrose and other derivatives, was the first donor to be discovered in the synthetase reaction but most recent emphasis has been on ADPG, since it is a superior donor in some systems and highly purified enzymes have been obtained which utilize ADPG almost exclusively·

The overall reaction is as follows:

$$(Glucose_n) + ADPG(UDPG) \longrightarrow (Glucose_{n+1}) + ADP(UDP)$$

and this is usually measured by the incorporation of labeled glucose into an insoluble form (starch) or by following the UDP (ADP) released in coupled enzyme reactions.

The sugar nucleotides are made from the appropriate triphosphate and glucose-1-P in a pyrophosphorylase reaction as follows:

$$UTP (ATP) + glucose\text{-}1\text{-}P \longrightarrow UDP (ADP)\text{-}glucose + PPi$$

The enzymes and their products have been detected in several species. The substrate is derived from glucose or fructose by the action of hexokinase and the appropriate isomerases.

The possibility has been raised (see Akazawa, 1965; Slabnik et al., 1968) that a somewhat more direct route to starch from sucrose is possible, since sucrose synthetase (one of two enzymes thought to bring about sucrose synthesis in the presence of ADP or UDP) can bring about the reverse reaction as follows:

$$Sucrose + ADP (UDP) \longrightarrow ADPG (UDPG) + Fructose.$$

The sugar nucleotide could then be used directly in starch synthesis and the fructose utilized as above. In this formulation the expenditure of ATP in starch synthesis from sucrose would be reduced by half, but it should be recognized that in the formation of sucrose itself, ATP is consumed, and no saving would result if the nucleotide sugars which are sucrose precursors were used directly in starch synthesis. The available evidence suggests that, even though sucrose is the form arriving at the sinks, hydrolysis occurs during uptake. If this is so, there would appear to be no advantage in forming sucrose as an intermediate in starch formation, and the formation of sucrose or starch would appear to be alternative fates for the nucleotide-hexoses. It remains to be proved that, even in leaves, sucrose normally intervenes as an intermediate in starch synthesis.

The question of how starch synthesis might be controlled by other metabolites has also received attention. Ghosh and Preiss (1966) showed that the purified starch synthetase from leaves which uses ADPG as a donor was not affected by a variety of glycolytic intermediates but that striking stimulations were observed when PGA and other intermediates were included in the ADPG pyrophosphorylase reaction. Similar, though smaller stimulations have been reported for the enzyme from maize endosperm (Dickinson and Preiss, 1968). If ADPG synthesis is a prime regulatory point in starch synthesis in seeds and tubers as it is believed to be in leaves, a possible control is afforded over the alternative fates of glucose as shown in Fig. 8-5. Active utilization of the glycolytic intermediates in the respiration of growing cells might, by keeping the concentration of PGA low, limit the formation of ADPG and thus of starch. Accumulation of PGA when utilization was slower might then bring about a more rapid rate of starch synthesis.

IV. INTERACTION BETWEEN SOURCE AND SINK

In the foregoing a purely passive relation between source and sinks has been implied; we have pointed out where the sinks are and what some of the metabolic reactions are which consume sucrose arriving in the translocation stream. The question of which of several alterna-

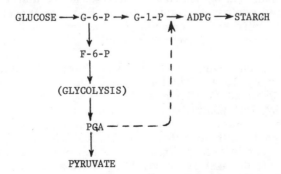

Fig. 8-5—Possible regulation of starch synthesis in sinks by glycolytic rate.

tive sinks pre-empts the photosynthate from a given leaf has been raised but not answered. However, it seems that the relationship can not be simply one of different concentration gradients between the source and sinks of different "strength" or metabolic activity.

Another subtle relationship which has been recognized for many years (see King, Wardlaw, and Evans, 1967; Neales and Incoll, 1968 for reviews) is that the size of activity in the sink may have an influence on the rate of photosynthesis in source leaves. The concept has grown that if assimilate is not transported to sinks the rate of photosynthesis is depressed, and if new sinks are provided, the rate is increased. Effects in response to changing status of sinks which suggest control of photo-synthesis by the level of assimilate in the leaf are shown in the following table (from summary by Neales and Incoll, 1968):

a) Decreased rate on detachment.
b) Fatigue effects: midday depression of photosynthetic rate.
c) Increased rate in remaining leaves following partial defoliation.
d) Decreased rate following interference with translocation or removing sink.
e) Decreasing rate at temperatures suboptimal for growth.
f) Influence of grafting different sinks.

A sort of mass action is frequently inferred. No biochemical evidence is available which would explain how accumulation of photosynthate would slow down the process, but distortion of the chloroplast by accumulating starch grains is surely not the only possibility, and in any event would not explain declines in rate in leaves which do not produce starch. Nor is it clear that the sugar concentration in the phloem is increased to the point where loading would be reduced, or indeed that inordinately high concentrations of assimilate always accumulate in leaves deprived of sinks.

Neales and Incoll (1968) conclude that although the evidence is suggestive the hypothesis is not proved. Many of the effects are long term and the possibility has been raised that other kinds of feed back from sink to source, including hormonal signals, may be operating. For example, Wareing, Khalifa, and Trehearne (1968) in a recent investigation of the stimulatory effect of partial defoliation on remaining leaves, showed that these had somewhat increased levels of protein, and particularly of carboxylating enzymes. They suggested that a correspondingly increased photosynthetic capacity, rather than increased relative demand by the sink, was responsible for the higher photosynthetic rate of surviving leaves, and favor a dynamic hormonal interaction between sink and source.

However, such an interpretation was shown to be unlikely for results obtained by King, Wardlaw, and Evans (1967). These authors showed that in wheat (Triticum aestivum L.), 2 weeks after anthesis, 45% of the flag leaf assimilates are transferred to the developing ear which is itself photosynthetic. Removal of the ear resulted in a 50% reduction in photosynthetic rate of the flag leaf within 15 hours. Darkening of the other leaves resulted in recovery of photosynthetic rate of the flag leaf, with the assimilate now being diverted to roots and shoots. Under some conditions inhibition of photosynthesis in the ear brought about an increased rate of photosynthesis in the flag leaf. In this system then there are relatively rapid interactions, and the photosynthetic rate of the source appears to be closely regulated by the demands of the sink.

LITERATURE CITED

Akazawa, T. 1965. Starch, Inulin, and other reserve polysaccharides, p. 258–297. In J. Bonner and J. E. Varner (ed.) Plant biochemistry. Academic Press, New York.

Beevers, H. 1961. Respiratory metabolism in plants. Harper and Rowe, New York, 232 p.

Bieleski, R. L. 1960. Characteristics of sugar uptake in slices of mature and immature storage tissue. Aust. J. Biol. Sci. 13:204-220.

Bieleski, R. L. 1962. The physiology of sugar cane. V. Kinetics of sugar accumulation. Aust. J. Biol. Sci. 15:429-444.

Crafts, A. S. 1961. Translocation in plants. Holt, Rinehart, and Winston, New York. 182 p.

Dickinson, D. B., and J. Preiss. 1968. ADPG-pyrophosphorylase from maize endosperm. Plant Physiol. 43:S-17.

Ghosh, H. P., and J. Preiss. 1966. ADPG-pyrophosphorylase. J. Biol. Chem. 241:4491-4504.

Grant, B. R., and H. Beevers. 1964. Absorption of sugars by plant tissues. Plant Physiol. 39:78-85.

Hatch, M. D., J. A. Sacher, and K. T. Glasziou. 1963. Sugar accumulation cycle in sugar cane. I. Studies on enzymes of the cycle. Plant Physiol. 38:338-343.

Hatch, M. D., and K. T. Glasziou. 1963. Sugar accumulation in sugar cane. II. Relationship of invertase activity to sugar content and growth rate in storage tissue of plants grown in controlled environments. Plant Physiol. 38:344-348.

King, R. W., I. F. Wardlaw, and L. T. Evans. 1967. Effect of assimilate utilization on photosynthetic in wheat. Planta 77:261-276.

Kriedemann, P., and H. Beevers. 1966a. Sugar uptake and translocation in the castor bean seedling. I. Characteristics of transfer in intact and excised seedlings. Plant Physiol. 42:161-173.

Kriedemann, P., and H. Beevers. 1966b. Sugar uptake and translocation in the castor bean seedling. II. Sugar transformations during uptake. Plant Physiol. 42:174-180.

Kursanov, A. L. 1963. Metabolism and the transport of organic solutes. Advance. Bot. Res. 1:209-278.

Leopold, A. C. 1964. Plant growth and development. McGraw Hill, New York. 466 p.

Loomis, R. S., W. A. Williams, and W. G. Duncan. 1967. Community architecture and the productivity of terrestrial plant communities, p. 291-308. In A. San Pietro, F. A. Greer and T. J. Army (ed.) Harvesting the sun. Academic Press, New York.

Mason, T. G., and E. Phillis. 1937. The migration of solutes. Bot. Rev. 3:47-71.

Neales, T. F., and L. D. Incoll. 1968. The control of leaf photosynthesis rate by level of assimilate concentration in the leaf: A review of the hypothesis. Bot. Rev. 34:107-125.

Sacher, J. A., M. D. Hatch, and K. T. Glasziou. 1963. Sugar accumulation cycle in sugar cane. III. Physical and metabolic aspects of cycle in immature storage tissues. Plant Physiol. 38:348-354.

Slabnik, E., R. B. Frydman, and C.E. Cardini. 1968. Some properties of potato UDPG-D-fructose-2-glucosyl transferase and UDPG-D-fructose-6-phosphate-2 glucosyl transferase. Plant Physiol. 43:1063-1068.

Swanson, C. A. 1959. Translocation of organic solutes, p. 481-545. In F. C. Steward (ed.) Plant physiology, Vol. II. Academic Press, New York.

Wardlaw, I. F. 1968. The control and pattern of movement of carbohydrates in
    plants. Bot. Rev. 34:79–105.
Wareing, P. F., M. M. Khalifa, and K. J. Trehearne. 1968. Rate-limiting pro-
    cesses in photosynthesis at saturating light intensities. Nature 220:453–457.

8 . . . DISCUSSION

JOHN B. HANSON

University of Illinois
Urbana, Illinois

Our topic here is metabolic sinks. Dr. Beevers has clearly outlined the state of our knowledge on the delivery of sucrose to such
sinks. The sucrose can be consumed in the biosyntheses which underlie
growth, or it can be sequestered in vacuoles or immobilized as starch
in plastids. In common, the cells involved must have boundary mechanisms for transport. "Sinks" then are cells not only with a high demand for carbohydrate, but also with intensely active mechanisms for
moving it across the limiting cell membranes.

It should be noted that more than sucrose is moved to sinks, particularly to sinks composed of rapidly growing tissues. Essential mineral nutrients flux as well, though not always through the phloem. One
of the earliest findings with P^{32} applied to roots was that it moved to
and became concentrated in active growth centers such as apical meristems and growing fruits. The bounding membranes of these must
avidly transport phosphate as well as sucrose. In turn, the transport
must "deepen" the sink and keep ions and sugars flowing to it.

It is appropriate to ask what sort of impulse or signal quickens the
metabolism of sinks. Our best response nowadays is to suggest an in-
volvement of hormones. The experiments of Professor Mothes come to
mind in which he places a drop of kinetin on a senescing leaf, with the
result that that area stays green at the expense of surrounding tissues.
Kinetin has here induced a sink in certain cells, and influences are sent
forth (or withdrawn) which command adjacent tissues to senesce in
order to nurture the sink. Something similar must happen normally
with ripening fruits and grain. In corn plants the growing and maturing
grain forms an intensely active sink which derives only half its nitrogen
directly from the soil—the other half is mobilized from the senescing
vegetative structure.

There is an interesting example of the induction of a sink with subsequent senescence in the use of the auxin herbicide, 2,4-D. It seems to me especially appropriate for this symposium as it provides one of the few instances where we make agricultural use of the induction of sinks.

Dr. Juan Cardenas in our laboratory studied the death of young cocklebur plants (Xanthium sp.) spot-treated on one leaf with 70 μg of 2,4-D (2, 4-dichlorophenoxyacetic acid) (Cardenas, 1968). There were 3 distinct periods in the growth toward death. Between 0-2 days the treated plants showed total growth similar to the control, but distributed in favor of the swelling stem-tap roof axis at the expense of new leaf and root formation. The axis swelled, but the meristems were "frozen." Immature leaves failed to expand properly. Between 2-7 days there was no net growth. However, the axis continued to gain in weight at the expense of leaves which were induced to senesce. In the period between 7 and 10 days the plants collapsed, withered, and died.

Roots were stimulated to greater ion uptake the first day after 2,4-D application, with the major portion of phosphate and potassium delivered to the sink in the swelling axis. Leaves received very little ion and after the second day the supply was virtually cut off.

Photosynthesis was also initially stimulated, but with a drastic decline by the second day. Photosynthate was delivered to the axis, the roots being starved.

Cardenas et al. concluded that the plant died because it failed to be autotrophic. Induction of the axis-sink caused senescence of those organs needed to exploit the environment.

Induction of the sink was ascribed to an accelerated nucleic acid metabolism in the axis, coupled with a "freezing" of nucleic acid metabolism in the apical meristems. There is insufficient time to discuss the evidence here. Key et al. (1966) have made a systematic study of the aberrant nucleic acid metabolism in 2,4-D-treated soybean seedlings (Glycine max L.), and correlated this with cell growth and division. O'Brien et al. (1968) show the induction of RNA polymerase in 2,4-D-treated soybeans.

The principal point to be made is that sinks can be manipulated to agronomic ends. When we know more about hormone action I feel certain that the manipulations can be extended to increasing crop yields. But we must first have more biochemical and physiological fact on the regulation of sink metabolism and on the transmission of signals for mobilization and senescence.

LITERATURE CITED

Cardenas, J., F. W. Slife, J. B. Hanson, and H. Butler. 1968. Physiological changes accompanying the death of cocklebur plants treated with 2,4-D. Weed Science 16:96-100.

Key, J. L., C. Y. Lin, E. M. Gifford, Jr., and R. Dengler. 1966. Relation of 2,4-D induced growth aberrations to changes in nucleic acid metabolism in soybean seedlings. Bot. Gaz. 127:87-94.

O'Brien, T. J., B. C. Jarvis, J. H. Cherry and J. B. Hanson. 1968. Enhancement by 2,4-D of chromatin RNA polymerase in soybean hypocotyl tissue. Biochim. Biophys. Acta 169:34-43.

8 ...DISCUSSION

GEORGE G. LATIES

University of California

Los Angeles, California

It was gratifying to have Professor Beevers dwell on the prospect that a hormonal feed-back may be significant in the determination of the influence of ultimate photosynthetic sinks in the plant on the photosynthetic apparatus. The regulation of metabolic events by mass law considerations is thermodynamically quite untenable, as calculations of the necessary substrate concentrations to effect synthesis of starch or protein by the reversal of hydrolytic processes will readily show. In the last analysis the ultimate metabolic sink is heat. While, with sunlight taken into consideration, metabolic cycles in plants may be taken as an example of a zero sum game—in the systems analysis terms of Dr. M. Clawson—such cycles may be far from a zero sum game in practical terms, when time, and perhaps location, are taken into consideration. A case in point is the role of the ocean as a sink par excellence for at least one critical component of metabolism.

While the major elements of photosynthesis are involved in prodigious quantities, they are totally recycled. The over-all constancy of the atmosphere and the level of the oceans attests to the regeneration of oxygen, carbon dioxide, and water. Phosphate, on the other hand, while recycled in metabolism, suffers a constant depletion from the earth's land surface to its underlying layers and particularly to the bottom of the oceans. Retrieval from these ultimate sinks is meager; for practical purposes the traffic is unidirectional. Insofar as the phosphate lost to the ocean bottom is primarily in organic combination, the ocean bottom is a metabolic sink.

While other elements as well are lost to the sea (in quantities greater than phosphate) their concentration in the sea permits the visualization of their role in marine agriculture. With phosphate (and with nitrogen as well) the concentration is so low that the energy of retrieval is perforce vast, and biological yields must be limited by the availability of these elements. In short the levels of phosphorus and nitrogen in the oceans do not realistically allow contemplation of the open oceans as a compensation for depleted agricultural potential on the land.

The fixation of carbon in photosynthesis per year over the land surface of the earth is enormous, being some 1.7×10^{10} metric tons. Estimates for photosynthesis in the oceans has ranged as high as 14×10^{10} metric tons of carbon fixed per year (see Rabinowitch, 1945). There is the prospect, based on the prevalence of $^{18}O_2$ in the air, compared with the prevalence of $H_2^{18}O$ in fresh water and sea water, respectively, that estimates for photosynthesis in the oceans may be several times too large. (R. Park and S. Epstein. Personal communication.) In any event the turnover of phosphorus on a molar basis is at least three times as great as carbon turnover, simply taking into account that three molecules of phosphate (as ATP) are required for each CO_2 fixed into carbohydrate. Respiratory breakdown leads to an even greater phosphate turnover—six molecules of phosphate for each O_2 utilized. In brief, the traffic in phosphate is prodigious, coming to some 27×10^{10} metric tons of phosphorus turned over in the terrestrial biosphere per year.

While phosphorus is not readily leached on the land (Black, 1965; Fried and Broeshart, 1967), considerable phosphate is lost from the land by erosion. In spite of the fact that the phosphate concentration in the earth's fresh waters is very low indeed, some 14.5×10^8 metric tons of phosphorus is delivered to the oceans each year by the world's rivers (see Rankama and Sahama, 1950). Withal, the concentration of phosphorus in the ocean is painfully low, ranging from almost nil at the ocean's surface, to but $3 \mu M$ at some 1,000 m in depth (see Sverdrup et al., 1942). Further, the concentration in the ocean is steadfast, approximately 14.5×10^8 metric tons of phosphorus being deposited in ocean sediments each year in the form of organic matter in residues of phyto- and zooplankton. For practical purposes such phosphorus is irretrievable. Surprisingly, the ocean bottom is not littered with calcium phosphate, and there is evidence that even the phosphorus-bearing concretions to be found on the ocean floor are not being laid down currently (Personal communication from Dr. I. Kaplan, Professor of Geophysics, UCLA.). Phytoplankton turn over approximately 1% of the phosphorus in the ocean per year, and in turn lose about 1% of what they turn over to the ocean sediments.

In querying the possible jeopardy to our agriculture of phosphate loss from the earth's land mass it is difficult to assign the source of the phosphorus lost by erosion. It seems likely that a disproportionate part of that lost to the oceans comes from arable land - which is currently estimated to be but 10% of the earth's land mass (Pehrson, 1945). In fact, a calculation of the total amount of phosphorus lost from arable land [11.9 kg/ha per year (see Black, 1965), $\times 1.4 \times 10^9$ ha (see Pehrson, 1945) = 16.7×10^8 metric tons] reveals a quantity very close to that lost to the oceans each year, e.g. 13.6×10^8 metric tons. This quantity represents the loss of roughly 1.0% of the phosphorus in a plowshare's depth of the earth's arable land per year. If an appreciable part of the phosphorus washed into the ocean in fact comes from nonarable land as well, the percent lost to agriculture will of course be less.

Finally, what of mariculture? The phosphorus concentration in the ocean is but $3 \mu M$, and nitrogen no more than $50 \mu M$. Plankton photosynthesis on an acre basis would appear to be but 5% that on land - and if the plankton product is converted to fish, so to speak, with 1% efficiency, the yield would be no more than 0.1 to 0.2% of the edible crop land yield (de Wit, 1967). Thus the prospect of extensive mariculture as a cure for the world's food needs is at best an illusion and at worst, a hoax. Further, with the current trend of ocean pollution, the ocean will unhappily assume an even greater role as an ultimate metabolic sink.

LITERATURE CITED

Black, C. A. 1965. Soil-plant relationships. John Wiley & Sons, New York.

de Wit, C. T. 1967. Photosynthesis: Its relationship to overpopulation, p. 315-320. In A. San Pietro, F. A. Greer, and T. J. Army (ed.) Harvesting the sun. Academic Press, New York.

Fried, M., and H. Broeshart. The soil-plant system. Academic Press, New York.

Pehrson, G. O. 1965. Report: Limited land in the world food problem. International Minerals & Chemical Corp., Skokie, Ill.

Rabinowitch, E. 1945. Photosynthesis. Interscience Publishers, New York.

Rankama, K., and Th. G. Sahama. 1950. Geochemistry. University of Chicago Press, Chicago. 1950.

Sverdrup, H. U., M. W. Johnson, and R. H. Fleming. 1942. The oceans. Prentice-Hall, Englewood Cliffs, N. J.

9

Interrelationships Among Photosynthesis, Respiration, and Movement of Carbon in Developing Crops

VOLKMAR STOY

Swedish Seed Association
Svalöf, Sweden

From the preceding lectures we have learned a great deal about how external conditions may influence various internal physiological processes within plants, and it therefore appears appropriate to consider briefly how these processes influence one another and also the manner in which they relate to yield. The main processes of interest in this connection are photosynthesis, respiration, and carbon assimilate translocation; but aspects of growth, development, mineral nutrition, etc., will also be considered when relevant.

I. INTERDEPENDENCE OF PHOTOSYNTHESIS AND RESPIRATION

A. Photosynthesis and Respiration in Individual Plants

According to the classical view, photosynthesis and respiration are two opposite processes, proceeding simultaneously and independently in all green tissues. Respiration has thus been believed to proceed at the same rate in light and in darkness, and as a consequence gross photosynthesis in illuminated plant parts has commonly been calculated by applying the formula:

gross photosynthesis = net photosynthesis + dark respiration.

However, the possibility that a light-dependent respiration exists different in nature and magnitude from ordinary dark respiration, and thus counteracting photosynthesis at a varying rate has been, to quote Rabinowitch (1945) "...a nightmare oppressing all who are concerned

185

Table 9-1—The magnitude of the Warburg effect in different plant species. The estimates refer to normal O_2 concentration in the air (20%), high light intensities, and temperatures between 20 and 25C

Species	CO_2 conc., %	% inhibition of photosynthesis	References
Chlorella pyrenoidosa (alga)	0.2	20	Warburg (1920)
Chlorella pyrenoidosa (alga)	0.03	0	Fock & Egle (1966)
Triticum sp. (wheat)	0.03	25	McAlister & Myers (1940)
Solidago virgaurea (European goldenrod)	0.03	33	Björkman (1967)
Mimulus cardinalis (Crimson monkeyflower)	0.03	32	Björkman (1967)
Zea mays (corn)	0.03	0	Björkman (1967)
Amaranthus edulis	0.03	0	Björkman (1967)

with the exact measurement of photosynthesis." Also to those dealing with problems of plant productivity, the question is of great interest and will therefore be briefly elucidated.

Warburg (1920) observed many years ago in Chlorella that the rate of apparent photosynthesis was considerably decreased when the concentration of oxygen in the surrounding medium was increased from 2 to 100%. At an oxygen concentration corresponding to that in normal air, inhibition was about 20%. The existence of the Warburg effect in higher plants was reported 20 years later by McAlister and Myers (1940), who observed the phenomenon in wheat leaves (Table 9-1).

Different explanations have been given for the Warburg effect (cf. Turner and Brittain, 1962), one of them being that it is caused by increased respiration. Since dark respiration is known to be practically independent of oxygen concentration within the range of 2 to 100% O_2, this presumptive respiration thus has to be light-dependent, and has consequently been termed photorespiration.

It is practically impossible—or at least extremely difficult—to make exact measurements of the rate of photorespiration under normal growth conditions since the simultaneously occurring photosynthesis interferes with and counteracts the respiratory gas exchange. For a long time, therefore, the existence of photorespiration was much questioned, but today the positive evidence is so overwhelming that there hardly can be any doubt about its reality (see e.g., Decker 1955, Tregunna, Krotkov, and Nelson 1961, 1964, 1966; Egle and Döhler 1963; Fock and Egle 1966; Moss 1966, 1968; Forrester, Krotkov, and Nelson 1966a,b; Holmgren and Jarvis 1967; Poskuta, Nelson, and Krotkov 1967; Poskuta 1968; Downton and Tregunna 1968a; Joliffe and Tregunna 1968; Fock, Schaub, and Hilgenberg 1969.

An important step towards a correct interpretation of the experimental results was the discovery of Hoch, Owens, and Kok (1963) (see also Ozbun, Volk, and Jackson, 1964; Tregunna et al., 1966; Forrester et al., 1966a,b; Holmgren and Jarvis, 1967) that dark respiration and photorespiration are quite different processes and that dark respiration is inhibited already at very weak light intensities. Moreover, the rate of photorespiration in normal air and at medium to high light intensities has in most cases been found to be one to two times that of dark respiration (Moss, 1966; Forrester et al., 1966a; Goldsworthy, 1966; see, however, Ozbun et al., 1964; Brix, 1968). On the other hand, in some species no photorespiration at all appears to exist (Tregunna et al., 1964; Forrester et al., 1966b; Björkman, 1967; Hesketh, 1967)(cf. Table 9-1). This observation has to be correlated with another phenomenon that had been reported already several years earlier.

If plants are placed in a closed assimilation chamber and subsequently illuminated, the CO_2 content of the air in this chamber soon reaches an equilibrium value, the magnitude of which is dependent on light intensity, temperature, O_2 concentration, etc. This value is called the compensation concentration (also designated Γ), and it has been shown by several workers (Meidner, 1962; Moss, 1962a) that Γ may attain rather different values for different species. As a matter of fact, two distinct groups of plant species can be distinguished, one exhibiting a compensation concentration of about 5 ppm and another one compensating at 50-100 ppm of CO_2 in the atmosphere. The first group comprises both a number of so-called tropical grasses (e.g., Zea, Sorghum, and Saccharum) and dicots, such as Amaranthus, whereas to the second group belong, amongst others, temperate grasses, such as Triticum Hordeum, Avena, Poa, Festuca (and also Oryza), as well as most of the investigated dicots (e.g., Glycine, Beta, Nicotiana, and Phaseolus).

The interesting thing is that all members of the low-compensating group appear not to be undergoing photorespiration whereas the high-compensating plants all seem to respire significantly when illuminated.

A biochemical mechanism to explain this phenomenon has been suggested by Zelitch (1958, 1959, 1966). According to his theory, glycolic acid is formed during the course of photosynthesis, and from the oxidation of glycolic acid CO_2 arises that is subsequently released in photorespiration, and thus causes the high compensation concentration. In low-compensating species the absence of CO_2 evolution might be due either to a block in some step in the oxidation of glycolic acid (as proposed by Tregunna, 1966 and Zelitch, 1966; see, however, Downton and Tregunna, 1968a) or to the lack of sufficient amounts of glycolic acid. The latter possibility has been considered as less probable (Zelitch, 1966).

In a recent study by Moss (1968), it was reported, however, that the production and subsequent oxidation of glycolate is not sufficiently large to account for the lower net photosynthesis found in, e.g., tobacco (Nicotiana tabacum L.) as compared with maize (which does not photorespire). It may be necessary therefore to consider also other mechanisms and this has, in fact, been done by some authors (El-Sharkawy, Loomis, and Williams, 1967; Hesketh and Baker, 1967). These authors proposed that the difference between the two groups of species may be explained instead by assuming that certain species possess a much stronger ability to reassimilate the CO_2 evolved than others and that the absence of photorespiration thus is only apparent. This interpretation has been rejected, however, by Downton and Tregunna (1968a).

One argument that has been raised to support the reassimilation hypothesis is founded on the observation that species showing low compensation concentration also possess certain characteristic anatomical features, such as a well-developed sheath of parenchymatous cells (rich in chloroplasts) around the vascular bundles and a particularly large, exposed cell surface per cell volume (Rhoades and Carvalho, 1944; El-Sharkawy and Hesketh, 1965; Downton and Tregunna, 1968b). These features are thought to facilitate a rapid gas exchange and thus a strong reassimilation of CO_2 released in photorespiration. Other factors favoring a rapid recycling of CO_2 might be faster rates of the dark enzymatic reactions in the chloroplasts (El-Sharkawy et al., 1967; Mansfield, 1968) or low cytoplasmatic resistance to CO_2 diffusion from the site of respiration to the site of assimilation (El-Sharkawy et al., 1967).

Another interesting difference between the high- and low-compensating plants has been revealed during the last few years. It has been reported by several groups (Kortschak, Hartt, and Burr, 1965; Hatch and Slack, 1966) that the biochemical pathway of photosynthesis in sugarcane (Saccharum officinarum L.) is different from the ordinary Calvin pathway starting with the carboxylation of ribulose diphosphate. This new pathway, often called the C_4-pathway, since a number of 4-carbon dicarboxylic acids form the primary product of the carboxylation, has later been found to be dominating in all those members of the low-compensating group that have been investigated for it (Slack and Hatch, 1967; Hatch, Slack, and Johnson, 1967; see also Downton and Tregunna, 1968b). This correlation can hardly be a mere coincidence, and it would be most interesting to know more about the biochemical similarities and differences between these groups of plants.

The two groups of plants differ in still another very important respect: they do not show the same rates of net photosynthesis. Whereas the low-compensating plants in normal air and at optimal light and temperature conditions all photosynthesize at a rate of about 50-60 mg $CO_2/dm^2/h$, the high-compensating plants rarely reach above 35 mg $CO_2/dm^2/h$ (El-Sharkawy and Hesketh, 1964, 1965; Moss, Musgrave, and Lemon, 1961; Hesketh and Moss, 1963; Murata and Iyama, 1963; Stoy, 1965). (Fig. 9-1). This difference could of course be attributed to the loss of carbon through photorespiration of the high-compensating

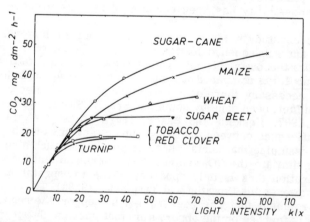

Fig. 9-1—Light response curves of photosynthesis for different crop plants. Attached leaves, CO_2 concentration = 0.03 vol.%, temperature = 20C (From Stoy, 1965).

plants, but it could also be caused by a real difference in the rate of gross photosynthesis. The previously mentioned study by Moss (1968), according to which the estimated rates of photorespiration appear to be too small to account for the total difference in rates of net photosynthesis, lends support to this possibility.

B. Photosynthetic Production and Respiratory Consumption in Plant Communities

In a plant community photosynthetic production rises with increasing size of the foliage per ground area (leaf area index, LAI). However, this rise does not go on indefinitely; but is limited by mutual shading of the leaves, whereby the mean photosynthetic production per unit leaf area (net assimilation rate, NAR) is decreased. It has been a matter of considerable disagreement whether an optimal LAI value exists at which the rate of total photosynthetic production (crop growth rate, C, according to Watson, 1958) reaches its maximum value, or whether this maximum is approached asymptotically with increasing LAI.

Results from work of Davidson and Philip (1958), Watson (1958), Davidson and Donald (1958), and Black (1963) indicated the existence of a definite optimal LAI; but other investigations (Brougham, 1956; Watson, Thorne, and French, 1963; Wang and Wei, 1964; Stoy, 1965; Nichiporovich and Malofeyev, 1965; Ludwig, Saeki, and Evans, 1965; Williams, Loomis, and Epley, 1965; Shibles and Weber, 1965; Wilfong, Brown, and Blaser, 1967; King and Evans, 1967) did in general not confirm these conclusions.

The reason for this discrepancy may be sought in the different light interception of the various plant species used in the investigations, and also in differences in environmental factors, such as light intensity, temperature, and plant density (Ludwig et al., 1965; King and Evans, 1967). For species with steeply inclined leaves (and consequently high light penetration), much higher LAI values can be expected, without any reduction in total photosynthetic productions, than for species with a flat leaf arrangement (Fig. 9-2). Moreover, differences in respiration rates may contribute to the varying experimental results. According to the models of Davidson and Philip (1958) and of Verhagen, Wilson, and Britten (1963), a reduction in the rate of net photosynthetic production is to be expected beyond a certain LAI value, since a constant value of respiration rate is attributed to all leaves. This assumption is rather doubtful, however, and direct estimates, as well as indirect evidence, have shown that the dark respiration rates of the bottom leaves in the canopy often are much lower than those of the top leaves (Ludwig et al., 1965; King and Evans, 1967). The bottom leaves are thus not parasitic in the sense of Nichiporovich (1956) and Davidson and Philip (1958) and will consequently not reduce the amount of assimilates produced by the top leaves to any greater extent. Moreover, the existence of photorespiration does steepen the gradient in respiration rates down the canopy still more (King and Evans, 1967), and will therefore contribute to reducing the occurrence of an optimal LAI under most conditions.

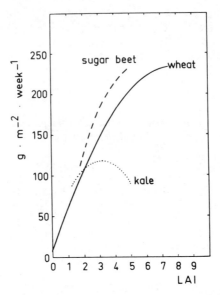

Fig. 9-2—The dependence of crop growth rate (C) on leaf area index (LAI). The data for kale and sugar beet are taken from Watson (1958), those for wheat from Stoy (1965).

II. THE INFLUENCE OF METABOLIC SINKS
ON THE RATE OF PHOTOSYNTHESIS

A. Experimental Evidence

When rates of photosynthesis are determined experimentally in the laboratory (and often even the field) for a given set of external conditions, they are frequently thought to represent specific values that are characteristic for the species and the conditions in question. However, this is certainly only rarely true. In most cases the figures obtained are maximum values that are only seldom reached under natural conditions and then only during limited periods. The reason for this behavior is that even when plants are growing under very constant external conditions internal regulation may occur that modifies the response of the plants to a great extent (see, e.g., Went, 1958). Also the respiration rates of the different living tissues are influenced by internal factors and may vary considerably during the lifetime of a plant (Kidd, West, and Briggs, 1921).

If plants are manipulated so that their normal assimilate distribution is disturbed, it is possible to change the rate of photosynthesis in their green parts rather drastically even if the plants are growing under constant external conditions. If, for instance, the tubers of a potato (Solanum tuberosum L.) plant (Burt, 1964; Nösberger and Humphries, 1965), the grains of a wheat plant (King, Wardlaw, and Evans, 1967)

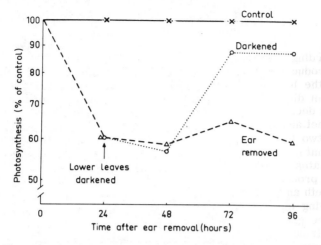

Fig. 9-3—The rate of net photosynthesis of wheat flag leaves after different treatments of the plants (From King, Wardlaw, and Evans 1967).

(cf. Fig. 9-3), the apples from an apple (Malus sylvestris) tree (Maggs, 1963; Hansen, 1967; see also Kazaryan, Balegezyan, and Karapetyan, 1965), or the fruits from a tomato (Lycopersicon esculentum Mill.) plant (Moss, 1962b) are removed soon after their appearance, the rate of photosynthesis in the leaves of these plants is decreased very significantly. Similarly, barren plants show a much lower photosynthetic rate than corresponding fertile specimens (Moss, 1962b).

Experiments in which the size of the source, instead of that of the sink, has been decreased have yielded reversed results. It has thus been reported that removing part of the leaves on maize plants (Kiesselbach, 1948; Wareing, Khalifa, and Treharne, 1968), apple trees (Maggs, 1964, 1965), pine (Pinus sp.) trees (Sweet and Wareing, 1966), and bean (Phaseolus sp.) or willow (Salix sp.) plants (Wareing et al., 1968) does very markedly increase the rate of photosynthesis in the remaining leaves. This increase may compensate for the loss of part of the green foliage, and has therefore been regarded by most authors as a response of the source to the demands of the sink.

B. Possible Mechanisms to Explain Sink Action

Two main theories have been advanced to explain the regulating ability of the sink—one rather old theory and a second more recent one.

One hundred years ago Boussingault (1868) proposed that the accumulation of assimilates in illuminated leaves might inhibit the rates of photosynthesis in the latter but it has still not been possible to prove or disprove this theory in a convincing manner (a thorough review of the problem is presented by Neales and Incoll, 1968). Several workers (e.g., Kurssanov, 1933; Went, 1958) have, however, adopted this idea and believe that removal of a metabolic sink induces a building-up of assimilates in the leaves, which in turn cause a reduction in the rate of photosynthesis.

According to a more recent hypothesis, the sink under normal conditions produces a certain amount of plant hormones that are translocated to the leaves where they increase the rate of photosynthesis. If the sink is disturbed or destroyed in any way, the amount of released hormones decreases, and, consequently, the rate of photosynthesis goes down (Sweet and Wareing, 1966; Bidwell and Turner, 1966).

The two theories have also been combined into a single one by assuming that growth regulators, produced in the sink, stimulate the flow of assimilates into the latter and thus prevent the accumulation of photosynthetic products that might depress the rate of photosynthesis at the source (Seth and Wareing, 1967; Hew, Nelson, and Krotkov, 1967).

Wareing et al. (1968) also found in their experiments that if the size of the green foliage was reduced, the activity of the carboxylating enzymes (ribulose-1,5-diphosphate carboxylase for beans and phosphoenolpyruvate carboxylase for maize) was raised significantly in the remaining leaves (Table 9-2). Based on this, they advanced the hypothesis that removal of part of the leaves stimulated the synthesis of proteins—and even enzymes—by reducing the competition for nutrients or growth substances.

Positive effects of treatment with growth substances on the rate of photosynthesis have been reported both for indole-3-acetic acid (Turner and Bidwell, 1965) and for gibberellin (Coulombe and Paquin, 1959; Alvim, 1960; Treharne and Stoddart, 1968), but many negative results have also been obtained (for a discussion see Hoffmann, 1968) and it is not clear, at the moment, whether growth substances actually exert a direct influence on photosynthesis or if their effects mainly are indirect, e.g., by an increased rate of translocation. However, Treharne and Stoddart (1968) found a close correlation in experiments with red clover (Trifolium pratense L.) between photosynthetic rate, activity of RuDP-carboxylase, and endogenous level of gibberellin in the leaves, a result that is suggestive of a direct influence on the photosynthesis rate in this case.

Table 9-2—Effect of partial defoliation on carboxylation reaction in remaining leaves. Enzyme activity was measured 3 days after defoliation (After Wareing, Khalifa, and Treharne, 1968)

Material	Treatment	Relative enzyme activity	Relative enzyme activity per unit leaf area
Phaseolus, RuDP carboxylase	Control	50.58	10.1
	Partial defoliation	59.28	11.9
Zea, PEP-carboxylase	Control	398.0	39.8
	Partial defoliation	466.0	46.6

III. GROWTH AND THE DISTRIBUTION
OF PHOTOSYNTHETIC PRODUCTS

A. The Distribution Pattern

Only a minor fraction of the products of photosynthesis remain at the site of production in fully expanded leaves, most of them are translocated to other organs where they are either used as building-blocks for various cell-constituents or deposited as storage products. A certain part is always lost through respiration during transport and at the final storage site.

Numerous investigations have clearly demonstrated that the translocation of photosynthates within the plant does not occur in a random fashion but that a very definite distribution pattern can be recognized (cf. reviews by Brouwer, 1962; Wardlaw, 1968). This pattern of movement changes continuously during the growth of the plant and exerts a profound effect on both the morphological form and the yielding properties of the plant. It is therefore of great interest for the plant physiologist, as well as for the agronomist, to know the manner in which the pattern changes, and also how these changes are regulated and controlled.

During the development of a single leaf, we can distinguish stages with different patterns of assimilate movement. When the leaf is very young, it imports photosynthetic products from other parts of the plant to build up its own structure; but very soon it becomes self-supporting and in a short time starts to export assimilates (see, e.g., Jones, Martin, and Porter, 1959; Shiroya et al., 1961; Thrower, 1962; Joy, 1964). As long as the plant is young this export is mainly directed towards centers of active growth, such as developing leaves, root tips, or shoot apices; but later on much of the assimilate transport is diverted to storage organs, such as fruits, grains, or tubers. This shift in direction may be rather sudden and dramatic as is shown by Fig. 9-4, which illustrates the flow of assimilates in a cereal plant at different periods after ear emergence.

Another expression of the distribution pattern is the fact that leaves in different positions on the plant may preferentially supply different growing organs with assimilates (Belikov, 1955, Belikov and Kostetskii, 1964; Fujiwara and Suzuki, 1957; Quinlan and Sagar, 1962; Stoy, 1963; Williams, 1964; Wardlaw, 1965; Bonnemain, 1966; Lupton, 1966). The photosynthates for the roots are thus mainly produced in the lower leaves and those for the apical parts in the upper leaves, whereas leaves in an intermediate position deliver assimilates in both directions. This general pattern is only relative, however, and may be modified both by external conditions, such as temperature or water supply and by differences in the internal organization of the vascular system (cf. Wardlaw, 1968).

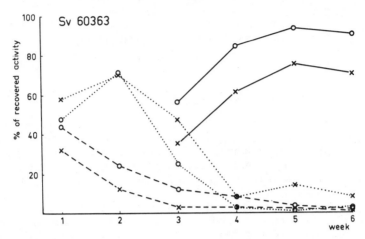

Fig. 9-4—The distribution of ^{14}C-photosynthates from the upper two leaves during the period from ear emergence to leaf senescence in spring wheat (Sv 60363); 7 days translocation period. ——————— = grains, - - - - - - = ears (minus grains), and · · · · = stems. Circles (o) represent photosynthates from the flag leaf and crosses (x) photosynthates from the second leaf from the top. (Unpublished results by Stoy).

B. Regulation of the Flow of Assimilates

There can hardly be any doubt that the centers of growth within the plants exert some attractive force on the flow of assimilates from the source to the sink (Aronoff, 1955; Crafts, 1961), and this force appears to determine both the direction and the intensity of the flow. Thus, different centers may exhibit various strengths of "demand" for assimilates, and therefore reproductive organs often (but not always!) dominate vegetative ones; shoot apices dominate root tips, etc.

The activity of the source, although not without importance, seems to be of secondary importance in this connection. This view is supported by the fact, amongst others, that several external factors, which may change the distribution pattern considerably (such as temperature or supply of water and nutrients) have a much greater influence on the rate of growth than on the rates of photosynthesis or translocation (Hsia, Waon, and Wang, 1963; Evans, Wardlaw, and Williams, 1964; Wardlaw, 1967, 1968).

Although the importance of active growth for the establishment of a polar movement of assimilates thus seems to be generally accepted, there does not exist any corresponding agreement as to the mechanism by which the attracting force of the sink is mediated. This is obviously due to the fact that we still do not know with certainty the mechanism that initiates, directs, and regulates the basic translocation process. The older theories of a passive mass flow along a concentration gradient are rejected by most workers and explanations involving an active loading and unloading of the phloem system are preferred by the majority (cf. Zimmermann, 1960; Kurssanov, 1963; Schumacher, 1967). In this connection, an action of growth substances has been postulated by many authors (De Stigter, 1961; Crane, 1964; Hew et al., 1967) and comparisons with the attracting effect of cytokinins on amino acids (Mothes, Engelbrecht, and Kulajewa, 1959) have frequently been made.

IV. THE DEPENDENCE OF YIELD ON PHOTOSYNTHETIC ACTIVITY

It may be appropriate at this stage, to recall that yield in the agronomic sense in most cases is not equivalent to total dry-matter production, but only to a certain fraction of the latter. However, this fraction is not constant even for a particular crop, but may change both with the environment and the genotype of the plant. An increase of this fraction can therefore be achieved by applying methods of plant husbandry, as well as of plant breeding.

In a recent book on the evolution of our cultivated plants, Schwanitz (1967) emphasizes strongly that the most outstanding feature of the evolution of the original wild forms into our present-day cultivated forms is the enormous increase in size of those parts of the plants that have come to be of special interest to man (Fig. 9-5). This nonuniform (allometric) growth is sometimes accompanied by a conspicuous enlargement also of the photosynthetically active organs (cf. Fig. 9-6), but in most cases this is not so and instead a remarkable increase in the photosynthetic efficiency of these organs obviously has been achieved in the course of evolution. This does not necessarily mean, however, that the maximum values of photosynthetic rate have been raised to any large extent; a more likely explanation is that in the wild forms (and even in many of the cultivated forms) photosynthesis proceeds at a considerably lower rate than is envisaged by its potential upper limit (von Sengbusch,

Allometric growth in Capsicum annuum

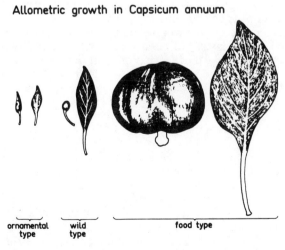

ornamental   wild   food type
type   type

Fig. 9-5—A typical example of allometric growth in a cultivated plant (After Schwanitz, 1967).

Evolution in Zea mays

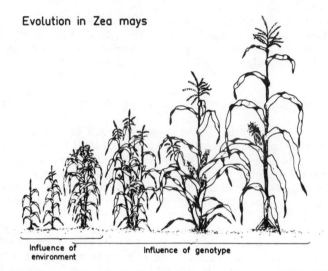

Fig. 9-6—Schematic representation of the relative importance of environmental and genotypical influences on the evolution of the maize plant (After Mangelsdorf, 1958).

1956; Went, 1958; Schwanitz, 1960) and that in the more high-yielding forms the actual rate of photosynthesis is closer to the potential limit.

The appreciable increase in yielding ability of these plants—when under cultivation, and thus subjected to a more or less conscious selection—may therefore be mainly attributed to an increased growth rate in particular organs, which is accompanied by a stronger flow of assimilates to these parts, as well as by a higher efficiency of the already existing photosynthetic apparatus. This evolutionary process should not be considered as terminated; there are, on the contrary, clear indications that it is still going on also in highly bred crops (van Dobben, 1962; Sandfaer, Jørgensen, and Haahr, 1965); but it should also be pointed out that in order to raise the maximum yielding capacity beyond its present level, it may be necessary in many cases to increase both the specific rate of photosynthesis and the fraction of total production that is diverted into those organs that are to be harvested (Nichiporovich, 1956; Donald, 1962; Stoy, 1965).

V. CHALLENGES FOR THE FUTURE

In concluding this lecture, I would like to draw attention to some of the problems just discussed that I believe deserve a particularly intensive study. One such problem regards photorespiration. We urgently need to know its exact biochemical nature and why it seems to be absent in some species. Of special importance is the question whether this lack is only apparent (due to rapid recycling of CO_2) or if it depends on a real biochemical difference among species. Thus a flux of CO_2 back to the atmosphere is equivalent to a loss of trapped energy and must therefore be prevented as much as possible. In this connection, it is also of great importance to learn if photorespiration has any essential function in plant life or not. If photorespiration is really absent in some species, it is hard to believe that it can play any vital role, particularly since these species include some of the most productive ones in the whole world.

Related to this problem is the question if it may be possible to convert, by methods of plant breeding, high-compensating plants into low-compensating ones? To answer this question, it seems to be necessary to know whether the phenomenon of light-dependent CO_2 evolution is closely linked to any specific anatomical features or if it is primarily caused by biochemical processes. The prospects for successful plant breeding seem to be considerably better in the latter case.

Another existing problem is to find out how near to potential photosynthetic production we can really come with different crops (and even varieties). For certain crops and at certain stages of development the limit has perhaps already been reached (cf. Stoy, 1966), but for others there seems to exist a fairly wide gap between what theoretically may be produced and what is actually achieved. The reasons for this discrepancy may be of different kinds; besides such obvious external influences as lack of water or nutrients, internal factors such as an inadequate assimilate distribution and inhibited rate of photosynthesis, or both, may be involved (Ermilov, 1962). In order to increase the productivity of the crop, it may, therefore, sometimes be desirable to effect a more or less radical change in the morphology and physiology of the plants. Plant breeding appears to be the method of choice to produce such changes (e.g., the tremendous success of the semidwarf varieties in wheat and rice) but the use of externally applied growth-regulators sometimes also gives spectacular results.

It is a distressing fact that we lack the basic physiological information in most cases to answer these questions. It is also embarrassing that we often know very little, for example, about the differences between species and varieties even with regard to major physiological processes and how they proceed quantitatively. There is a definite trend throughout the world, however, to try to fill the existing gaps in our knowledge in this particular respect, and it is to be hoped that within a relatively few years we will be able to understand much better the way in which different crop plants absorb, distribute, and store the energy they derive from the sun and how to utilize this information to produce more food for mankind.

LITERATURE CITED

Alvim, P. de T. 1960. Net assimilation rate and growth behavior of beans as affected by gibberellic acid, urea, and sugar sprays. Plant Physiol. 35:285–288.

Aronoff, S. 1955. Translocation from soybean leaves. Plant Physiol. 30:184–185.

Belikov, I. F. 1955. Movement and distribution of photosynthetic products in soybean plants during the vegetation period (In Russian). Fiziol. Rast. 4:345–357.

Belikov, I. F., and E. Ya. Kostetskii. 1964. The distribution of assimilates in sugar beet during the growth period. Soviet Plant Physiol. 11:508–511.

Bidwell, R. G. S., and Wendy B. Turner. 1966. Effect of growth regulators on CO_2 assimilation in leaves, and its correlation with the bud break response in photosynthesis. Plant Physiol. 41:267-270.

Björkman, O. 1967. Further studies of the effect of oxygen concentration on photosynthetic CO_2 uptake in higher plants. Carnegie Inst. Washington Yearbook 66:310-318.

Black, J. N. 1963. The interrelationship of solar radiation and leaf area index in determining the rate of dry matter production of swards of subterranean clover (Trifolium subterraneum L.). Aust. J. Agr. Res. 14:20-38.

Bonnemain, M. J. 1966. Sur les transport des produits de la photosynthèse chez la Tomate lors de la fructification. Compt. Rend. Acad. Sci. (Paris) 262:366-369.

Boussingault, J. B. 1868. Agronomie, chimie agricole et physiologie. 2e Ed. Mallet Bachelier, Paris, 1860-1874, 5 vols. (p. 236-312).

Brix, H. 1968. Influence of light intensity at different temperatures on rate of respiration of Douglas-fir seedlings. Plant Physiol. 43:389-393.

Brougham, R. W. 1956. Effect of intensity of defoliation on regrowth of pasture. Aust. J. Agr. Res. 7:377-387.

Brouwer, R. 1962. Distribution of dry matter in the plant. Neth. J. Agr. Sci. 10 (Special Issue):361-376.

Burt, R. L. 1964. Carbohydrate utilization as a factor in plant growth. Aust. J. Biol. Sci. 17:867-877.

Coulombe, L.-J. et R. Paquin. 1959. Effects de l'acide gibberellique sur le métabolisme des plantes. Can. J. Bot. 37:897-901.

Crafts, A. S. 1961. Translocation in plants. Holt, Rinehart, and Winston, New York. 182 p.

Crane, J. C. 1964. Growth substances in fruit setting and development. Ann. Rev. Plant Physiol. 15:303-326.

Davidson, J. L., and C. M. Donald. 1958. The growth of swards of subterranean clover with particular reference to leaf area. Aust. J. Agr. Res. 9:53-72.

Davidson, J. L. and J. R. Philip. 1958. Light and pasture growth, p. 181-187. In Climatology and microclimatology, Proc. Canberra Symp. 1956, Unesco, Paris.

Decker, J. P. 1955. A rapid, postillumination deceleration of respiration in green leaves. Plant Physiol. 30:82-84.

De Stigter, H. C. M. 1961. Translocation of ^{14}C-photosynthates in the graft muskmelon (Cucurbita ficifolia). Acta Bot. Neerl. 10:466-473.

Dobben, W. H. van. 1962. Influence of temperature and light conditions on dry-matter distribution, development rate and yield in arable crops. Neth. J. Agr. Sci. 10 (Special Issue):377-388.

Donald, C. M. 1962. In search of yield. J. Aust. Inst. Agr. Sci. 28:171-178.

Downton, W. J. S., and E. B. Tregunna. 1968a. Photorespiration and gycolate metabolism: A re-examination and correlation of some previous studies. Plant Physiol. 43:923-929.

Downton, W. J. S., and E. B. Tregunna. 1968b. Carbon dioxide compensation - its relation to photosynthetic carboxylation reactions, systematics of the Graminae, and leaf anatomy. Can. J. Bot. 46:207-215.

Egle, K., and G. Döhler 1963. Uber Induktionserscheinungen der Photosynthese und der Lichtatmung bei einzelligen Grünalgen. Beitr. Biol. Pfl. 42:213-239.

El-Sharkawy, M. A., and J. D. Hesketh. 1964. Effects of temperature and water deficit on leaf photosynthetic rates of different species. Crop Sci. 4:514-518.

El-Sharkawy, M. A., and J. D. Hesketh. 1965. Photosynthesis among species in relation to characteristics of leaf anatomy and CO_2 diffusion resistances. Crop Sci. 5:517-521.

El-Sharkawy, M. A., Loomis, R. S., and W. A. Williams. 1967. Apparent reassimilation of respiratory carbon dioxide by different plant species. Physiol. Plant. 20:171-186.

Ermilov, G. B. 1962. Dependence of leaf productivity of corn on the internal plant processes. Soviet Plant Physiol. 9:315-317.

Evans, L. T., I. F. Wardlaw, and C. N. Williams. 1964. Environmental control of growth, p. 102-125. In C. Barnard (ed.) Grasses and grasslands. Macmillan, London.

Fock, H., and K. Egle. 1966. Über die "Lichtatmung" bei grünen Pflanzen. I. Die Wirkung von Sauerstoff und Kohlendioxyd auf den CO_2-Gaswechsel während der Licht- und Dunkelphase. Beitr. Biol. Pfl. 42:213-239.

Fock, H., H. Schaub, und W. Hilgenberg. 1969. Über den Sauerstoff und Kohlendioxidgaswechsel von Chlorella und Conocephalum während der Lichtphase. Z.f.Pflanzenphysiol. 60:56-63.

Forrester, Marlene L., G. Krotkov, and C. D. Nelson. 1966a. Effect of oxygen on photosynthesis, photorespiration and respiration in detached leaves. I. Soybean. Plant Physiol. 41:422-427.

Forrester, Marlene L., G. Krotkov, and C. D. Nelson. 1966b. Effect of oxygen on photosynthesis, photorespiration and respiration in detached leaves. II. Corn and other monocotyledons. Plant Physiol. 41:428-431.

Fujiwara, A., and M. Suzuki. 1957. Studies on the carbon metabolism in higher plants. II. Structural distribution of the carbon-14 absorbed through the leaf in the rice plant. Tohoku J. Agr. Res. 8:89-97.

Goldsworthy, A. 1966. Experiments on the origin of CO_2 released by tobacco leaf segments in the light. Phytochem. 5:1013-1019.

Hansen, P. 1967. ^{14}C-studies on apple trees. I. The effect of the fruit on the translocation and distribution of photosynthates. Physiol. Plant. 20:382-391.

Hatch, M. D., and C. R. Slack. 1966. Photosynthesis by sugarcane leaves. A new carboxylation reaction and the pathway of sugar formation. Biochem. J. 101:103-111.

Hatch, M. D., C. R. Slack, and Hilary S. Johnson. 1967. Further studies on a new pathway of photosynthetic carbon dioxide fixation in sugarcane and its occurrence in other plant species. Biochem. J. 102:417-422.

Hesketh, J. 1967. Enhancement of photosynthetic CO_2-assimilation in the absence of oxygen, as affected by species and temperature. Planta 76:371-374.

Hesketh, J., and D. Baker. 1967. Light and carbon assimilation by plant communities. Crop Sci. 7:285-293.

Hesketh, J. and D. N. Moss. 1963. Variation in the response of photosynthesis to light. Crop Sci. 3:107-110.

Hew, C., C. D. Nelson, and G. Krotkov. 1967. Hormonal control of translocation of photosynthetically assimilated ^{14}C in young soybean plants. Amer. J. Bot. 54:252-256.

Hoch, G., Olga v. H. Owens, and B. Kok. 1963. Photosynthesis and respiration. Arch. Biochem. Biophys. 101:171-180.

Hoffman, P. 1968. Zur Physiologie der Photosynthese bei höheren Pflanzen. Botanische Studien. 18. VEB Gustav Fischer, Jena. 151 p.

Holmgren, P., and P. G. Jarvis. 1967. Carbon dioxide efflux from leaves in light and darkness. Physiol. Plant. 20:1045-1051.

Hsia, C.-A., S.-S. Waon, and F.-T. Wang. 1963. The influence of temperature on the physiological changes in wheat during the grain formation stage (In Chinese with English summary). Acta Bot. Sinica. 11:338-349.

Joliffe, P. A., and E. B. Tregunna. 1968. Effect of temperature, CO_2 concentration, and light intensity on oxygen inhibition of photosynthesis in wheat leaves. Plant Physiol. 43:902-906.

Jones, H., R. V. Martin, and Helen K. Porter. 1959. Translocation of ^{14}carbon in tobacco following assimilation of ^{14}carbon dioxide by a single leaf. Ann. Bot. N.S. 23:493-508.

Joy, K. W. 1964. Translocation in sugar beet. I. Assimilation of $^{14}CO_2$ and distribution of materials from leaves. J. Exptl. Bot. 15:485-494.

Kazaryan, V. O., N. V. Balagezyan, and K. A. Karapetyan. 1965. Influence of the fruits of apple trees on the physiological activity of the leaves. Soviet Plant Physiol. 12:265-269.

Kidd, F., C. West, and G. E. Briggs. 1921. A quantitative analysis of the growth of Helianthus annuus. Part I. The respiration of the plant and its parts throughout the life cycle. Proc. Roy. Soc. London. Ser. B. 92:368-384.

Kiesselbach, T. A. 1948. Endosperm type as a physiological factor in corn yield. J. Amer. Soc. Agron. 40:216-236.

King, R. W., and L. T. Evans. 1967. Photosynthesis in artificial communities of wheat, lucerne, and subterranean clover plants. Aust. J. Biol. Sci. 20:623-635.

King, R. W., I. F. Wardlaw, and L. T. Evans. 1967. Effect of assimilate utilization on photosynthetic rate in wheat. Planta 77:261-276.

Kortschak, H. P., Constance E. Hartt, and G. O. Burr. 1965. Carbon dioxide fixation in sugarcane leaves. Plant Physiol. 40:209-213.

Kurssanov, A. L. 1933. Über den Einfluss der Kohlenhydrate auf den Tagesverlauf der Photosynthese. Planta 20:535-548.

Kurssanov, A. L. 1963. Metabolism and the transport of organic substance in the phloem. Advance Bot. Res. 1:209-278.

Ludwig, L. J., T. Saeki, and L. T. Evans. 1965. Photosynthesis in artificial communities of cotton plants in relation to leaf area. I. Experiments with progressive defoliation of mature plants. Aust. J. Biol. Sci. 18:1103-1118.

Lupton, F. G. H. 1966. Translocation of photosynthetic assimilates in wheat. Ann. Appl. Biol. 57:355-364.

Maggs, D. H. 1963. The reduction in growth brought about by fruiting. J. Hort. Sci. 38:119-128.

Maggs, D. H. 1964. Growth rates in relation to assimilate supply and demand. I. Leaves and roots as limiting regions. J. Exp. Bot. 15:574-583.

Maggs, D. H. 1965. Growth rates in relation to assimilate supply and demand. II. The effect of particular leaves and growing regions in determining the dry matter distribution in young apple trees. J. Exp. Bot. 16:387-404.

Mangelsdorf, P. C. 1958. Reconstructing the ancestor of corn. Proc. Amer. Philos. Soc. 102. No. 5.

Mansfield, T. A. 1968. Carbon dioxide compensation points in maize and Pelargonium. Physiol. Plant. 21:1159-1162.

McAlister, E. D., and J. Myers. 1940. The time course of photosynthesis and fluorescence observed simultaneously. Smithson. Misc. Coll. 99:6-26.

Meidner, H. 1962. The minimum intercellular-space CO_2-concentration (Γ) of maize leaves and its influence on stomatal movements. J. Exp. Bot. 13:284-293.

Moss, D. N. 1962a. The limiting carbon dioxide concentration for photosynthesis. Nature 193:587.

Moss, D. N. 1962b. Photosynthesis and barrenness. Crop Sci. 2:366-367.

Moss, D. N. 1966. Respiration of leaves in light and darkness. Crop Sci. 6:351-354.

Moss, D. N. 1968. Photorespiration and glycolate metabolism in tobacco leaves. Crop Sci. 8:71-76.

Moss, D. N., R. B. Musgrave, and E. R. Lemon. 1961. Photosynthesis under field conditions: II. Some effects of light, carbon dioxide, temperature, and soil moisture on photosynthesis, respiration, and transpiration of corn. Crop Sci. 1:83-87.

Mothes, K., L. Engelbrecht, und O. Kulajewa. 1959. Über die Wirkung des Kinetins auf Stickstoffverteilung und Eiweissynthese in isolierten Blättern. Flora 147:445-464.

Murata, Y., and J. Iyama. 1963. Studies on the photosynthesis of forage crops. II. Influence of air-temperature upon the photosynthesis of some forage and grain crops. Proc. Crop Sci. Soc. Japan 31:315-322.

Neales, T. F., and L. D. Incoll. 1968. The control of leaf photosynthesis rate by the level of assimilate concentration in the leaf: A review of the hypothesis. Bot. Rev. 34:107-125.

Nichiporovich, A. A. 1956. Photosynthesis and the theory of obtaining high crop yields. 15th Timiryazev lecture. USSR Acad. Sci., Moscow. 94 p. (Engl. Transl.: Dept. Sci. Industr. Res. Gt. Brit. 1959).

Nichiporovich, A. A., and V. Malofeyev. 1965. Principles of the formation of highly productive photosynthesizing systems. Soviet Plant Physiol. 12:1-8.

Nösberger, J., and E. C. Humphries. 1965. The influence of removing tubers on dry matter production and net assimilation rate of potato plants. Ann. Bot. N.S. 29:579-588.

Ozbun, J. L., R. J. Volk, and W. A. Jackson. 1964. Effects of light and darkness on gaseous exchange of bean plants. Plant Physiol. 39:523-527.

Poskuta, J. 1968. Photosynthesis, photorespiration and respiration of detached spruce twigs as influenced by oxygen concentration and light intensity. Physiol. Plant. 21:1129-1136.

Poskuta, J., C. D. Nelson, and G. Krotkov. 1967. Effects of metabolic inhibitors on the rates of CO_2 evolution in light and in darkness by detached spruce twigs, wheat and soybean leaves. Plant Physiol. 42:1187-1190.

Quinlan, J: D., and G. R. Sagar. 1962. An autoradiographic study of the movement of ^{14}C-labelled assimilates in the developing wheat plant. Weed Res. 2:264-273.

Rabinowitch, E. I. 1945. Photosynthesis and related processes. I. Interscience Publ., New York. 602 p.

Rhoades, N. M., and A. Carvalho. 1944. The function and structure of the parenchyma sheath plastids of the maize leaf. Bull. Torrey Bot. Club 71:335-346.

Sandfaer, J., J. H. Jørgensen, and V. Haahr. 1965. The effect of nitrogen fertilization on old and new barley varieties. Roy. Vet. Agr. Coll. Yearbook 1965: 153-180.

Schumacher, W. 1967. Die Fernleitung der Stoffe im Pflanzenkörper. In W. Ruhland (ed.) Handb.d.Pflanzenphysiol. XIII:61-177.

Schwanitz, F. 1960. Das Ertragsproblem in entwicklungsphysiologischer Sicht. Züchter 30:45-56.

Schwanitz, F. 1967. Die Evolution der Kulturpflanzen. BLV, München, Basel, Wien. 463 p.

Sengbusch, R. von. 1956. Untersuchungen über die Ursachen der Leistungen unserer Nahrungskulturpflanzen. Jb. Max-Planck-Ges. 200-209.

Seth, A. K., and P. F. Wareing. 1967. Hormone directed transport of metabolites and its possible role in plant senescence. J. Exp. Bot. 18:65-77.

Shibles, R. M., and C. R. Weber. 1965. Leaf area, solar radiation interception and dry matter production by soybeans. Crop Sci. 5:575-577.

Shiroya, T., G. R. Lister, C. D. Nelson, and G. Krotkov. 1961. Translocation of C^{14} in tobacco, at different stages of development following assimilation of $C^{14}O_2$ by a single leaf. Can. J. Bot. 39:855-864.

Slack, C. R., and M. D. Hatch. 1967. Comparative studies on the activity of carboxylases and other enzymes in relation to the new pathway of photosynthetic carbon dioxide fixation in tropical grasses. Biochem. J. 103:660-665.

Stoy, V. 1963. The translocation of the C^{14}-labelled photosynthetic products from the leaf to the ear in wheat. Physiol. Plant. 16:851-866.

Stoy, V. 1965. Photosynthesis, respiration, and carbohydrate accumulation in spring wheat in relation to yield. Physiol. Plant. Suppl. IV:1-125.

Stoy, V. 1966. Photosynthetic production after ear emergence as yield-limiting factor in the culture of cereals. Acta Agr. Scand. Suppl. 16:178-182.

Sweet, G. B., and P. F. Wareing. 1966. Role of plant growth in regulating photosynthesis. Nature 210:77-79.

Thrower, Stella L. 1962. Translocation of labelled assimilates in soybean. II. The pattern of translocation in intact and defoliated plants. Aust. J. Biol. Sci. 15:629-649.

Tregunna, B. 1966. Flavin mononucleotide control of glycolic acid oxidase and photorespiration in corn leaves. Science 151:1239-1241.

Tregunna, G., G. Krotkov, and C. D. Nelson. 1961. Evolution of carbon dioxide by tobacco leaves during the dark period following illumination with light of different intensities. Can. J. Bot. 39:1045-1056.

Tregunna, B., G. Krotkov, and C. D. Nelson. 1964. Further evidence on the effects of light on respiration during photosynthesis. Plant Physiol. 42:989-997.

Tregunna, B., G. Krotkov, and C. D. Nelson. 1966. Effect of oxygen on the rate of photorespiration in detached tobacco leaves. Physiol. Plant. 19:723-733.

Treharne, K. J., and J. L. Stoddart. 1968. Effects of gibberellin on photosynthesis in red clover (Trifolium pratense L.). Nature 220:457-458.

Turner, Wendy B., and R. G. S. Bidwell. 1965. Rates of photosynthesis in attached and detached bean leaves, and the effect of spraying with indoleacetic acid solution. Plant Physiol. 40:446-451.

Turner, J. S., and Brittain, E. G. 1962. Oxygen as a factor in photosynthesis. Biol. Rev. 37:130-170.

Verhagen, A. M. W., J. H. Wilson, and E. J. Britten. 1963. Plant production in relation to foliage illumination. Ann. Bot. N. S. 27:627-640.

Wang, T. D. and J. Wei. 1964. The CO_2 assimilation rate of plant communities as a function of leaf area index. Acta Bot. Sinica 12:154-158.

Warburg, O. 1920. Über die Geschwindigkeit der photochemischen Kohlensäurezersetzung in lebenden Zellen. II. Biochem. Z. 103:188-217.

Wardlaw, I. F. 1965. The velocity and pattern of assimilate translocation in wheat plants during grain development. Aust. J. Biol. Sci. 18:269-281.

Wardlaw, I. F. 1967. The effect of water stress on translocation in relation to photosynthesis and growth. I. Effect during grain development in wheat. Aust. J. Biol. Sci. 20:25-39.

Wardlaw, I. F. 1968. The control and pattern of movement of carbohydrates in plants. Bot. Rev. 34:79-105.

Wareing, P. F., M. M. Khalifa, and K. J. Treharne. 1968. Rate-limiting processes in photosynthesis at saturating light intensities. Nature 220:453-457.

Watson, D. J. 1958. The dependence of net assimilation rate on leaf area index. Ann. Bot. N.S. 22:37-54.

Watson, D. J., Gillian N. Thorne, and S. A. W. French. 1963. Analysis of growth and yield of winter and spring wheats. Ann. Bot. N.S. 27:1-22.

Went, F. W. 1958. The physiology of photosynthesis in higher plants. Preslia 1:225-240.

Wilfong, R. T., R. H. Brown, and R. E. Blaser. 1967. Relationships between leaf area index and apparent photosynthesis in alfalfa (Medicago sativa L.) and Ladino clover (Trifolium repens L.). Crop Sci. 7:27-30.

Williams, R. D. 1964. Assimilation and translocation in perennial grasses. Ann. Bot. N.S. 28:419-426.

Williams, W. A., R. S. Loomis, and C. R. Lepley. 1965. Vegetative growth of corn as affected by population density. II. Components of growth, net assimilation rate and leaf area index. Crop Sci. 5:215-219.

Zelitch, I. 1958. The role of glycolic acid oxidase in the respiration of leaves. J. Biol. Chem. 233:1299-1303.

Zelitch, I. 1959. The relationship of glycolic acid to respiration and photosynthesis in tobacco leaves. J. Biol. Chem. 234:3077-3081.

Zelitch, I. 1966. Increased rate of net photosynthetic carbon dioxide uptake caused by the inhibition of glycolate oxidase. Plant Physiol. 41:1623-1631.

Zimmermann, M. H. 1960. Transport in the phloem. Ann. Rev. Plant. Physiol. 11:167-190.

9 ... DISCUSSION

DALE N. MOSS

University of Minnesota
St. Paul, Minnesota

For a long time I have admired Dr. Stoy's scholarly and thorough work. His presentation this morning has done nothing to detract from that esteem. In the time allotted to me I would like to enlarge on three points which he has discussed in his paper. First, let us consider the topic of chloroplast arrangement in low compensation and high photosynthetic efficiency species. Some years ago Paul Rasmussen and I were interested in where, within leaves, CO_2 was being fixed and how the pattern of fixation was affected by internal shading, stomatal arrangement, etc. We fed illuminated leaves a short burst of $^{14}CO_2$, quickly froze the tissue in isopentane cooled in liquid N, freeze-dried the tissue, and determined where the $^{14}CO_2$ was located, which, presumably, would still be in the cells where it was originally fixed. To our surprise we found that, in contrast to the widespread fixation in all green cells in sugar beet (Beta vulgaris L.) (a high CO_2 compensation species), corn (Zea mays L.) (a low compensator) fixed its CO_2 in cells surrounding the vascular bundles. (Unknown to us, a somewhat similar experiment was done with corn and barley (Hordeum vulgare L.) by N. A. Pristupa in Moscow, Fiziologiya Rastenii 11:38-42, 1964). We now know that these bundle-sheath cells contain specialized chloroplasts which differ markedly in ultrastructure from chloroplasts in mesophyll cells. These can be separated from other mesophyll chloroplasts by density gradient centrifugation and we are studying their physiology.

This fixation pattern raises some most interesting questions. Why do corn bundle sheath cells fix most of the CO_2 during photosynthesis to the practical exclusion of other green mesophyll cells? Does the peculiar form of these bundle sheath chloroplasts have special meaning in terms of C-4 pathway of photosynthesis? If so does the Calvin cycle operate in the "normal" appearing chloroplasts of other mesophyll cells?

Such questions have special implications in terms of the second point I would like to consider, the inheritance of the efficient "corn-type" photosynthesis. All evidence to date indicates that CO_2 compensation concentrations are either less than 10 ppm or greater than 40 ppm. If both Calvin and C-4 pathways should be found in corn this would mean that all the cells in a corn plant, and presumably, then, other plants as well, had the genetic potential for either system. Something about the environment of the corn bundle sheath, however, might dictate that the C-4 pathway predominates in those cells. If low compensation points were the result, through affinity of enzymes for CO_2, of the presence of a C-4 pathway both Calvin and C-4 pathways could be present but the CO_2 compensation be controlled by C-4 enzymes.

The mode of inheritance of efficient photosynthesis is not known. Crosses between high and low compensation species and obtaining segregating populations would permit us to determine whether leaf anatomy, photorespiration, carbon pathway, etc., were all required for high rates of CO_2 fixation or just which factors were the essential ones for efficient photosynthesis. Such crosses have never been made because high and low compensation has not been known in closely related species. In our laboratory we have classified several hundred species for compensation concentration, and in most cases, the taxonomic classification accurately predicts which photosynthetic system a plant will have. We have found four genera, however, which contain both high and low compensation species. We are attempting interspecific crosses between high and low compensating species to study the control mechanisms for these many interesting and correlated traits.

Finally to the subject of breeding plants for photosynthetic efficiency—You cannot look at a plant and tell the kind of photosynthetic mechanism it has and to measure CO_2 uptake or CO_2 compensations take much too much time to be practical as breeding tools. We have been seeking ways to rapidly screen individual plants for photosynthetic efficiency and we now have a method which is reliable and rapid and may be of interest to you. In our system we take advantage of the fact that plants which have the efficient corn-type photosynthesis are able to grow quite well in an atmosphere so deficient in CO_2 that the nonefficient plant is below its compensation concentration. Thus, by growing together in a closed system, our test population to be screened and some low compensating plants such as corn or sorghum (Sorghum vulgare Pers.), the efficient plants keep the CO_2 concentration below the compensation of inefficient plants. They survive on the CO_2 being continually respired by the nonefficient plants. The nonefficient plants rapidly die. There is opportunity to spread the difference between efficient and nonefficient plants to very wide margins by increasing the O_2 concentration and air temperature. If there were any efficient plants in our test population they would survive and grow as does the corn. This system is working very well for us and permits us to actively proceed with a breeding program to introduce high photosynthetic efficiency into nonefficient small grains.

If we can change the photosynthetic capacity of leaf tissue can we change the capacity to produce grain? I do not know of any example of yield differences among varieties or lines within a single species that can be attributed directly to differences in photosynthetic capacity. On the other hand, there is ample evidence that changing the photosynthetic rate does markedly alter yield. Consider, for example, the advantage of CO_2 fertilization in glasshouses or the many experiments showing yield reductions due to shading. Would within-species material, differing in photosynthetic capacity, allow us to better evaluate the role of translocation, strength of sinks, or location with respect to sinks? These and other questions we hope to answer through genetic manipulation of some of these most interesting plant traits.

9...DISCUSSION

GILLIAN N. THORNE

Rothamsted Experimental Station
Harpenden, Herts, England

It seems an appropriate place in this symposium to summarize the physiological characters of a high yielding crop, i.e., one that produces a large yield of the economically useful part rather than of total dry matter, and to discuss which physiological characters limit yields of particular crops.

Firstly, there must be plenty of leaf surface arranged to use the available radiation efficiently (see R.S. Loomis, Chapter 3, this book). The leaf area at a particular time may be especially important. For example, in European wheat (Triticum aestivum L.) and barley (Hordeum vulgare L.) crops, grain yield is closely correlated with the leaf area after flowering but not with that earlier, because almost all the carbohydrate in the grain is produced by photosynthesis after flowering (Thorne, 1966). Secondly, the net CO_2 uptake by the crop should be fast, which requires fast photosynthesis or slow respiration.

To accommodate the carbohydrate produced by the efficient leaves the crop must have an efficient sink. Sink capacity may affect the distribution of carbohydrate within the plant even when it has no or little effect on photosynthesis of the leaves, as often occurs in barley and wheat (Nösberger and Thorne, 1965; Thorne, Ford, and Watson, 1968). Although it can be shown experimentally that yield depends on adequate production of carbohydrate and an adequate sink to accept this, it is often difficult to decide whether supply or sink capacity is restricting yield in any particular situation. Both seem to control yield of wheat and barley in Britain. Evidence comes from a study of the apparent efficiency in grain production of the leaf area present after flowering (Welbank, Witts, and Thorne, 1968). The efficiency can be expressed as the ratio of grain yield to the leaf area duration between flowering and maturity. In controlled environments and in the field this ratio increases with increase in radiation, presumably because the leaves photosynthesize faster. It also increases with increase in temperature, although photosynthesis and total dry weight are not increased, probably because the grains grow faster and use more carbohydrate; i.e., they are a more efficient sink.

These suggestions about the physiological control of yield of wheat and barley apply to European varieties; the semidwarf varieties derived from the Japanese variety Norin 10 behave slightly differently. When grown in Britain, they have grain yields similar to European varieties but only about half the leaf area after flowering. We do not know whether the apparently greater efficiency of the leaves is caused by faster photosynthesis, less respiration, or more efficient translocation (Thorne, Welbank, and Blackwood, 1969).

LITERATURE CITED

Nösberger, J., and G. N. Thorne. 1965. The effect of removing florets or shading the ear of barley on production and distribution of dry matter. Ann. Bot. N.S. 29:635-44.

Thorne, G. N. 1966. Physiological aspects of grain yield in cereals, p. 88-105. In F. L. Milthorpe and J. D. Ivins (ed.). The growth of cereals and grasses. Butterworths, London.

Thorne, G. N., M. A. Ford, and D. J. Watson. 1968. Growth, development, and yield of spring wheat in artificial climates. Ann. Bot. N. S. 32:425-426.

Thorne, G. N., P. J. Welbank and G. C. Blackwood. 1969. Growth and yield of six short varieties of spring wheat derived from Norin 10 and of two European varieties. Ann. Appl. Biol. 63:241-251.

Welbank, P. J., K. J. Witts, and G. N. Thorne. 1968. Effect of radiation and temperature on efficiency of cereal leaves during grain growth. Ann. Bot. N.S. 32:79-95.

10

Mechanisms of Carbon Fixation and Associated Physiological Responses

ISRAEL ZELITCH

The Connecticut Agricultural Experiment Station
New Haven, Connecticut

I. CONTROL OF STOMATAL APERTURE BY SPECIFIC INHIBITION OF GUARD CELL ACTIVITY

A. Control of Stomatal Opening in Light

Recent work in this laboratory has been directed towards increasing net photosynthesis or decreasing the transpiration rate in higher plants by exercising biochemical control over these processes. In these experiments, the fact that both photosynthesis and transpiration involve diffusion processes that might be regulated by varying appropriate diffusive resistances has been exploited (Gaastra, 1959; Zelitch and Waggoner, 1962a). Since in most instances the pathway of diffusion of water vapor in transpiration is shorter than that of CO_2 uptake in photosynthesis, and both gases must pass through the stomata, it was predicted that closing the stomata in a specific manner would diminish transpiration more than net photosynthesis.

To detect effective biochemical inhibitors of stomatal opening, a leaf disk assay was developed (Zelitch, 1961), and criteria were described for judging whether an inhibitor acts primarily on guard cells (Zelitch and Waggoner, 1962a; Zelitch, 1965a; Waggoner and Zelitch, 1965). Thus we found that the effects of spraying a 10^{-4} M solution of phenylmercuric acetate on excised tobacco leaves (Nicotiana tabacum L.) fit these criteria since stomatal widths were decreased and transpiration was inhibited more then photosynthesis (Zelitch and Waggoner, 1962a). When sprayed on leaves, this inhibitor closed stomata and increased efficiency of water use in tobacco plants in a greenhouse (Zelitch & Waggoner, 1962b), sunflower (Helianthus annuus L.) outdoors (Shimshi, 1963a), maize (Zea mays L.) in a chamber (Shimshi,

207

1963b), cotton (Gossypium hirsutum L.) in a greenhouse (Slatyer and Bierhuizen, 1964), and on grass in a growth room and outdoors (Davenport, 1967). However, if an inhibitor of stomatal opening also greatly affected photosynthesis in the mesophyll tissue, then net photosynthesis would likely be decreased as much as transpiration, and probably even more than transpiration. Thus a comparison of the effect of a stomatal inhibitor on these two processes provides a simple test of whether or not the inhibitor acts primarily on the guard cells to cause an increased stomatal diffusive resistance.

Several workers in England have described experiments which led them to conclude that the CO_2 concentration inside leaves in the light largely controls stomatal opening (Meidner and Mansfield, 1965). They suggested that stomata open in the light because CO_2 concentration inside the leaf is decreased by photosynthesis, and that stomata close when the CO_2 concentration increases, as in darkness. Slatyer (1967) in his book on plant-water relations also states that the primary factor controlling stomatal apertures appears to be the CO_2 concentration in the intercellular space.

There is ample experimental evidence which is not in favor of this hypothesis (Zelitch, 1965a, 1967, 1969). An additional troublesome problem would arise if it were in fact necessary to close stomata by inhibiting photosyntheses or increasing respiration in order to raise the internal CO_2 concentration. Raising the CO_2 concentration in the intercellular space would diminish the CO_2 concentration gradient between the leaf interior and the ambient atmosphere, and this would likely decrease net photosynthesis more then transpiration. However, as already indicated, it is possible to close stomata by spraying an inhibitor on leaf surfaces and to decrease net photosynthesis proportionately less then transpiration. This finding raises further doubts about the significance of the intercellular space CO_2 concentration in controlling stomatal apertures in normal air.

B. Effect of Inhibitors of Stomatal Opening on the CO_2 Compensation Point

Several investigators have recently carried out experiments on stomatal control by inhibitors supplied to excised leaves through the petiole (Heath, Mansfield, and Meidner, 1965; Meidner and Mansfield 1966; Mansfield, 1967; Allaway and Mansfield, 1967). They observed that such treatments closed the stomata, but concluded that this occurred largely because photosynthesis in the mesophyll was inhibited. This was inferred because in a closed system the CO_2 compensation point, the steady-state concentration at which there is no net photosynthesis or net respiration, was increased by the inhibitors. However, when such inhibitors are supplied to the epidermis of tobacco leaves where it is more likely to affect primarily the guard cells, rather than through the petiole, where it will first reach the mesophyll, stomata closed with no apparent change in the CO_2 compensation point.

Thus Fig. 10-1 shows the results of epidermal treatment when half of a tobacco leaf was sprayed on both surfaces with 5×10^{-5} M phenyl-

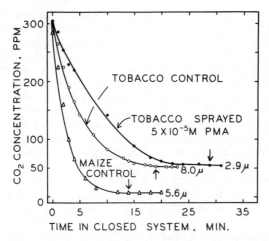

Fig. 10-1—Rate of CO_2 depletion in a closed system containing tobacco with open or closed stomata or maize leaf disks in light. Disks were cut (5 disks, 3.2-cm diameter) from a Havana Seed tobacco leaf that had been sprayed 24 hr earlier in one portion with 5×10^{-5} M phenylmercuric acetate in 0.02% Triton X-100 and in another part with Triton. After the disks were at least one hr in air in light while floated upside down on water at about 25C, the CO_2 concentration was measured in a closed system with an infrared CO_2 analyzer. Arrows indicate the CO_2 compensation point. Chamber volume, 0.95 liter. Gas flow, 8.5 liters/min. Light intensity from tungesten lamps, 2,000 ft-c. Temperature, 30 C. At the end of the experiments, mean stomatal widths were determined from silicone rubber impressions (Zelitch, 1961).

mercuric acetate in 0.02% Triton X-100, and the other half was sprayed only with Triton. On the next day 3.2-cm diameter disks were cut from each side of the leaf and the disks were floated on water in the light for at least 1 hour in air with the lower epidermis up. The disks were then transferred to a closed chamber, and the CO_2 concentration in the system was measured continuously. Initially net photosynthesis in the control disks was 10.5, and in the disks sprayed with inhibitor it was 7.7 mg CO_2 dm^{-2} hr^{-1}. The disks sprayed with inhibitor required a longer time to reach the compensation point from the initial 300 ppm of CO_2, as expected, but the steady-state concentration was about the same in each, 54 ppm in the control and 55 ppm in the disks treated with inhibitor. The stomatal widths at the end of the experiment were much narrower in disks sprayed earlier with phenylmercuric acetate. An additional control showed that untreated disks of hybrid maize had an initial rate of photosynthesis of 17.4 mg CO_2 dm^{-2} hr^{-1}, 66% greater than the tobacco control, and a compensation point of only 7 ppm of CO_2 (Moss, 1962; Meidner, 1962).

Bravdo (1968) has described a model, in which stomata play the role of variable resistances to diffusion, that predicts the manner in which the CO_2 concentration should increase from near zero CO_2 to the compensation point if gross photosynthesis, respiration, and the diffusive resistance through the stomata remain constant when leaves are placed in a closed system in the light. Figure 10-2 shows the manner in which tobacco leaf disks with open and closed stomata increase the CO_2 concentration from near zero to the compensation point. The control disks in this experiment also reached the CO_2 compensation point more quickly and the stomata were more widely open, although the compensation point of 48 ppm was similar to that of leaf disks sprayed earlier with phenylmercuris acetate to close the stomata which was 50 ppm. These data give straight lines with different slopes when plotted by the method of Equation IV in Bravdo (1968), and this further indicates that the rates of CO_2 evolution, stomatal diffusive resistance, and the physical and chemical resistances to CO_2 fixation were constant as the CO_2 concentration increased to the CO_2 compensation point. The stomata were thus functioning as expected as variable resistances to diffusion and the treatment with phenylmercuric acetate did not greatly effect gross photosynthesis or the CO_2 concentration in the leaf interior while the stomata were closed.

Similar results on the closing of stomata without affecting the CO_2 compensation point have also been obtained by applying other inhibitors, such as α-hydroxysulfonates, at appropriate concentrations to the leaf surface. Thus increasing the CO_2 concentration in the intercellular space, as by supplying inhibitors through the petiole, is not a necessary condition for stomatal closure. Finding inhibitors that function still more exclusively on guard cell metabolism should therefore create an increased stomatal resistance and permit increased water use efficiency and exert a beneficial influence on the hydrologic cycle in a more effective manner than has already been accomplished (Waggoner and Bravdo, 1967; Turner and Waggoner, 1968).

II. DIFFERENCES IN PHOTOSYNTHETIC EFFICIENCY AMONG SPECIES

A. The Carboxylation Reactions

As is shown in Fig. 10-3, the rate of net photosynthesis per unit leaf area at high light intensities in normal air is at least twice as great in certain species including maize, sugarcane (Saccharum officinarum L.) and sorghum (Sorghum vulgare Pers.) as in most species such as tobacco and sugar beet (Beta vulgaris L.) (Hesketh, 1963; Hesketh and Moss, 1963). At lower light intensities, the differences in photosynthetic efficiency between such species becomes smaller (Waggoner, Moss, and Hesketh, 1963). It therefore seems important to determine the factors responsible for the increased photosynthetic efficiency shown by these tropical grasses with the view to altering the other species so as to make them equally productive photosynthetically. An obvious consideration is whether the more efficient species fix CO_2 by a biochemically more effective enzymatic carboxylation reaction.

In spite of the considerable work in this area, it is not yet known how much CO_2 is fixed by one or another of the carboxylation reactions that are demonstrably present in the chloroplasts of leaves. The brilliant contributions of Calvin, Benson, and their colleagues elucidated the

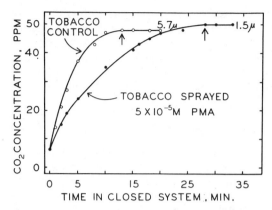

Fig. 10-2—Rate of CO_2 concentration increase in a closed illuminated chamber containing tobacco with open or closed stomata. Conditions of the experiment were the same as in Fig. 10-1. The CO_2 concentration was depleted to 7 ppm of CO_2 by means of a CO_2 absorbent, and the absorbent was then removed from the system at zero time.

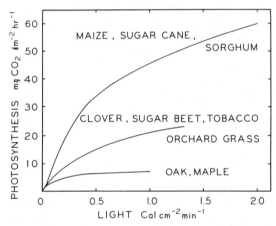

Fig. 10-3—Diagrammatic representation of the effect of light intensity on net photosynthesis at 30C and 300 ppm CO_2 in air (adapted from Hesketh (1963) and Hesketh and Moss (1963)).

photosynthetic carbon reduction cycle. The main features of this scheme are the carboxylation of ribulose 1,5-diphosphate to produce 3-phospho-D-glyceric acid as the first stable intermediate. The phosphoglyceric acid is then reduced to triose phosphate, and the CO_2 acceptor is regenerated in a cyclic process. In kinetic photosynthetic experiments with barley leaves (Hordeum vulgare L.) in which $^{14}CO_2$ was supplied during progressively shorter periods, phosphoglyceric acid was the first detectable radioactive product and it contained most of its ^{14}C in the carboxyl-carbon atom as was demanded by the functioning of the ribulose diphosphate carboxylase reaction (Bassham, 1964).

However, as was pointed out by Stiller (1962), other carboxylation reactions could fix more carbon and not be,detected in kinetic experiments if the early intermediates are unstable during isolation or are undetectable in small amounts. Accordingly, unless it is certain that there is only one carboxylation reaction, it is unsafe on the basis of such kinetic experiments to conclude that the Calvin-Benson cycle accounts for most of the CO_2 fixed by a tissue.

Another troublesome aspect of the Calvin-Benson cycle is that the CO_2 concentration at which the isolated carboxylating enzyme or isolated chloroplasts are half-saturated, (K_m), is considerably higher (Racket, 1957; Jensen and Bassham, 1966) than the 300 ppm (or about 7×10^{-6} $\underline{M}$ free CO_2 in solution) which provides half the maximal rate of photosynthesis in intact plant tissues (Hesketh, 1963). The phosphoenolpyruvate carboxylase reaction is another CO_2-fixing reaction known to occur in higher plants (Bandurski, 1955), and this enzyme is half-saturated at only about 440 ppm CO_2 (Walker, 1962). In this reaction, CO_2 and phosphoenolpyruvate react to produce oxaloacetate as the first product, which may be rapidly converted into malic or aspartic acid. In kinetic $^{14}CO_2$ experiments with one of the efficient species, sugarcane, the first detectable radioactive products were malic and aspartic acids, which were labeled with ^{14}C it was shown that oxaloacetate also became labeled before phosphoglyceric acid in maize and sorghum as well as in sugarcane leaves (Slack and Hatch, 1967). These results still do not tell us how much carbon is fixed by the phosphoenolpyruvate carboxylase reaction any more than do the kinetic experiments that demonstrated phosphoglyceric acid to be the "first product." They do, however, provide convincing evidence that multiple carboxylation reactions occur in photosynthetic tissues.

When $^{14}CO_2$ of known specific activity at low concentrations was supplied to tobacco leaf tissue in the light, glycolic acid was produced with a specific activity similar to that of the added $^{14}CO_2$ and in excess of the specific activity of the carboxyl-carbon atom of phosphoglyceric acid (Zelitch, 1965b). This suggested that glycolic acid was synthesized by still another unknown carboxylation reaction. Recently it was shown, in kinetic $^{14}CO_2$ experiments carried out on photosynthetic bacteria, that glycolate is labeled with ^{14}C before the phosphate esters, again suggesting that glycolate is the "first product" of photosynthesis in this organism (Anderson and Fuller, 1967).

Doubt is cast on whether the carboxylation reaction need be limiting photosynthetic efficiency since, at high light intensities and saturating CO_2 concentrations, there is little difference in net photosynthesis between leaves of the highly efficient species, such as maize and sugarcane, and those of the less efficient species such as tobacco (Zelitch, 1967b; Goldsworthy, 1968). Moreover, Goldsworthy (1968) showed that if net photosynthesis was measured at low concentrations of oxygen in the ambient atmosphere, there was little difference in the overall K_m, about 300 ppm, between these species. I have confirmed his findings (Fig. 10-4),and will discuss these experiments in more detail in a later section.

Thus although multiple carboxylation reactions probably occur in each tissue, it is still uncertain how much each contributes to the total

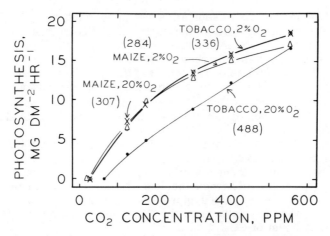

Fig. 10-4—Effect of oxygen concentration on the atmosphere on net photosynthesis in tobacco and maize at various CO_2 concentrations. Leaf disks were floated upside down on water in light for a preliminary period and measurements were made in the system used in Fig. 10-1. Net photosynthesis was measured at about 30C and 3,000 ft-c. After measurements were made at 1,800 ppm, the CO_2 concentration was lowered with an absorbent to 600 ppm. After several measurements near 600 ppm, the leaf disks were allowed to deplete the CO_2 to the CO_2 compensation point. The system was then flushed with nitrogen (final concentration of oxygen eas less than 2%), and the measurements were then repeated. Each point on the curves is the mean of three experiments. The overall K_m is given in parentheses and was determined graphically. (●), tobacco in 20% oxygen; (o), tobacco in 2% oxygen; (x) maize in 20% oxygen; (Δ) maize in 2% oxygen. Only the data from 550 ppm to the compensation point are shown.

CO_2 fixation. Nevertheless, a lower rate of net photosynthesis (compared with maize) in a species does not seem to be attributable to severe limitations in the biochemical mechanism of carboxylation or in the photochemistry. Hence we must seek other causes for these large differences in net photosynthesis between species in normal air. As can be shown in several independent ways, these differences seem to be related to the rate of CO_2 evolution in the light by the process known as photorespiration. Therefore this process must be considered as an important factor in causing a diminished net photosynthesis.

B. Photorespiration and its Measurement

Since CO_2 uptake in bright light in air exceeds dark respiration by 10- to 20-fold, even if photorespiration contributes additional CO_2 inside a leaf, evaluating the gross CO_2 evolution in the light will present difficulties. Any method of measurement of photorespiration will underestimate the CO_2 evolution because some fraction of the respired CO_2 that is evolved will be refixed by the more active photosynthetic system.

Decker (1955, 1959a) observed that, when tobacco leaves were placed in darkness after a period in the light, there was a burst of CO_2

evolution before the dark respiration resumed its lower steady rate. He deduced that the post-illumination burst of CO_2 release is derived from a substrate that was synthesized exclusively in the light, and that, when photosynthesis was interrupted, the substrate continued to be oxidized until its supply was exhausted. In Mimulus, he found that photorespiration was about 3.3 times greater than dark respiration (Decker, 1959b). Soybean leaves (Glycine max L.) also exhibited such a post-illumination burst, but maize leaves did not (Forrester, Krotkov, and Nelson, 1966a, 1966b).

With use of this assay in tobacco, Decker (1959a) found that photorespiration had the following characteristics: it increased with increasing light intensity in a manner similar in proportion to net photosynthesis; it increased 3.4-fold when the leaf temperature was raised from 17.5C to 33.5C, while net photosynthesis changed little; photorespiration differed little when leaves were at the CO_2 compensation point (45 ppm) or in air at 300 ppm of CO_2.

A different assay of photorespiration was developed (Decker, 1957) based on extrapolation of the curve for net photosynthesis at varying CO_2 concentrations from the CO_2 compensation point to "zero" CO_2 concentration. The intercept was taken to be the photorespiration, and in tobacco as well as in eight other species photorespiration exceeded the dark respiration. Recently it has been shown algebraically (Bravdo, 1968; Samish and Koller, 1968) that the intercept is a function of stomatal diffusive resistance and internal diffusive resistances as well as of photorespiration, and thus evaluation of photorespiration by the extrapolation method clearly underestimates the gross CO_2 evolution by an amount that depends on the size of the other resistances.

Photorespiration has also been estimated by observing the rate of dilution by normal respiratory CO_2 of $^{14}CO_2$ of known specific activity added to the atmosphere surrounding leaves in light in a closed system (Krotkov, Runeckles, and Thimann, 1958). In spite of the diffusive resistances that would tend to slow the rate of dilution in light, in wheat leaves (Triticum sp.), photorespiration was still found to be twice the dark respiration.

In CO_2-free air in the light, the CO_2 flux would be reversed and CO_2 is then released from the leaf at a rate that is a function of the photorespiration as well as internal and stomatal diffusive resistances. This principle was utilized by El-Sharkawy and Hesketh (1965), who showed that CO_2 released in the light in cotton leaves exceeded dark respiration at 35C, while no CO_2 release was detected in the light in maize. By this method Moss (1966) also found CO_2 released in the light to be greater than dark respiration in five species but again none was released in maize. This technique was modified by first labeling tobacco leaf disks with $^{14}CO_2$, and then measuring the $^{14}CO_2$ released in the light in CO_2-free air (Goldsworthy, 1966). Again photorespiration was found to exceed dark respiration, and further modifications of this method that will be discussed later have provided additional evidence that photorespiration greatly exceeds dark respiration in tobacco leaves but not in maize (Zelitch, 1968).

Thus although all of the methods described undoubtedly underestimate photorespiration by differing amounts, all indicate that photorespiration exceeds dark respiration in many species, but not in maize.

C. The CO_2 Compensation Point

The steady-state CO_2 concentration found when a leaf is placed in light in a closed system is also well correlated inversely with differences in photosynthetic efficiency between species, and this is also likely related to differences in photorespiration. The magnitude of the CO_2 compensation point is determined by the product of the rate of CO_2 evolution inside the leaf times the "resistance" to fixation of CO_2 in the the chloroplasts (Bravdo, 1968; Samish and Koller, 1968). Thus a low compensation point could result from a low photorespiration or a low internal "resistance" to CO_2 fixation. The compensation point for maize is less than 10 ppm and for tobacco it is about 50 ppm of CO_2 at 25C, although it will be demonstrated later that the internal "resistance" is not greatly different in these species. Therefore these differences are largely related to differences in photorespiration.

It has long been known that oxygen in excess of 2% in the atmosphere surrounding a leaf decreases net photosynthesis in most species. Part of this effect results from an increase in photorespiration, as may be inferred from the increase in the CO_2 compensation point with increasing oxygen concentration in species like tobacco, wheat, and soybean (Forrester, Krotkov, and Nelson, 1966a; Downton and Tregunna, 1968). On the other hand, even 100% oxygen in the ambient atmosphere did not increase the low CO_2 compensation point in maize leaves (Forrester, Krotkov, and Nelson, 1966b).

In those species with a high CO_2 compensation point, the compensation point also doubles when leaf temperature is increased from 25C to 35C (Zelitch, 1967b). This indicates that photorespiration may even increase more rapidly than gross photosynthesis, and the increase in respiratory CO_2 probably accounts for the lack of increase in net photosynthesis in normal air in tobacco between about 25C and 35C (Decker, 1959a). In maize, net photosynthesis approximately doubles between 25C and 35C (Moss, 1963).

Thus a higher CO_2 compensation point in the less efficient photosynthetic species, and its increase with temperature and increasing outside oxygen concentration all point to an increased photorespiration as the cause of lowered net photosynthesis in species with a high CO_2 compensation point.

D. Net Photosynthesis in Atmospheres Low in Oxygen

If differences in photosynthetic efficiency among species is only little affected by differences in gross photosynthetic rates, but is decreased in the less efficient species because of photorespiration, net photosynthesis should be little different among these species at low oxygen concentrations. Moreover, if the biochemical carboxylation mechanism is not limiting the photosynthetic rate, the overall K_m for

CO_2 concentration in the atmosphere should be similar in such species if photorespiration is largely eliminated.

Goldsworthy (1968) measured net photosynthesis at various CO_2 concentrations at high light intensities in leaf disks of tobacco, maize, and sugarcane with nitrogen in the ambient atmosphere. He found the maximal rates of photosynthesis at saturating concentrations of CO_2 to be about the same in all three species as well as the overall K_m, 300 ppm CO_2. Thus he concluded that the greater photosynthetic efficiency of maize and sugarcane is not the result of a more effective carboxylation system, with a lower K_m in maize than in tobacco.

I have repeated and extended Goldsworthy's experiment (Fig. 10-4). Net photosynthesis was measured in large brightly illuminated leaf disks of tobacco and maize floating upside down on water in a closed system with either 20% oxygen or less than 2% oxygen in the ambient atmosphere. The CO_2 concentration was varied from 1,800 ppm to the CO_2 compensation point. At 1,800 ppm there was little difference in the rate of net photosynthesis between the species in 20% or 2% oxygen; they were all about 22 mg CO_2 dm^{-2} hr^{-1}. The overall K_m for maize in both atmospheres and for tobacco in 2% oxygen was about the same and close to 300 ppm of CO_2. The overall K_m for tobacco in air was considerably higher, 488 ppm of CO_2. In a companion experiment, stomatal opening was similar under these photosynthetic conditions in both species. Thus Goldsworthy's (1968) observations were confirmed. In addition, since net photosynthesis in tobacco with low oxygen outside is similar to that in maize at all concentrations of CO_2 (Fig. 10-4), differences in the internal diffusive resistances between these species cannot account for their differences in net photosynthesis in normal air.

Net photosynthesis in soybean leaves was inhibited 35% in air in comparison with an oxygen-free system, while in maize leaves it was not inhibited even in 50% oxygen (Forrester, Krotkov, and Nelson, 1966a, 1966b). Hesketh (1967) compared net photosynthesis in a number of species in air and in an oxygen-free atmosphere. There was no enhancement in an oxygen-free environment in maize and sorghum leaves, but a considerable enhancement occurred in cotton, tobacco, and bean. However, the enhancement did not increase net photosynthesis to the rates observed with maize, although no information was provided about limitations of stomatal diffusion or the hydration of the leaves in the bright light used in these experiments.

E. The Glycolate Oxidase Reaction as a Source of CO_2
in Photorespiration

The data presented already suggest that if one could diminish the photorespiration in species active in this process, one might obtain faster rates of net photosynthesis approaching those of maize. Previously I suggested (Zelitch, 1959, 1964) for several reasons that glycolate is a likely candidate for the primary substrate of photorespiratory CO_2. This metabolite is synthesized in leaves by an unknown mechanism exclusively in the light as an early product of photosynthesis (Zelitch, 1959; Tolbert, 1963). Since it is synthesized in tobacco from $^{14}CO_2$ with little dilution in specific activity, it must be produced rather directly from CO_2 (Zelitch, 1965b). It is readily synthesized at low CO_2 concentrations in the atmosphere in tobacco (from "zero" to 0.2% CO_2), but its synthesis is inhibited at CO_2 concentrations above 0.2% (Zelitch and Walker, 1964; Zelitch, 1965b). Oxygen is necessary in the atmosphere for rapid synthesis of glycolate (Tolbert, 1963; Zelitch and Walker, 1964), and oxygen is also utilized by an active flavoprotein enzyme, glycolate oxidase, in photosynthetic tissue. This enzyme catalyzes the following reaction in which glycolate is oxidized to CO_2 primarily from the carboxyl-carbon atom:

$$CH_2OH\text{-}\overset{*}{C}OO^- + O_2 \longrightarrow CHO\text{-}\overset{*}{C}OO^- + H_2O_2 \longrightarrow HCOO + \overset{*}{C}O_2 \; .$$

Glycolate   Glyoxylate   Formate

α-Hydroxysulfonate

The glycolate oxidase reaction is effectively inhibited by analogues of glycolate, the α-hydroxysulfonates (Zelitch, 1959, 1965b).

As discussed earlier, changes in the CO_2 compensation point and the post-illumination burst indicate that photorespiration increases greatly with increasing temperature. When glycolate-1-^{14}C was supplied to tobacco leaf disks, the release of $^{14}CO_2$ increased about three times faster at 35C compared with 25C than the gross photosynthesis. The relative increase in release of $^{14}CO_2$ was smaller when either glycolate-2-^{14}C or acetate-1-^{14}C were added to the leaf disks. However, in maize leaf disks such effects with glycolate-1-^{14}C could not be obtained. Thus the carboxyl-carbon atom of glycolate appeared as an important final substrate of photorespiration.

F. Increasing Net Photosynthesis by Inhibition of Glycolate Oxidation

If glycolate oxidation is ultimately the source of the CO_2 evolved in photorespiration, a specific inhibition of this reaction should reveal the magnitude of this process. The inhibition might also cause net photosynthesis to increase to values like those in maize. Experiments to test this hypothesis were carried out on tobacco leaf disks with an α-hydroxysulfonate as inhibitor. Between 25C and 30C net photosynthesis was not adversely affected, although glycolate accumulated rapidly, indicating that the glycolate oxidase reaction was being inhibited in vivo (Zelitch, 1965b). When the disks were warmed to 35C, however, the inhibitor made net photosynthesis about 3-fold greater (Zelitch, 1966). In similar experiments with maize, net photosynthesis was not increased by the inhibitor at either temperature. The results were thus consistent with the hypothesis that the CO_2 is evolved in the light in tobacco leaves as a result of glycolate oxidation, and this normally diminishes net photosynthesis in these species especially at higher temperatures when photorespiration accounts for a greater portion of gross photosynthesis.

The data suggested that the internal turnover of CO_2 evolved by photorespiration accounted for 60% of the gross photosynthesis at 35C and 25% of the gross CO_2 uptake at 25C. The data also permitted an estimate that at 25C in tobacco tissue the CO_2 evolved in the light was about 2.5 times the dark respiration, while at 35C the ratio of light to dark CO_2 evolution was about 6.7 (Table III in Zelitch, 1966).

III. THE RELATION BETWEEN PHOTORESPIRATION AND NET PHOTOSYNTHESIS

A. A Sensitive ^{14}C-Assay of Photorespiration

Because none of the methods of measuring photorespiration, except the post-illumination burst studied by Decker (1955, 1959b), showed such large excesses of photorespiration over dark respiration, I have investigated this process with a more sensitive assay (Zelitch, 1968). Since photorespiration is largely independent of CO_2 concentration up to 300 ppm (Decker, 1959a), I observed the release of $^{14}CO_2$ in CO_2-free air from leaf tissue that had previously fixed $^{14}CO_2$ in the light. Under such circumstances, the CO_2 flux is outward (El-Sharkawy and Hesketh, 1965; Moss, 1966; Goldsworthy, 1966), and the amount released will depend upon the rate of CO_2 evolved inside the leaf and the "resistance" to refixation of evolved CO_2 as well as the diffusive resistance from the intercellular space to the ambient atmosphere (Bravdo, 1968; Samish and Koller, 1968).

Thus in order to release more of the evolved CO_2 in the light and to permit less to be refixed, one should use higher temperatures, rapid flow rates of CO_2-free air over the leaf tissue, and insure that the stomatal pores are open. In the ^{14}C-assay of photorespiration, leaf disks were exposed to the light for 45 min, and were then allowed to fix a known quantity of $^{14}CO_2$ in a closed system at 30C to 35C. Then moistened CO_2-free air was passed rapidly over the leaf disks, and the $^{14}CO_2$ released was collected and its radioactivity determined. Leaf disks of a standard variety of tobacco, Havana Seed, and those of hybrid maize were compared in the assay, Fig. 10-5. In tobacco there was an approximately linear release of $^{14}CO_2$ at a rate that was 3 to 5 times greater than the rate of release in darkness. However, in maize, only 2% as

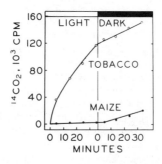

Fig. 10-5—Comparison of $^{14}CO_2$ released in the light and dark by tobacco and maize leaf disks in the ^{14}C-assay of photorespiration (from Zelitch, 1968).

much $^{14}CO_2$ was released in the light as from tobacco, although the dark respiration was about the same in these species. I have earlier indicated that it is unlikely that the carboxylation reaction or the photochemistry in tobacco operates at 2% of the rate of maize (Fig. 10-4). Thus I conclude that the difference in efficiency of net photosynthesis between such species is largely caused by the smaller photorespiration in maize, about 2% of that in tobacco.

B. Comparison of Turnover of CO_2 to the Quantity Released in CO_2-Free Air in the Light

These results suggested the desirability of decreasing the apparently wasteful photorespiration in order to obtain rates of net photosynthesis approaching that of maize. Experiments in this connection will be discussed in the last section. However, first a biochemical method will be described for evaluating the extent of internal refixation of CO_2 in the light in comparison with the amount released to the atmosphere during assays of photorespiration in CO_2-free air. Thus Lake (1967) and Begg and Jarvis (1968) have clearly recognized this problem and stated that light respiration was at least twice the dark respiration.

When an α-hydroxysulfonate was added to tobacco leaf disks in the photorespiration assay, under conditions that did not close the stomata, the amount of $^{14}CO_2$ released in the light was strongly inhibited (Fig. 10-6), but not the dark respiration, showing the respiratory CO_2 has different origins in light and darkness. If glycolate is the ultimate source of CO_2 evolved in photorespiration, and this evolution is blocked by the inhibitor, then the ^{14}C present in the glycolate accumulating should be at least equal to the decrease in the quantity of $^{14}CO_2$ released. However, if more glycolate-^{14}C accumulated than the decrease of $^{14}CO_2$ released from the tissue, it would indicate that part of the evolved $^{14}CO_2$ was refixed and only some fraction of the evolved $^{14}CO_2$ was normally released to the atmosphere. These assumptions therefore provide a basis for a quantitative evaluation of this fraction of the evolved $^{14}CO_2$ that is released, x (Zelitch, 1968).

The assumptions in this analysis are shown diagrammatically in

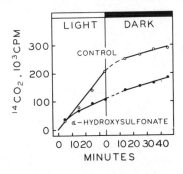

Fig. 10-6—$^{14}CO_2$ released by tobacco leaf disks in the presence of 10^{-2} $\underline{M}$ α-hydroxy-2-pyridinemethanesulfonic acid at 35C (from Zelitch, 1968).

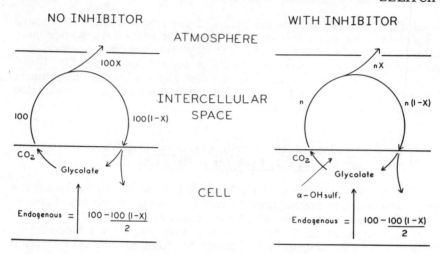

Fig. 10-7—Diagrammatic representation of $^{14}CO_2$ evolved into the intercellular space and the fraction released to the atmosphere in CO_2-free air.

Fig. 10-7. If 100 units of $^{14}CO_2$ were evolved to the intercellular space without inhibitor, and x is the fraction of the $^{14}CO_2$ that is released to the atmosphere, then 100 x would be the quantity released and 100 (1-x) the portion refixed. About 50% of the refixed CO_2 goes into glycolate (Zelitch, 1959, 1965b), and this is represented as 100 (1-x)/2. Since there is negligible accumulation of ^{14}C-glycolate without inhibitor, it is shown in Table 10-1 that the rate of change of ^{14}C-glycolate from endogenous carbon plus that from refixation of $^{14}C_2$ less the $^{14}CO_2$ evolved equals zero. With inhibitor (Fig. 10-7), since the inhibitor is used under conditions such that net photosynthesis is not adversely affected, the

Table 10-1—Method of calculating fraction $^{14}CO_2$ evolved in light that is released to the atmosphere and the fraction that is refixed in the leaf

Rate of change of ^{14}C-glycolate				
From endogenous carbon	From refixation of intercellular space $^{14}CO_2$	Rate $^{14}CO_2$ Evolved	Net change ^{14}C-glycolate	Rate $^{14}CO_2$ released outside leaf
Without Inhibitor				
$100 - \dfrac{100(1-x)}{2}$ $+$	$\dfrac{100(1-x)}{2}$	100	0	100x
With Inhibitor				
$100 - \dfrac{100(1-x)}{2}$ $+$	$\dfrac{n(1-x)}{2}$	n	(See below)	nx

$$z = \frac{\text{Rate change } ^{14}C\text{-glycolate with inhibitor}}{\text{Decrease in } ^{14}CO_2 \text{ released outside leaf with inhibitor}} = \frac{100 - \dfrac{100(1-x)}{2} + \dfrac{n(1-x)}{2} - n}{100x - nx}$$

Therefore, x, fraction $^{14}CO_2$ released outside leaf $= \dfrac{1}{2z-1}$

rate of endogenous synthesis of glycolate is assumed to be unaffected. It follows that if n equals the percentage of $^{14}CO_2$ evolved in the presence of α-hydroxysulfonate, then n (1-x) is the quantity of evolved $^{14}CO_2$ that is refixed. The rate of ^{14}C-glycolate accumulation (Table 10-1) with inhibitor would be equal to that arising from unchanged endogenous carbon plus that from refixation of $^{14}CO_2$, n (1-x)/2, less the carbon lost from glycolate oxidation, n. The quotient of the rate of change of ^{14}C-glycolate with inhibitor to the decrease in $^{14}CO_2$ output with inhibitor, z, can then be represented as shown in Table 10-1. It follows that x = 1/(2z-1).

Therefore if the ratio of the ^{14}C-glycolate accumulated with inhibitor to the decrease in $^{14}CO_2$ in a given time were 2.0, then x = 0.33, indicating that one-third of the CO_2 evolved by photorespiration was released and two-thirds were refixed. Such a result was in fact realized at 35C (Table 10-2) even though the quantity of ^{14}C-glycolate is somewhat underestimated by the method (Zelitch, 1968), emphasizing how much greater in magnitude photorespiration may be than can be directly revealed even by the sensitive ^{14}C assay. This would be true in spite of a possible overestimation because recently fixed $^{14}CO_2$ may provide preferred substrates (Zelitch, 1968).

C. Effect of Genetic Control of Photorespiration on Net Photosynthesis

Since rapid CO_2 evolution in the light seemed to diminish net photosynthesis in many species, then a plant with a less active photorespiration might be expected to have a photosynthetic rate approaching that of maize. Such an inhibition of photorespiration and consequent increased photosynthetic efficiency could conceivably be accomplished by means of suitable biochemical inhibitors or perhaps more easily by genetic manipulation. Experiments aimed at testing this hypothesis have been described in great detail (Zelitch and Day, 1968), and can only be summarized here.

Using the ^{14}C assay of photorespiration (Zelitch, 1968; Zelitch and Day, 1968) we searched for leaf material with a lower rate of photorespiration than appeared normal for a given species. A yellow heterozygous mutant of John Williams Broadleaf tobacco (JWB Mutant) and its dark green homozygous recessive sibling (JWB Wild) had been described by Burk and Menser (1964). The ratios of photorespiration to dark respiration were compared in this tobacco as well as in a standard variety, Havana Seed, and in hybrid maize leaves (Table 10-3). Photorespiration was greatest in JWB Mutant (ratios from 3.7 to 6.6 in three experiments with a mean of 4.7), next possibly in Havana Seed (ratios from 3 to 5 in Zelitch, 1968), followed by JWB Wild (ratios from 0.82 to 2.3 in 5 experiments with a mean of 1.6), and least in maize (ratios less than 0.1; Zelitch, 1968). Thus the assay revealed that JWB Wild tobacco has an unusually low photorespiration for tobacco, while its yellow sibling, JWB Mutant, has a high photorespiration rate, perhaps even greater than in Havana Seed.

If the hypothesis is valid that net photosynthesis is diminished because of photorespiration, one would expect from these differences in photorespiration among the three varieties that the net photosynthesis

Table 10-2—Comparison of decrease in $^{14}CO_2$ and accumulation of ^{14}C-glycolate in presence of a–hydroxy-2-pyridinemethane-sulfonic acid in the ^{14}C-assay of photorespiration at 35C (from Zelitch, 1968)

Exp. no.	Fluid	Total $^{14}CO_2$ fixed	Time in CO_2-free air	Flow rate CO_2-free air	$^{14}CO_2$ released	Decrease $^{14}CO_2$ released with inhibitor	^{14}C-glycolate	Increase ^{14}C-glycolate/ decrease $^{14}CO_2$ released
		10^8 count/min	min.	Flask vol/min		count/min		ratio
1	Water	4.63	6	2.7	42,600	--	2,400	
	Inhibitor	4.63	6	2.7	19,400	23,200	31,900	1.3
2	Water	2.95	15	6.7	108,000	--	7,140	
	Inhibitor	2.95	15	6.7	75,400	32,600	71,200	2.0

Table 10-3—Comparison of $^{14}CO_2$ released in light and darkness and net photosynthesis in three tobacco varieties and hybrid maize (adapted from Zelitch, 1968; Zelitch and Day, 1968). The light-to-dark ratio was obtained from the ^{14}C-assay of photorespiration. Net photosynthesis was measured in excised leaves in air at about 30C and 300 ppm CO_2 at 1,500 ft-c. The number of determinations of net photosynthesis is given in parentheses next to the standard error of the mean.

Species	Ratio $^{14}CO_2$ released, Light/dark in photorespiration assay	Net photosynthesis	Comparison net photosynthesis, Havana Seed = 100
		mg CO_2 dm^{-2} hr^{-1}	
Tobacco (JWB Mutant)	3.7 to 6.6	10.8 ± 0.6 (21)	79
Tobacco (Havana Seed)	3 to 5	13.6 ± 0.5 (17)	100
Tobacco (JWB Wild)	0.82 to 2.3	16.8 ± 0.4 (22)	124
Maize (Hybrid Penn 602A)	< 0.1	26.5 ± 0.7 (8)	195

should be clearly superior in JWB Wild to that in JWB Mutant and possibly greater than that in Havana Seed. The results of such measurements are given in Table 10-3. At about 30C and 300 ppm of CO_2, JWB Wild was 25% more efficient than Havana Seed and JWB Mutant was 21% less efficient than the standard variety. Thus differences in net photosynthesis between species, which had previously been suggested as being caused by the marked differences in their photorespiration, were also found within varieties of a single species that differed in their photorespiration as revealed by the ^{14}C-assay.

Although net photosynthesis in JWB Mutant tobacco was clearly inferior at normal CO_2 concentrations, Schmid and Gaffron (1967) have shown that at 0.45% to 5.0% CO_2 this tissue has a superior net photosynthesis. This efficient photosynthetic system in JWB Mutant is not capable of rapid net photosynthesis because its active photorespiration restricts CO_2 uptake from normal air and hence its growth is also normally severely restricted. Thus blocking photorespiration by genetic manipulation may permit us to increase net photosynthesis greatly. Although the genetic basis for the differences between JWB Mutant and Wild was clearly established by Burk and Menser (1964), these differences may include factors that bear no relation to photorespiration. The genetic aspects of control of photorespiration are still unknown, and further work will be required before we will learn how to control photorespiration in various genetic backgrounds. This genetic and biochemical approach, however, appears to offer hope for a rational means of increasing photosynthetic efficiency.

LITERATURE CITED

Allaway, W. G., and T. A. Mansfield. 1967. Stomatal responses to changes in carbon dioxide concentration in leaves treated with 3-(4-chlorophenyl)-1, 1-dimethylurea. New Phytol. 66:57-63.

Anderson, L., and R. C. Fuller, 1967. The rapid appearance of glycolate during photosynthesis in Rhodospirillum rubrum. Biochim. Biophys. Acta 131:198-201.

Bandurski, R. S. 1955. Further studies on the enzymatic synthesis of oxalace-
tate from phosphoenolpyruvate and carbon dioxide. J. Biol. Chem. 217:137-
150.

Bassham, J. A. 1964. Kinetic studies of the photosynthetic carbon reduction
cycle. Ann. Rev. Plant Physiol. 15:101-120.

Begg, J. E., and P. G. Jarvis. 1968. Photosynthesis in Townsville lucerne (Stylosanthes Humilis H.B.K.). Agr. Meteorol. 5:91-109.

Bravdo, B.-A. 1968. Decrease in net photosynthesis caused by respiration.
Plant Physiol. 43:479-483.

Burk, L. G., and H. A. Menser. 1964. A dominant aurea mutation in tobacco.
Tobacco Sci. 8:101-104.

Davenport, D. C. 1967. Effects of chemical antitranspirants on transpiration
and growth of grass. J. Exp. Bot. 18:332-347.

Decker, J. P. 1955. A rapid, postillumination deceleration of respiration in
green leaves. Plant Physiol. 30:82-84.

Decker, J. P. 1957. Further evidence of increased carbon dioxide production
accompanying photosynthesis. J. Solar Energy Sci. and Eng. 1:30-33.

Decker, J. P. 1959a. Comparative responses of carbon dioxide outburst and
uptake in tobacco. Plant Physiol. 34:100-102.

Decker, J. P. 1959b. Some effects of temperature and carbon dioxide concentration on photosynthesis of Mimulus. Plant Physiol. 34:103-106.

Downton, W. J. S., and E. B. Tregunna. 1968. Photorespiration and glycolate
metabolism: A re-examination and correlation of some previous studies.
Plant Physiol. 43:923-929.

El-Sharkawy, M., and J. Hesketh. 1965. Photosynthesis among species in relation to characteristics of leaf anatomy and CO_2 diffusion resistances. Crop
Sci. 5:517-521.

Forrester, M. L., G. Krotkov, and C. D. Nelson. 1966a. Effect of oxygen on
photosynthesis, photorespiration and respiration in detached leaves. I. Soybean. Plant Physiol. 41:422-427.

Forrester, M. L., G. Krotkov, and C. D. Nelson. 1966b. Effect of oxygen on
photosynthesis, photorespiration and respiration in detached leaves. II. Corn
and other monocotyledons. Plant Physiol. 41:428-431.

Gaastra, P. 1959. Photosynthesis of crop plants as influenced by light, carbon
dioxide, temperature, and stomatal diffusion resistance. Mededel. Land-
bouwhogesch. Wageningen 59:1-68.

Goldsworthy, A. 1966. Experiments on the origin of CO_2 released by tobacco
leaf segments in the light. Phytochemistry 5:1013-1019.

Goldsworthy, A. 1968. Comparison of the kinetics of photosynthetic carbon
dioxide fixation in maize, sugar cane and tobacco, and its relation to photorespiration. Nature 217:849.

Heath, O. V. S., T. A. Mansfield, and H. Meidner. 1965. Light-induced stomatal
opening and the postulated role of glycollic acid. Nature 207:960-962.

Hesketh, J. D. 1963. Limitations to photosynthesis responsible for differences
among species. Crop Sci. 3:493-496.

Hesketh, J. 1967. Enhancement of photosynthetic CO_2 assimilation in the absence of oxygen, as dependent upon species and temperature. Planta 76:371-
374.

Hesketh, J. D., and D. N. Moss. 1963. Variation in the response of photosynthesis to light. Crop Sci. 3:107-110.

Jensen, R. G., and J. A. Bassham. 1966. Photosynthesis by isolated chloroplasts. Proc. Nat. Acad. Sci. U.S. 56:1095-1101.

Kortschak, H. P., C. E. Hartt, and G. O. Burr. 1965. Carbon dioxide fixation in
sugarcane leaves. Plant Physiol. 40:209-213.

Krotkov, G., V. C. Runeckles, and K. V. Thimann. 1958. Effect of light on the
CO absorption and evolution by Kalanchoe, wheat, and pea leaves. Plant
Physiol. 33:289-292.

MECHANISMS OF CARBON FIXATION

225

Lake, J. V.   1967.   Respiration of leaves during photosynthesis. I. Estimates from an electrical analogue. Aust. J. Biol. Sci. 20:487-493.

Mansfield, T. A.   1967.   Stomatal behavior following treatment with auxin-like substances and phenylmercuric acetate. New Phytol. 66:325-330.

Meidner, H.   1962.   The minimum intercellular-space CO_2-concentration (Γ) of maize leaves and its influence on stomatal movements. J. Exp. Bot. 13:284-293.

Meidner, H., and T. A. Mansfield.   1965.   Stomatal responses to illumination. Biol. Rev. 40:483-509.

Meidner, H., and T. A. Mansfield.   1966.   Rates of photosynthesis and respiration in relation to stomatal movements in leaves treated with α-hydroxysulfonate and glycollate. J. Exp. Bot. 17:502-509.

Moss, D. N.   1962.   The limiting carbon dioxide conecntration for photosynthesis. Nature 193:587.

Moss, D. N.   1963.   The effect of environment on gas exchange of leaves. In Stomata and water relations in plants. Conn. Agr. Exp. Sta. (New Haven) Bull. 664:86-101.

Moss, D. N.   1966.   Respiration of leaves in light and darkness. Crop Sci. 6:351-354.

Racker, E.   1957.   The reductive pentose phosphate cycle. I. Phosphoribulokinase and ribolose diphosphate carboxylase. Arch. Biochem. Biophys. 69:300-310.

Samish, Y., and D. Koller.   1968.   Estimation of photorespiration of green plants and of their mesophyll resistance to CO_2 uptake. Ann. Bot. 32:687-694.

Schmid, E. H. and H. Gaffron.   1967.   Light metabolism and chloroplast structure in chlorophyll-deficient tobacco mutants. J. Gen. Physiol. 50:563-582.

Shimshi, D.   1963a.   Effect of chemical closure of stomata on transpiration in varied soil and atmospheric environments. Plant Physiol. 38:709-712.

Shimshi, D.   1963b.   Effect of soil moisture and phenylmercuric acetate upon stomatal aperture, transpiration, and photosynthesis. Plant Physiol. 38:713-721.

Slack, C. R., and M. D. Hatch.   1967.   Comparative studies on the activity of carboxylases and other enzymes in relation to the new pathway of photosynthetic carbon dioxide fixation in tropical grasses. Biochem. J. 103:660-665.

Slatyer, R. O.   1967.   Plant-water relationships. p. 249-253. Academic Press, London and New York.

Slatyer, R. O., and J. F. Bierhuizen.   1964.   The influence of several transpiration suppressants on transpiration, photosynthesis, and water-use efficiency of cotton leaves. Aust. J. Biol. Sci. 17:131-146.

Stiller, M.   1962.   The path of carbon in photosynthesis. Ann. Rev. Plant Physiol. 13 :151-171.

Tolbert, N. E.   1963.   Glycolate pathway, p. 648-662. In Photosynthetic mechanisms of green plants. Nat. Acad. Sci.-NRC, Washington, D. C.

Turner, N. C., and P. E. Waggoner.   1968.   Effects of changing stomatal widths in a red pine forest on soil water content, leaf water potential, bole diameter and growth. Plant Physiol. 43:973-978.

Waggoner, P. E., and B.-A. Bravdo.   1967.   Stomata and the hydrologic cycle. Proc. Nat. Acad. Sci. U. S. 57:1096-1102.

Waggoner, P. E., D. N. Moss, and J. D. Hesketh.   1963.   Radiation in the plant environment and photosynthesis. Agron. J. 55:36-39.

Waggoner, P. E., and I. Zelitch.   1965.   Transpiration and the stomata of leaves. Science 150:1413-1420.

Walker, D. A.   1962.   Pyruvate caroxylation and plant metabolism. Biol. Rev. 37:215-256.

Zelitch, I.   1959.   The relationship of glycolic acid to respiration and photosynthesis in tobacco leaves. J. Biol. Chem. 234-3077-3081.

Zelitch, I. 1961. Biochemical control of stomatal opening in leaves. Proc. Nat. Acad. Sci. U.S. 47:1423-1433.

Zelitch, I. 1964. Organic acids and respiration in photosynthetic tissues. Ann. Rev. Plant Physiol. 15:121-142.

Zelitch, I. 1965a. Environmental and biochemical control of stomatal movement in leaves. Biol. Rev. 40:463-482.

Zelitch, I. 1965b. The relation of glycolic acid synthesis to the primary photosynthetic carboxylation reaction in leaves. J. Biol. Chem. 240:1869-1876.

Zelitch, I. 1966. Increased rate of net photosynthetic carbon dioxide uptake caused by the inhibition of glycolate oxidase. Plant Physiol. 41:1623-1631.

Zelitch, I. 1967a. Control of leaf stomata - Their role in transpiration and photosynthesis. Amer. Sci. 55:472-486.

Zelitch, I. 1967b. Water and CO_2 transport in the photosynthetic process, p. 231-248. In A. San Pietro, F. A. Greer, and T. J. Army (ed.) Harvesting the Sun: Photosynthesis in plant life. Academic Press, New York and London.

Zelitch, I. 1968. Investigations on photorespiration with a sensitive ^{14}C-assay. Plant Physiol. 43:1829-1837.

Zelitch, I. 1969. Stomatal control. Ann. Rev. Plant Physiol. 20: In press.

Zelitch, I., and P. R. Day. 1968. Variation in photorespiration. The effect of genetic differences in photorespiration on net photosynthesis in tobacco. Plant Physiol. 43:1838-1844.

Zelitch, I., and P. E. Waggoner. 1962a. Effect of chemical control of stomata on transpiration and photosynthesis. Proc. Nat. Acad. Sci. U.S. 48:1101-1108.

Zelitch, I. and P. E. Waggoner. 1962b. Effect of chemical control of stomata on transpiration and photosynthesis of intact plants. Proc. Nat. Acad. Sci. U.S. 48:1297-1299.

Zelitch, I., and D. A. Walker. 1964. The role of glycolic acid metabolism in opening of leaf stomata. Plant Physiol. 39:856-862.

10 ... DISCUSSION

DOV KOLLER

The Hebrew University
Jerusalem, Israel

Dr. Zelitch has shown that, for comparable conditions, the "efficiency of water use" could be improved by partial stomatal closure, because diffusion of water-vapor is dependent on stomatal resistance to a greater extent than diffusion of CO_2. However, any stomatal closure will reduce CO_2 uptake and thus also reduce photosynthesis. Dr. Zelitch was also quite justified in indicating the futility of using photosynthetic inhibitors, or promoters of photorespiration to increase CO_2 concentration in the mesophyll, thereby inducing stomatal closure. It is worth bearing in mind that, for crops grown under glass or plastic, both efficiency and overall CO_2 fixation have been improved by manipulating

ERRATUM---PHYSIOLOGICAL ASPECTS OF CROP YIELD

For Chapter 10--Discussion, by Dov Koller, pages 226-231

After this book had gone to the press, the author of the Discussion for Chapter 10, p. 226-231 showed[1] that the generally used relationship $R_C = R_W' + r_m$ is inapplicable in photorespiring plants. This necessitated the following changes to be made in the text, as well as replacing the APPENDIX: -

page 227, line 8: substitute 'intracellular' for 'residual "internal" '.
   line 9: delete 'i.e. $r_m = R_C - R_W'$'.
   line 14: should read 'then, if photorespiration is negligible'

page 230, equation (4) should read

$$R_W' = G \cdot (r_2 - r_1)/(\Gamma_2 - \Gamma_1) = G \cdot (r_3 - r_2)/(\Gamma_3 - \Gamma_2)$$
$$= G \cdot (r_4 - r_3)/(\Gamma_4 - \Gamma_3) = \text{etc.}$$

The APPENDIX on pages 230-231 should be replaced with the following:

APPENDIX 1 (FIG. 10D-4)

Let:
   R and r represent R_C and r_m, respectively; L_X and L_i represent rates of photorespiration, measured externally and inside the mesophyll intercellular spaces, respectively; suffixes 1 and 2 designate lines 1 and 2, respectively.

Then:

$$L_{X1} = \Gamma_1/R_1 ; \quad L_{X2} = \Gamma_2/R_2 \tag{1}$$

$$(L_{X1}/L_{X2}) \cdot (\Gamma_2/\Gamma_1) = R_2/R_1 \tag{2}$$

$$L_{i1} = L_{i2} = \Gamma_1/r_1 = \Gamma_2/r_2 \tag{3}$$

$$\Gamma_1/\Gamma_2 = r_1/r_2 \text{ and } r_1 \cdot \Gamma_2 = r_2 \cdot \Gamma_1 \tag{4}$$

According to Samish and Koller (1968)

$$L_{i1} = L_{i2} = L_{X1} \cdot (1 + R_W'/r_1) = L_{X2} \cdot (1 + R_W'/r_2) \tag{5}$$

---

[1] Koller, D. 1969. Characteristics of the photosynthetic apparatus derived from its response to natural complexes of environmental factors. Proc. IBP/PP Technical Meeting "Productivity of Photosynthetic Systems, Models and Methods". Trebon, Czechoslovakia. (I. Setlik, editor). In press.

(over)

Rearranging equation (5) and substituting from equation (2)

$$(r_2 + R'_W)/(r_1 + R'_W) = (L_{X1}/L_{X2}) \cdot (r_2/r_1)$$
$$= (L_{X1}/L_{X2}) \cdot (\Gamma_2/\Gamma_1) = R_2/R_1 \quad (6)$$

$$R'_W \cdot (R_2 - R_1) = r_2 \cdot R_1 - r_1 \cdot R_2 \quad (7)$$

Dividing by R_2

$$R'_W \cdot (1 - R_1/R_2) = r_2 \cdot (R_1/R_2) - r_1 \quad (8)$$

From Fig. 10D-4

$$(\Gamma_1 + G)/R_1 = (\Gamma_2 + G)/R_2 \quad (9)$$
$$R_1/R_2 = (\Gamma_1 + G)/(\Gamma_2 + G) \quad (10)$$

Substituting equation (10) and (4) in equation (8)

$$R'_W [1 - (\Gamma_1 + G)/(\Gamma_2 + G)] = r_2 \cdot (\Gamma_1 + G)/(\Gamma_2 + G) - r_1 \quad (11)$$

From which

$$R'_W \cdot (\Gamma_2 - \Gamma_1) = G \cdot (r_2 - r_1) \quad (12)$$
$$R'_W = G \cdot (r_2 - r_1)/(\Gamma_2 - \Gamma_1) \quad (13)$$

mesophyll CO_2 through judicious increase of ambient CO_2 (C_x). Thus, if

P = net-photosynthetic flux of CO_2

R_w' = diffusive resistance to CO_2 over the same pathway taken by transpiration vapor

R_c = total "resistance" to photosynthetic CO_2 uptake from the ambient atmosphere

r_m = residual "internal," or "mesophyll" resistance to CO_2 uptake, i.e., $r_m = R_c - R_w'$

C_m = intercellular CO_2 concentration at the mesophyll evaporating surfaces.

C_i = intracellular CO_2 concentration (=0, after carboxylating its acceptor)

then

$$P = (C_x - C_i)/R_c = (C_x - C_m)/R_w' = (C_m - C_i)/r_m \qquad (1)$$

from which, taking $C_i = 0$,

$$C_x/R_c = (C_x - C_m)/R_w' = C_m/r_m \qquad (2)$$

$$C_m/C_x = r_m/R_c = r_m/(R_w' + r_m). \qquad (3)$$

Thus, doubling C_x will double the gradient, so long as the increase in C_m does not increase R_w' (by inducing stomatal closure) and r_m (by overloading the acceptor sites for CO_2). The increase in P will not be as large if R_w' increases. If, however, r_m increases, the degree to which P may increase would depend on the magnitude of the increase in C_m relative to the increase in r_m [equation (1)].

My second comment relates to the CO_2 compensation point, Γ. The value of this parameter is (i) it is easily obtained, (ii) it is the point at which photorespiratory output and photosynthetic input of CO_2 are exactly equal, and (iii) it is the state at which $C_x = C_m$. However, it is not an independent plant characteristic, but the product of two such characteristics, namely photorespiration and r_m, and any attempt to use it as a unique indicator of photorespiration, or of photosynthetic efficiency, may be entirely misleading. Thus, increase in Γ may result from inhibition of photosynthesis alone, or from enhancement of photorespiration alone (Fig. 10D-1). In both cases, however, stomatal closure associated with increase in Γ may be attributable to increased C_m. By the same reasoning, the fact that PMA treatment (phenylmercuric acetate) caused stomatal closure, without affecting Γ, does not constitute proof that PMA was affecting the stomata directly, not through changing C_m. If PMA were to affect stomatal closure without affecting photorespiration (L), R_c would increase, and so would Γ. The very lack of effect of PMA on Γ seems to indicate that PMA may be inhibiting the same apparatus which fixes CO_2 photosynthetically and releases CO_2 in photorespiration (Fig. 10D-2), so that at Γ, $P - \Delta P = L - \Delta L$.

I would also like to question the significance of the conclusion drawn

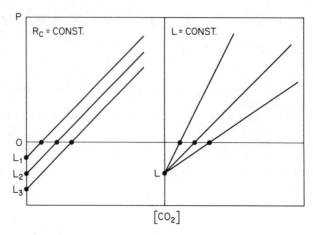

Fig. 10D-1—The CO_2 compensation point may change solely as a result of changes in photorespiration, L, (left), or of changes in resistance to CO_2 uptake R_C, (right). In the former, R_C is constant, in the latter, L is constant.

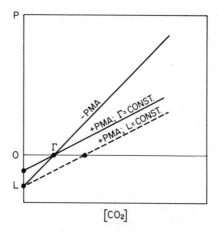

Fig. 10D-2—PMA may affect the CO_2 compensation point, Γ, by affecting photorespiration, L, (dashed line), without acting on photosynthetic efficiency (slope). Γ may remain unchanged, though photosynthetic efficiency and hence also photorespiration, are affected by PMA (solid line).

from Goldsworthy's K_m value being nearly equal for tobacco, sugarcane, and maize. (For references, see chapter by I. Zelitch.) Goldsworthy's (1968) data show that maximal photosynthesis was far from equal (tobacco > sugarcane > maize), probably resulting from nonsaturation with light of the tropical grasses. Furthermore, the apparent "K_m" has very little in common with the K_m value of enzyme kinetics, which characterizes the interaction between a single enzyme and its substrate. Photosynthetic rates, on the other hand, depend on several reactions, controlled by different environmental factors, and to a different degree in different

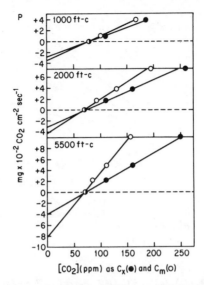

Fig. 10D-3—Effects of light intensity (sunflowers). Estimate of photorespiration (the extrapolated intercept with the ordinate) is greater when P is plotted as a function of CO_2 at the evaporating surfaces of the mesophyll, C_m, than in the external atmosphere, C_X (after Samish & Koller, 1968).

species. Therefore, the fact that the "K_m" values were nearly the same is an insufficient indication to equality in the "carboxylation efficiency."

My last comment is on the effects of oxygen tension on net photosynthesis. Dr. Zelitch attributes the inhibitory effects of increased $[O_2]$ on P largely to enhancement of photorespiration. One of the best examples of these effects is given by Forrester, Krotkov, and Nelson (1966a), showing P of soybeans as a function of C_X (their Fig. 7). From equation (1) above it is clear that $C_m = C_X - P \cdot R_W^t$, so that when P is plotted as a function of C_m, not C_X, the lines become steeper, and the intercept with the ordinate (L) becomes more negative (i.e., estimate of photorespiration increases) (Fig. 10D-3). Samish and Koller (1968) have shown that photorespiration estimated within the mesophyll (L_i) is greater than that estimated outside the leaf (L_X) by a factor of $1 + R_W^t/r_m$. Thus, when R_W^t is constant, L_i/L_X will increase as r_m becomes smaller. Therefore, relating P to C_m, instead of C_X, would increase the difference in slopes and decrease the difference in intercepts. Effects of oxygen on photosynthesis therefore appear to be concerned more with carboxylation efficiency (or r_m, to be exact) than with photorespiration. It turns out that the linear P/C_X relationships at all oxygen concentrations, as provided by Forrester, Krotkov and Nelson (1966a), can be extrapolated to a mutual point of intersection (Fig. 10D-4). Assuming that R_W^t was constant, as well as unaffected by oxygen concentration (these data were not provided), it can be shown (Appendix 1) that transformation of the results to the P/C_m relationship will cause the lines to converge on the ordinate (i.e., where $C_m = 0$), if

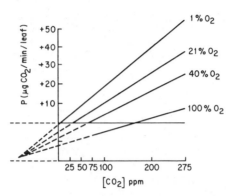

Fig. 10D-4—Effects of oxygen concentration, when P is plotted as a function of CO_2 in the ambient atmosphere. (Adapted from Forrester, Krotkov & Nelson, 1966a. Dashed lines extrapolated.)

$$R'_W = G \cdot (R_2 - R_1)/(\Gamma_2 - \Gamma_1) = G \cdot (R_3 - R_2)/(\Gamma_3 - \Gamma_2) = G \cdot (R_4 - R_3)/(\Gamma_4 - \Gamma_3)$$

$$= G \cdot (r_2 - r_1)/(\Gamma_2 - \Gamma_1) = \ldots \text{ etc.} \tag{4}$$

where G is the projection on the abscissa of the original point of intersection, R and r are abbreviated symbols for R_C and r_m, respectively, and the numerical suffixes refer to the appropriate lines. The derived intersection on the ordinate will be the estimate of intercellular photorespiration, which is equal at all oxygen concentrations. (This does not rule out the possibility that very low oxygen concentrations may indeed inhibit photorespiration, as they also inhibit dark respiration.) If indeed increased oxygen concentration inhibits net photosynthesis largely, if not uniquely, by increasing "resistance" to carboxylation, it may play the role of an end-product inhibitor of an initial and essential reaction in photosynthesis.

APPENDIX 1 (FIG. 10D-4)

Let:
R and r represent R_C and r_m, respectively $(R = r + R'_W)$
L_X and L_i represent rates of photorespiration, measured externally and inside the mesophyll intercellular spaces, respectively.
Suffixes 1 and 2 designate lines 1 and 2, respectively.

Then:

$$L_{X1} = \Gamma_1/R_1 = \Gamma_1/(r_1 + R'_W); \quad L_{X2} = \Gamma_2/R_2 = \Gamma_2/(r_2 + R'_W). \tag{1}$$

According to Samish and Koller (1968)

$$L_i = L_X \cdot (1 + R'_W/r) = L_X \cdot R/r. \tag{2}$$

Substituting L_x values from equation (1) we obtain

$$L_{i1} = (\Gamma_1/R_1) \cdot (R_1/r_1) = \Gamma_1/r_1; \quad L_{i2} = (\Gamma_2/R_2) \cdot (R_2/r_2) = \Gamma_2/r_2 \quad (3)$$

If $L_{i1} = L_{i2}$, then

$$\Gamma_1 \cdot r_2 = \Gamma_2 \cdot r_1. \quad (4)$$

From Fig. 10D-4:

$$(\Gamma_1 + G)/R_1 = (\Gamma_1 + G)/(r_1 + R'_W) = (\Gamma_2 + G)/R_2 = (\Gamma_2 + G)/(R'_W + r_2). \quad (5)$$

Solving to obtain R'_W

$$(r_2 + R'_W)\cdot(\Gamma_1 + G) = (r_1 + R'_W)\cdot(\Gamma_2 + G)$$
$$r_2\cdot(\Gamma_1 + G) - r_1\cdot(\Gamma_2 + G) = R'_W\cdot(\Gamma_2 - \Gamma_1)$$
$$G\cdot(r_2 - r_1) + \Gamma_1\cdot r_2 - \Gamma_2\cdot r_1 = R'_W\cdot(\Gamma_2 - \Gamma_1). \quad (6)$$

Substituting equation (4) in equation (6)

$$G\cdot(r_2 - r_1) = R'_W\cdot(\Gamma_2 - \Gamma_1) \quad (7)$$

$$\text{or } R'_W = G\cdot(r_2 - r_1)/(\Gamma_2 - \Gamma_1) = G\cdot(R_2 - R_1)/(\Gamma_2 - \Gamma_1). \quad (8)$$

10...DISCUSSION

T. A. MANSFIELD

University of Lancaster
Lancaster, England

Dr. Zelitch raised the question of the control of stomatal aperture by the CO_2 concentration inside the leaf. The fact that increases in CO_2 concentration cause stomatal closure cannot reasonably be disputed in view of the vast amount of evidence available. Freudenberger (1940), Heath (1948), Scarth and Shaw (1951), Kuiper (1961) and Stalfelt (1967) are a few of the workers who have observed that stomatal aperture is influenced by changes in CO_2 concentration in the physiological range, that is, around 300 ppm. Their observations were made on a variety of species and between them they used all the major techniques for observing stomatal aperture. I have recalculated some of the data of Heath and Russell (1954) to show how a change in CO_2 concentration affects stomatal

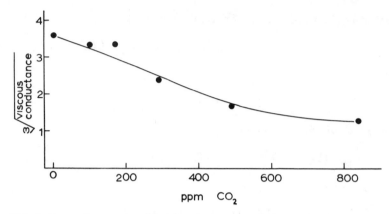

Fig. 10D-1—Dependence of stomatal opening on CO_2 concentration in 'Charter' wheat (Triticum sp.). Light intensity 8,000 lux. The cube-root of the viscous conductance was used for the ordinate to indicate the effect of CO_2 on the diffusive conductance of the stomata. Recalculated data of Heath and Russell (1954).

diffusive conductance in light (Fig. 10-D-1). It is data like these that have led to the view that internal changes in CO_2 concentration contribute to changes in stomatal aperture. The relevant concentration is presumably that inside the guard cells and if a photosynthetic inhibitor like phenylmercuric acetate is sprayed on to the leaf surface it is not surprising that the stomata close. In my opinion phenylmercuric acetate is a successful antitranspirant because it is taken up by the guard cells but is not translocated to the mesophyll, and it therefore has the desired effect of causing stomatal closure without impairing the photosynthetic activities of the major part of the leaf.

In spite of the evidence presented by Dr. Zelitch I remain unconvinced that maize possesses a low CO_2 compensation point merely because it lacks photorespiration. I think that the answer is more likely to lie in the efficiency of photosynthetic carboxylation, and I am concerned about the quality of the evidence that is quoted relating to the efficiency of carboxylation in maize, and comparing it with that in plants having a high CO_2 compensation point. In particular I consider that experiments of the type performed by Goldsworthy (1968) are open to serious objections. Determining K_m values in vivo is always likely to be hazardous because there is the possibility of interference from other systems, and in this case there is likely to have been interference from the stomata in addition to intracellular factors. In Goldsworthy's experiments the stomata constituted a resistance between the supply of substrate (CO_2 in the ambient atmosphere) and the reaction sites. At the start of the determinations the material was exposed to conditions likely to cause stomatal closure, namely, a high CO_2 concentration (6,000 ppm) and anaerobic conditions. Thus there was almost certainly a considerable resistance to diffusion in the path from the main source of substrate to the carboxylation centers, and the CO_2 concentration at the latter must have been much lower than in the atmosphere. The quoted values of K_m

are the CO_2 concentrations in the atmosphere and they depend, therefore, not only on the efficiency of carboxylation, but also on the magnitude of the diffusion resistance. Stomata are, however, a variable resistance, and if they opened during the determinations (as is likely since the CO_2 concentration was decreasing), the kinetics of uptake are further complicated. If the same diffusion resistance occurred at given CO_2 concentrations for both maize and tobacco the errors would cancel out in a comparison between the two species. However, it is most unlikely that the diffusion resistances are the same since the stomata are different in size, number, distribution, and physiology (maize stomata are more sensitive to CO_2 than those of most species).

The ·view that carboxylation is not more efficient in maize is thus based on very flimsy evidence. There is, however, good evidence from in vitro studies that phosphoenolpyruvate carboxylase, which is now thought to be responsible for photosynthetic carboxylation in maize, has a higher affinity for CO_2 than ribulosediphosphate carboxylase. In some succulents, where it has long been known that PEP carboxylase is responsible for dark CO_2 fixation, Wilkins (1959) found no CO_2 output into a stream of CO_2-free air in the dark. This is equivalent to a CO_2 compensation point of zero.

ADDITIONAL LITERATURE CITED

Freudenberger, H. 1940. Die Reaktion der Schliesszellen auf Kohlensaüre-und Sauerstoff-Entzug. Protoplasma 35:15-54.

Heath, O.V.S. 1948. Control of stomatal movement by a reduction in the normal carbon dioxide content of the air. Nature, Lond. 161-179-81.

Heath, O.V.S., and J. Russell. 1954. An investigation of the light responses of wheat stomata with the attempted elimination of control by the mesophyll. Part 2. Interactions with external carbon dioxide, and general discussion. J. Exp. Bot. 5:269-92.

Kuiper, P.J.C. 1961. The effects of factors on the transpiration of leaves, with special reference to the stomatal light response. Meded. Landb Hoogesch. Wageningen 61:1-49.

Scarth, G. W., and M. Shaw. 1951. Stomatal movement and photosynthesis in Pelargonium. I. Effects of light and carbon dioxide. Plant Physiol. 26:207-25.

Stalfelt, M. G. 1967. The components of the CO_2-induced stomatal movements. Physiol. Plant. 20:634-42.

Wilkins, M. B. 1959. An endogenous rhythm in the rate of carbon dioxide output of Bryophyllum. J. Exp. Bot. 10:377-90.

11

Physiological Responses to Nitrogen in Plants

YOSHIO MURATA

National Institute of Agricultural Sciences
Konosu, Saitana, Japan

I. INTRODUCTION

Recent advances in crop physiology have given us some clues for analysis of the complex relationships of environmental factors, cultural conditions and genetic factors to crop yield. However, in order to accomplish this analysis, it is quite necessary to have concrete knowledge about the causal relationships and the time sequence of the processes of yield-formation.

In grain crops, the process of yield-formation may be divided into the following three phases:

1) Formation of organs for nutrient absorption and photosynthesis,
2) Formation of flower organs and "yield-container," and
3) Production, accumulation and translocation of "yield-contents."

The effect of nitrogen, which has been quite popularly used to promote the growth of crop plants, also will be expressed through these processes.

In the following presentation, an attempt has been made to demonstrate the pattern and meaning of physiological responses of crop plants, especially of rice plants (Oryza sativa L.), to nitrogen as associated with their grain production, putting emphasis on the second and third phases.

II. NITROGEN AND FORMATION OF "YIELD-CONTAINER"

A. The Number of Spikelets and Nitrogen

According to Matsushima (1957), an upper limit of kernel growth is imposed in rice plants by the size of hulls which is determined already 1 week before heading (flowering). Thus, the "physical" capacity

235

for grain yield which can be broken down into the following three components is determined at a comparatively early stage of growth:

$$\text{Capacity of "yield-container"} = \left(\begin{array}{c}\text{Number of}\\\text{panicles per m}^2\end{array}\right) \times \left(\begin{array}{c}\text{Number of spike-}\\\text{lets per panicle}\end{array}\right) \times \left(\begin{array}{c}\text{Size of}\\\text{hull}\end{array}\right).$$

The number of panicles is determined by about 10 days after the maxi-
mum-tiller-number stage, and the number of spikelets per panicle, by
about 10 days before flowering.

According to Kumura (1956a), there is a very close correlation between the number of spikelets per panicle and the average nitrogen content of leaf blades during the 1-4 week period before flowering. In this
connection Matsushima (1957) observed that, during the process of
spikelet-formation, some of the differentiated spikelets degenerated.
The degeneration occurred at the stage of reduction division of pollen
mother cells. It was also found that both differentiation and degeneration were quite sensitive to outside conditions—especially nitrogen supply and solar radiation—the most sensitive period for nitrogen supply
being 30-32 days before flowering and for solar radiation, 15-16 days
before flowering.

Yamada et al. (1957) dealt with this problem at the stand level and
found close correlations between the number of spikelets per hill and
the total nitrogen content of the top at flowering. Wada and Matsushima
(1962) found that in a number of their experiments, the amount of total
nitrogen absorbed by the end of the spikelet-differentiation stage (17-18
days before flowering) had the closest correlation with the number of
differentiated spikelets per hill (Fig. 11-1), whereas the amount of

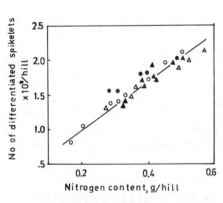

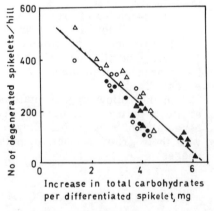

Fig. 11-1—Effect of total nitrogen content in the shoot at the late spikelet-
differentiation stage on the number of
differentiated spikelets in rice plants
(Wada and Matsushima, 1962). Various plots differing in variety, transplanting date, N level, and shaded
period are included.

Figure 11-2—Effect of the amount of
carbohydrate per differentiated spikelet during the late spikelet-differentiation stage to flowering on the number of degenerated spikelets (Wada
and Matsushima, 1962). Plots same as
in Fig. 11-1.

carbohydrate-increase per differentiated spikelet during the period from spikelet-differentiation to flowering, showed the highest, negative correlation with the number of degenerated spikelets (Fig. 11-2).

Thus, it was established that the differentiation of spikelets was strongly promoted by nitrogen supply and their degeneration was effectively prevented by carbohydrate supply. However, as the number of degenerated spikelets is comparatively smaller than that of differentiated spikelets, the final number of spikelets usually is closely correlated with the amount of total nitrogen absorbed up to the flowering stage (Wada, 1969).

B. Effect of Nitrogen Topdressing for Increasing the Capacity of "Yield-Container"

Judging from the above-entitled results, it may be obvious that the main effect of the nitrogen topdressing applied at 3-4 weeks before heading (so-called "panicle fertilizer," widely used in Japan), lies in increasing the number of spikelets. However, it is possible that the "panicle fertilizer" is also effective in increasing the size of hulls.

Recently, a new nitrogen application method called "deep-layer-application," in which nitrogen fertilizer is injected into a depth of 10-12 cm at a time about 30-40 days before heading, is gaining popularity in northern Japan with increased grain yields (Wada and Kudo, 1965). Matsuura, Iwata, and Hasegawa (1969) very recently have shown, as is indicated in Table 11-1, that this method is quite effective in increasing the size of hulls, thereby increasing the 1,000-grain weight proportionally, and that this effect is due to the promotion of net assimilation rate (NAR) caused by the nitrogen thus applied.

C. The Number of Spikelets and LAI

As previously described, the number of spikelets per unit area has a close correlation with the amount of nitrogen absorbed up to heading stage. As this amount of nitrogen may be considered to be nearly proportional to the leaf area index (LAI) at the heading stage, it naturally

Table 11-1—Effect of "deep-layer-application" of nitrogen topdressing on the 1,000-weight of husks and kernels and NAR (Matsuura et al., 1969)

Plot	Nitrogen supplied as		Planting density hill/m^2	1,000 weight of				NAR g/m^2 day‡
				Husks attached to		Kernels attached to		
	Basal	Top dressing		Primary rachis	Secondary rachis	Primary rachis	Secondary rachis	
Control	80	20*	22.2	3.3 g	2.9 g	20.1 g	18.5 g	5.7
"Deep" 1	50	50†	22.2	3.7	3.3	21.7	19.9	6.8
"Deep" 2	50	50†	29.7	3.9	3.4	23.0	20.7	7.8
"Deep" 3	50	50†	29.7	3.9	3.8	22.8	21.6	9.9

* Applied at the soil surface. † Applied at 10-12 cm deep. ‡ NAR: Average value for the ear-initiation to heading.

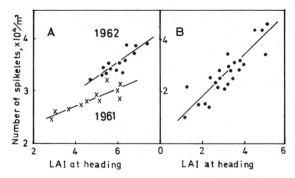

Fig. 11-3—Two examples for close correlation between LAI at flowering and the number of spikelets per area. (A) Plots of various combinations in plowing depth, planting density, and N level are included (Murata et al., 1966). (B) Plots of various seasons of culture are included (Tokaikinki Exp. Sta., 1967).

follows that quite high, positive correlations are observed between LAI and the number of spikelets (Fig. 11-3). The example shown here indicates that the relationship may vary considerably according to the year. Comparison of experimental conditions between the two years revealed that the factor most probably responsible was the difference in the average temperature (2.8C lower in 1962 than in 1961) during the 1-month period prior to heading when differentiation and development of spikelets took place.

On the other hand, Murayama (1967) recently has found that the nitrogen-spikelet number relationship differs according to the area of production (Fig. 11-4). The data indicate that in northern districts more spikelets are formed than in the southern districts at the same nitrogen level. Rice plants grown in northern districts contain more nitrogen and pass their ear-initiation stage under lower temperatures than those grown in southern districts (Ishizuka and Tanaka, 1956a,b; Yamada, 1963; Yanagisawa and Takahashi, 1964). From these results it may be concluded that in southern districts, rice plants tend to have

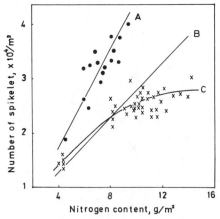

Fig. 11-4—Relationships between the amount of nitrogen contained in plants at heading and number of spikelets per area (Murayama, 1967). (A) Northern Japan (Hokkaido Exp. Sta., 1965). (B) Middle Japan (Experimentally obtained line by Shimizu, 1967). (C) Southern Japan (Kyushu Exp. Sta., 1961).

a larger leaf area but a smaller number of spikelets, so that they must contend with more severe mutual shading than in northern districts, to insure the same capacity for yield.

D. Fertilization (Pollination) and Nitrogen

It is by fertilization (pollination) that spikelets are given the "accepting ability" for carbohydrates and other food material. In the case of a japonica rice, the occurrence of sterile paddy due to failure of fertilization usually amounts to no more than several percent. When, however, a heavy dose of nitrogen is applied, especially in combination with weak light, sterility of spikelets is greatly increased as was demonstrated by Togari and Kashiwakura (1958) (Fig. 11-5). They found the cause to be in the reduced number of germinated pollen at the stigma (Fig. 11-6), and this in turn was attributed to the increased occurrence of incomplete dehiscing of anthers and abnormal behavior of filaments at the time of flowering.

In indica rice which is believed to have a higher sterility percentage than japonica rice, it was found that the sterility was closely correlated with the degree of nitrogen-response. According to the work of Ota and Yamada (1965) in Ceylon, heavy doses of nitrogen fertilizer greatly increased the sterility percentage, sometimes to almost 100%, in a low nitrogen-response variety, whereas the increase was far smaller in a high nitrogen-response variety.

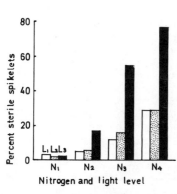

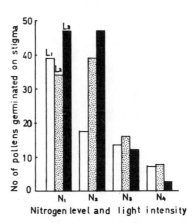

Fig. 11-5—Effect of nitrogen-fertilizer and light intensity on sterility of rice (Togari and Kashiwakura, 1958). N_1 = 37.5, N_2 = 94, N_3 = 150, N_4 = 300 kg/ha; L_3 = strongly shaded, L_2 = weakly shaded, L_1 = nonshaded.

Fig. 11-6—Effect of nitrogen-fertilizer and light intensity on the number of pollens germinated on the stigma (Togari and Kashiwakura, 1958). Plots same as in Fig. 11-5.

III. THE AMOUNT OF "CONTENTS" IN RELATION TO
THE CAPACITY FOR YIELD

When the "capacity" for yield has been determined and pollination has been smoothly performed, the next problem is the extent to which the "container" will actually be filled.

As for the quantitative relation between the capacity of the "container" (V) and the amount of "contents" produced (C), three cases are possible: (i) V < C, (ii) V > C, and (iii) V = C. The capacity can be expressed by the product of the spikelet number, S, and the average size of hull. The variation due to different conditions is generally far greater in the former than in the latter. It follows, therefore, that V can be roughly represented by S. Thus, the first case occurs when S is very small. Here, close correlations are usually found between grain yield, Y, and S, but no correlation, between Y and the percentage of filled grains, F, as is shown in Fig. 11-7A and 7B. This is because Y is limited by the capacity of the container.

The second case is observed when S is extremely large. Here Y is usually closely correlated with F, but not with S (Fig. 11-7C and 7D). In this case, the contents limit the yield.

The third case is observed when the capacity and contents are in good harmony, so that a high F value is obtained in spite of a large S value. Close correlations are observed between Y and S (Fig. 11-8), as in the first case.

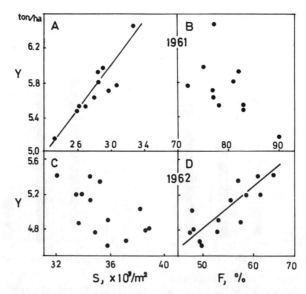

Fig. 11-7—Relationships of brown rice yield, Y, to the spikelets number, S, and the percentage of completely filled grains, F, of rice plants cultured under various combinations of plowing depth, planting density, and nitrogen level (Murata et al., 1966).

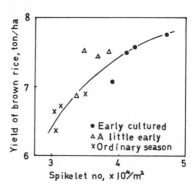

Fig. 11-8—Relation between brown rice yield, Y, and spikelet number, S, in rice plants cultured in different seasons (Kyushu Agr. Exp. Sta., 1967).

These principles have been established by many experiments in Japan starting from the work of Kumura (1956a) which will be explained later. The existence of such a simple principle is largely due to the characteristics of rice plants whose grain yield is very likely to be limited by the capacity of "container." On this point, it is not likely that in wheat (Triticum aestivum L.) and corn (Zea mays L.), for example, such a severe "physical" limitations will exist, judging from the morphological structure of their grain. The following facts may be a reflection of these circumstances: In some varieties of wheat a yearly deviation of as high as 50% in 1,000-grain weight is cited by Thorne (1965), while in rice plants the deviation seldom exceeds 10%.

IV. PRODUCTION OF RESERVE SUBSTANCES, RIPENING, AND NITROGEN

A. Accumulation of Organic Substances and Nitrogen

According to the works of Togari, Okamoto, and Kumura (1954), Togari and Sato (1954), Murayama et al. (1955), Soga and Nozaki (1957), and others, the following patterns were observed in the production and accumulation of organic substances in rice plants (Fig. 11-9). At early stages, protein synthesis is most active and this is immediately followed by accumulation of cell wall substances such as lignin and cellulose. In close succession to this, accumulation of hemicellulose takes place, while accumulation of sugars and starch begins at intermediate stage of growth and becomes dominant at later stages. The accumulation of starch and sugars usually begins in culms and leaf sheaths at around the ear-initiation stage, which is about 30 days before flowering. The highest content is reached at the flowering stage. (Fig. 11-9B). Immediately after flowering, translocation of the temporarily reserved carbohydrates to the panicles begins. The grain makes a rapid growth under the influence of both the stored, and currently synthesized, carbohydrates.

Being one of the most important constituents of proteins, nitrogen always gives a marked, promoting influence on protein synthesis. On

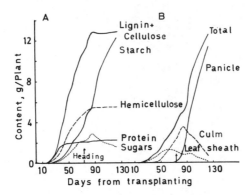

Fig. 11-9—Changes in various organic substances in rice plants according to growth stage (Togari et al., 1954). (A) Various organic substances. (B) Starch content in various organs.

the other hand, nitrogen produces a complex influence on carbohydrate metabolism: Sometimes it remarkably promotes the production of carbohydrates, but on other occasions it greatly reduces carbohydrate accumulation. At the elongation stage of rice plants, the content of total nitrogen and protein-nitrogen increases with increasing supply of nitrogen, while the content of sugars and starch drastically decreases (Table 11-2).

It is a widely recognized fact that in rice plants the smaller the nitrogen supply at the heading stage, the greater is the carbohydrate accumulation (Fujiwara et al., 1951; Takahashi et al., 1957; Matsushima, 1957; and others). The same situation is recognized also in some other species, for example, in orchardgrass (Griffith, Teel, and Parker, 1964; Colby et al., 1965; Auda et al., 1966) and coastal bermudagrass (Adegbola and McKell, 1966).

Large differences in effect were induced by varying the time and combination of nitrogen application, as is shown in Fig. 11-10. Thus, the nitrogen applied at the earlier stage of growth is always effective in increasing the carbohydrate accumulation at maturity, but the nitrogen applied at the later stage of growth is effective only when the level of nitrogen at the earlier stage is not too high. These effects may be

Table 11-2—Composition of the leaf blade and stem of rice plants at the elongation stage under different levels of nitrogen supply (Takahashi et al., 1955)

	Plant part							
	Leaf blade				Stem (sheath and culm)			
Composition	N_0	N_1	N_3	N_5	N_0	N_1	N_3	N_5
Total N	1.93	2.38	3.15	3.61	0.91	0.88	1.49	1.74
Protein	1.68	2.09	2.74	3.14	0.73	0.68	1.21	1.34
Total sugars	6.05	5.24	5.30	4.61	3.79	4.04	3.15	1.52
Starch	5.16	2.34	4.69	3.78	12.10	12.90	7.50	3.60

Notes: N_0 - No nitrogen; N_1 - 37.5 kg nitrogen; N_3 - 113 kg nitrogen; N_5 - 188 kg nitrogen/ha.

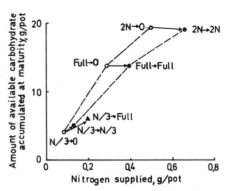

Fig. 11-10—Effect of the amount and time of nitrogen application on the carbohydrate accumulation at maturity in rice plants (Kumura, 1956b). Plot name, e.g., 2N—2N means two times normal level of nitrogen applied before heading, and the same amount applied after heading.

explained from the fact that the earlier application primarily promotes leaf area expansion, while the later application stimulates the photosynthetic activity of the leaf as well as preventing the decline of leaf area (Murata, 1961).

Generally speaking, nitrogen topdressing after the spikelet-differentiation stage increases carbohydrate accumulation both at heading and at maturity (Sato, 1956; Wada, 1969). After this stage, the growth-stimulating effect of nitrogen greatly decreases.

B. Ripening and Nitrogen

Kumura (1956b) found in a pot experiment an interesting relationship between the C/S ratio—the ratio of the amount of total available carbohydrates (sugars plus starch) accumulated in plants at maturity, C, to the total number of spikelets, S—and the distribution ratio, C_E/C, (the ratio of the amount of carbohydrates accumulated in the ears, C_E, to C) as is shown in Fig. 11-11. The data indicate that when the C/S ratio is small under high nitrogen level, almost all of the carbohydrates

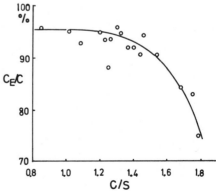

Fig. 11-11—Relationship between the amount of carbohydrate at maturity per spikelet (C/S) and its distribution rate to ears (C_E/C) in rice plants supplied with various amount of nitrogen (Kumura, 1956b).

accumulated in the plant are translocated to the ear, so that the distribution ratio becomes nearly 100%. When the C/S ratio is large under low nitrogen level, the carbohydrates in excess of the capacity of the grains remain in the straw, and as a result the distribution ratio decreases. In the former case, as was mentioned earlier, grain yield is limited by the amount of carbohydrates produced, and in the latter case, by the number of spikelets.

Also Matsushima (1957) showed in field experiments that the smaller the basal dose of nitrogen, the larger the effect of topdressing on the percentage of filled grains and 1,000-grain weight. Thus, the degree of filling of grains is determined basically by the ratio between the number of spikelets and the total amount of carbohydrates accumulated at the time of maturity.

C. Photosynthetic Activity, Respiratory Activity, and Nitrogen

As to the effect of nitrogen in promoting or maintaining the photosynthetic activity as well as respiratory activity, there are already sufficient data, especially in rice plants, since the work of Mitsui and Ishii (1938, 1939) (c.f. Murata, 1965). Recently other results have been added by Osada (1964, 1966), Osada and Murata (1965a,b), Murata et al. (1966), and Tanaka, Kawano, and Yamaguchi (1966). Also in other species, for example, soybean (Ojima, Fukui, and Watanabe, 1965), and sweet potato (Tsuno and Fujise, 1965), results similar to those with rice have been obtained. Based upon the work with rice, photosynthetic activity measured under normal conditions has a very close, positive correlation with the total or protein nitrogen content of the leaf over a wide range, usually up to 5% nitrogen, irrespective of the growth stage, as is shown in Fig. 11-12. Fujiwara and co-worker found that in developing rice leaves the photosynthetic activity was proportional to the nitrogen content corrected by subtracting the nitrogen content of the very young leaf which had, as yet, no photosynthetic capacity (Fujiwara, 1965).

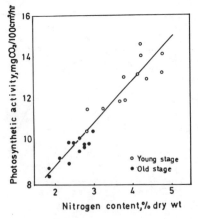

Fig. 11-12—Relation between N content and photosynthetic activity of the rice leaf (Murata et al., 1966). Leaves were sampled from those plants grown in the field under various combinations in plowing depth, planting density, and nitrogen level and measured under saturating light intensity and normal CO_2 concentration.

On the other hand, higher nitrogen supply does not always bring about higher photosynthetic activity, though the photosynthetic capacity of the plant or stand may be greatly enhanced (Murata, 1961). This is because, under high nitrogen supply, growth and development of leaves are greatly stimulated, so that the nitrogen content of each leaf is 'diluted,' making the difference of nitrogen content comparatively small, and increasing the possibility of relative deficiency in other nutrients. If, however, nitrogen is applied at a stage when the growth of leaves is slowed down or stopped due to a certain inner or outer condition, then photosynthetic activity will be stimulated in most cases. Herein lies the reason for the typical effect of nitrogen topdressing applied at later growth stages (Murata, 1961).

In higher plants, chloroplasts account for 25% of the total dry weight, and 40% of the total nitrogen, of the leaf (Bonner, 1952). About 50% of the dry weight of the chloroplast is composed of various proteins. The stroma protein, responsible for reduction of CO_2 makes up about one-third of the protein of the chloroplast. The remaining two-thirds consists of the structural proteins responsible, in combination with chlorophyll, for the primary processes in photosynthesis (Menke, 1966). Although little information is available, it is supposed that the effect of nitrogen on photosynthetic activity is basically exerted through the metabolism of these chloroplast proteins and chlorophyll. According to Bourdu et al. (1965, 1966), not only decreases in the content of chlorophyll and protein but also changes in structure and function of chloroplast were observed in the nitrogen-deficient Bryophyllum leaf. The chloroplasts were filled with large starch inclusions which disorganized the lamellar system, some chloroplasts were membraneless, and Hill-reaction and photophosphorylation activities were very low.

Nitrogen also affects photosynthesis in another way. Navasero and

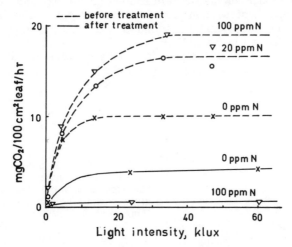

Fig. 11-13—Photosynthetic rate at different light intensities of 'Peta' leaves before and after a 13-day, 400 lux dark treatment (Tanaka et al., 1966). The respiratory rates in mg CO_2/dm^2 per hr were: before—0 N = 0.757, 20 N = 1.004, 100 N = 1.807; after—0 N = 0.84, and 100 N = 0.86.

Tanaka (1966) have made the very interesting observation that when rice plants supplied with abundant nitrogen were kept under a reduced light condition (400 lux) for 13 days, their leaves completely lost photosynthetic activity, but retained respiratory activity, as is shown in Fig. 11-13. This finding could explain one of the common causes for the death of lower leaves of plants under heavy mutual shading: Lack of respiratory substrates induces protein breakdown, as is shown in Table 11-3, leading to the production of amino acids, amides, and ammonium ion which is toxic to the cell and eventually kills the leaves.

D. Root Activity and Photosynthetic Activity

A close correlation between nitrogen content and photosynthetic activity is not found in cases where root injury is probable, for example, in a poorly drained, strongly reduced soil (Murata et al., 1966). Here, two problems are involved. One is the influence of toxic substances produced in the soil, and the other is the role of the root for maintaining the photosynthetic activity.

Concerning the first problem, Baba and Tajima (1962) and Yanagisawa and Takahashi (1964) observed that addition of hydrogen sulfide to the culture medium reduced the photosynthetic activity of rice leaves, and caused an abnormal acceleration of respiration and decreased absorption of nutrients. As to the second problem, Murata, Iyamm, and Honma (1965) demonstrated a close interdependence between root activity and photosynthetic activity in water-cultured rice plants. The root system was subjected to various unfavorable conditions such as addition of hydrogen sulfide or ferrous iron into the solution, depletion of oxygen from the solution, and others. After a few days considerable differences developed in the protein content of the leaf, though the plants were uniformly kept without added nitrogen supply. The difference in protein content was clearly associated with changes in photosynthetic activity as is shown in Fig. 11-14.

That the presence of the root is closely correlated with the protein level of the shoot has been shown by Chibnall (1954), Mothes and Engel-

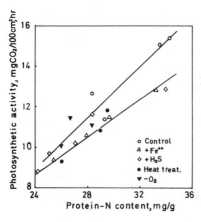

Fig. 11-14—Relationships between protein-nitrogen content of the leaf and photosynthetic activity in rice plants given various treatments to the root (Murata et al., 1965).

brecht (1956), Oritani (1963), Oritani and Yoshida (1967) and others. On the other hand, evidence is now accumulating indicating the necessity of simultaneous synthesis of ribonucleic acids (RNA) for protein synthesis (McKee, 1962). In plants without roots, the ability to synthesize RNA decreases, followed by reduced protein synthesis (Togari and Oritani, 1960; Oritani, 1963). These facts suggest the possibility that the root may in some way influence RNA synthesis and thereby control the protein level of the leaf, and as a result may influence photosynthetic activity.

V. DRY MATTER AND GRAIN PRODUCTION UNDER ABUNDANT NITROGEN SUPPLY

This topic will be discussed both from the standpoint of direct effect of heavy doses of nitrogen on the plant itself, and from the standpoint of indirect influence of the environment which the plants have created under such conditions.

A. Disruption of Photosynthesis-Respiration Balance

With the advance of growth from the initial stage dominated by differentiation to the stage of rapid growth, the demand for carbohydrates increases, and therefore, the problem of keeping the balance between photosynthesis and respiration (P-R balance) becomes increasingly important. The LAI of a rice stand reaches its maximum a little before heading. In order to hasten the expansion rate of LAI and enlarge the "capacity" for yield, a heavy application of nitrogen at an early stage is quite effective. On the other hand, such an application is very likely to deteriorate the P-R balance of the crop stand, adversely affecting the accumulation of carbohydrates and grain-filling.

The existence of an optimum leaf area for the maximum dry matter production of a plant community was shown theoretically by Monsi and Saeki (1953), and experimentally by Takeda (1961), Murata (1961) and Tanaka et al. (1966) in rice stands. These authors also demon-

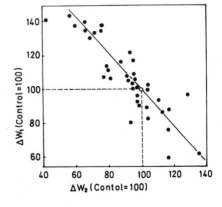

Fig. 11-15—Relationship between dry matter increase before (ΔW_1) and after heading (ΔW_2) in rice plants grown in the field under various combinations of plowing depth, planting density, and nitrogen level (Murata et al., 1966).

strated that one of the fundamental, physiological causes responsible
for various difficulties occurring under an abundant supply of nitrogen
lies in the deterioration of P-R balance due to increased mutual shading. Thus, under these conditions, a phenomenon occurs such as that
reported by Murata et al. (1966) and Tanaka et al. (1966) in which the
more vigorous the growth of the stand before heading stage, the smaller
is the dry matter increase in the grain-filling stage. (Fig. 11-15).

B. Influence of Solar Radiation on Nitrogen Effect

The disruption of P-R balance of crop stands due to heavy application of nitrogen is intensified under conditions of low solar radiation.
Murata (1961) observed that in some extreme cases those plants supplied with high rates of nitrogen temporarily lost dry weight when the
solar radiation was very poor (approximately 200 cal/cm^2/day) at
around the heading stage. Wada (1969) has recently concluded from a
number of his experiments (Fig. 11-16) that dry matter increase in rice
during the ripening period is most closely correlated with the following product: $(N + \Delta N)Q$, where N stands for the total nitrogen content of
leaves at heading, ΔN for the amount of nitrogen absorbed during the
filling period, and Q for the average solar radiation during the same
period. Chernavskaya and Nichiporovich (1966) also have concluded
from many data that, when nitrogen supply and light level are within the

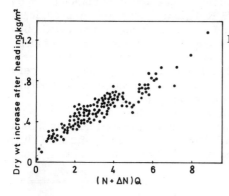

Fig. 11-16—Relation between dry matter increase after heading and the
product of the amount of solar radiation (Q) and the sum of nitrogen content in leaf blade (N) and the amount
of nitrogen absorbed after heading
(ΔN) in rice plants (Wada, 1969). Various plots differing in time of culture,
degree of shading, N level, and year
are included.

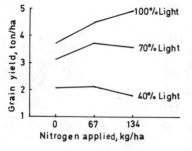

Fig. 11-17—Rough rice yield at different light intensities and nitrogen fertility (Stansel et al., 1965).

range of "harmonious combination," the efficiencies of photosynthesis, growth, and dry matter production are highest.

In the case of grain production, another circumstance adds to the importance of solar radiation during the filling period. Grain-filling depends almost entirely upon the currently produced carbohydrates under a heavy nitrogen application as was shown by Murayama et al. (1955). Also, Stansel et al. (1965) found, as is shown in Fig. 11-17, that the higher the radiation level during the critical 6 weeks—3 weeks before heading plus 3 weeks after it—the larger was the effect of nitrogen on the grain yield of rice.

C. Disturbance of Nitrogen Metabolism

An abundant supply of nitrogen can stimulate growth as long as there are sufficient supplies of growth hormone(s), carbohydrates, water and other nutrients as well as environmental conditions suitable for rapid growth. At present we do not know the exact mechanism for the growth process. However, it is clear that growth which is stimulated by nitrogen supply is inseparably combined with protein synthesis which is carried out at the expense of carbohydrates in reserve or currently under production. Therefore, if nitrogen supply is too abundant in comparison to the rate of carbohydrate production, plants will sooner or later be depleted of carbohydrate reserve. Such plants will face the danger of ammonium toxicity, having insufficient carbohydrates to promote the conversion of ammonium to amides or amino acids. To make the situation worse, in paddy soil which is in a highly reduced state under flooded water, most of the available nitrogen is in the form of the ammonium ion. Thus, the possibility of severe ammonium toxicity for rice plants is expected from the highest-tiller-number stage through the heading stage. Carbohydrate accumulation is still very small during this time. A large increase in the content of ammonium ion and amides in the cells of rice plants supplied with a topdressing of ammonium sulfate was demonstrated by Ito and Sakamoto (1942) and this was considered as an important causal factor for the increased susceptibility of rice plants to the blast disease. In lower leaves, increase of soluble nitrogen due to protein degradation is also expected (c.f. Table 11-3).

Another problem to be considered here is the disturbance of nitrogen metabolism following decreased nitrate reductase activity under shaded conditions. This problem has recently been actively studied by Hageman and Flesher (1960), Hageman, Flesher, and Gitter (1961),

Table 11-3—Nitrogen in various fractions in leaves of rice grown in the dark for 7 days compared to that grown in the light (Navasero and Tanaka, 1966)

Nitrogenous fractions	Content, mg/g fresh wt	
	Control	Dark
Ammonium-N	.09	.34
Amino-N	.68	3.04
Amide-N	.14	.36
Protein-N	11.64	8.08

Knipmeyer et al. (1962), Beevers et al. (1965), Harper and Paulsen (1967), and others, in corn, wheat and other species. Knipmeyer et al. (1962), studying three corn hybrids which were artificially shaded or placed under competitive plant shading, observed increased nitrate accumulation in spite of unchanged total nitrogen content. They concluded that nitrogen metabolism was more adversely affected by shading than was carbohydrate metabolism. This conclusion has led them to denial of the common idea that nitrogen metabolism is limited by carbohydrate metabolism under such conditions.

The same situation is expected under heavy mutual shading caused by abundant nitrogen supply. Thus, a large amount of nitrate accumulation is reported in grasses. However, the ability to store nitrogen as nitrate differs greatly from species to species, being high in such plants as sugar beet, tobacco, wheat, and soybean (McKee, 1962), and very low in rice plants, at least when grown with ammonium nitrogen (Izawa, Oji, and Okamoto, 1966; etc.). Many upland crops accumulate nitrate which is far less harmful than ammonium for the plant, thus they can store a considerable amount of nitrogen without consuming carbohydrates. In contrast to this, it is inevitable for rice plants to consume stored carbohydrates to avoid the toxic effect of ammonium under heavy nitrogen supply. That is to say, in rice plants nitrogen metabolism is quite closely combined with, and likely to be limited by, carbohydrate metabolism, whereas in many upland species nitrogen metabolism is more or less loosely combined with, and to some extent independent of, carbohydrate metabolism due to the ability of the plants to store nitrates.

D. Decrease of Root Activity

The root system of a plant requires adequate supplies of carbohydrates and other nutrients to maintain its activity. Under stand conditions in the field, root activity is quite often limited by carbohydrate supply from the shoot. Thus, Thomas and Hill (1949) observed in alfalfa that the daily change of root respiration quite closely resembled a 3-day running average of net assimilation. Such a situation may become serious under an abundant supply of nitrogen.

According to the studies of Tanaka (1958) in rice, division of work is seen concerning the carbohydrate supply among the leaves different in their position on the stem; upper leaves supply carbohydrates to the developing new leaves and ears, while lower leaves supply the root system. This observation was also reported in bean (Biddulph and Cory, 1965), field pea (Pate, 1966), and tobacco (Tokitsu et al., 1957). As was mentioned earlier, under heavy nitrogen supply, lower leaves are very likely to die due to carbohydrate deficiency. Thus, the root system loses both activity for nutrient absorption and also resistance to toxic substances in the soil. Root rot develops, in turn the death of lower leaves intensifies (Okajima, 1960; Baba, 1961), and the photosynthetic activity of the remaining leaves decreases (Murata et al., 1965). According to Okajima (1960), if under such conditions nitrogen supply is temporarily suspended, the root loses oxidative activity and as a result turns the surrounding medium to a more reduced state, intensifying the production of hydrogen sulfide. However, according to recent work of Hoshino, Matsushima, and Matsuzaki (1969) such adverse effects of nitrogen-depletion can be largely eliminated by addition of small amount of nitrogen to the root media.

Tanaka et al. (1964) observed a larger dry weight increase in those rice plants which could continue absorption of nitrogen after the heading stage. Tsuno (1968) showed, in several rice varieties with which he succeeded in obtaining yields in excess of 8 tons of brown rice per hectare, that the amount of nitrogen absorbed after heading was equivalent to as much as 19-78% of the nitrogen accumulated in ears at harvest. He stressed that such active absorption of nitrogen from the soil made it possible to maintain a large LAI as well as high photosynthetic activity until a very late stage, contributing greatly to the high yield.

E. Translocation and Distribution of Substances and Nitrogen

Nitrogen can affect, though indirectly, the translocation and distribution of various substances in plants. Such an influence of nitrogen is based on the fact that different parts of the plant respond to nitrogen to different degrees. For example, as is shown in Table 11-4, at a lower level of nitrogen supply, there exists a larger stimulus to the growth of root than shoot, increasing translocation of carbohydrates to the root. At a higher level of nitrogen supply, however, shoot growth is greatly stimulated and this in turn decreases the translocation of carbohydrates to the root, thereby suppressing its growth. In this way, nitrogen influences the distribution of substances among different organs.

Shimizu (1967) found that the higher the nitrogen content in the rice leaf, the larger was the portion of dry matter allotted for the formation

Table 11-4—Distribution of ^{14}C between the shoot and root of rice plant 4 days after $^{14}CO_2$ given (5th Laboratory of Physiology, Nat. Inst. Agr. Sci., 1960)

Plot Amount of (N added)	Part	Dry wt g/plant	Amount of ^{14}C count/min /plant × 10^3	Relative to total
Low - N	Leaf blade	0.91	5.8	40
(0 g)	Leaf sheath	0.94	2.8	19
	Root	0.76	5.9	41
	Total	2.61	14.5	100
Medium-N	Leaf blade	4.29	15.3	51
(3 g/plant)	Leaf sheath	3.12	10.1	34
	Root	2.11	4.7	15
	Total	9.52	30.1	100
High-N	Leaf blade	4.97	19.5	52
(6 g/plant)	Leath sheath	3.43	13.8	37
	Root	2.33	4.2	11
	Total	10.73	37.5	100

Note: $^{14}CO_2$ applied, 50 μc/plant, for 1 hour, at the max-tiller – number stage.

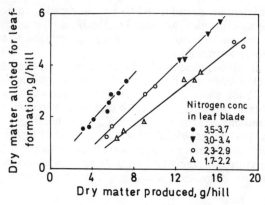

Fig. 11-18—Relationships between nitrogen conc. in leaf blade and the amount of dry matter allotted for leaf formation in rice plants (Shimizu, 1967).

of new leaves (Fig. 11-18). Interesting results were also reported by Tsuno and Fujise (1965) in the sweet potato (Ipomoea batatas L.). Here both potassium and nitrogen were shown to play important roles in determining the relative distribution of dry matter between shoot and root.

It is also possible that nitrogen can influence translocation through its effect on the development or longevity of conducting tissues. Matsushima (1957) found that the cross-sectional area of the conducting tissues of the main culm of rice plants was made considerably larger by removing all the tillers except the main culm, thereby giving a more favorable environment to the plants.

In the "deep-layer-application" of nitrogen which was mentioned earlier, the grain yield of the treated plot was higher than the control (Table 11-5), in spite of the fact that dry matter increase during the filling period was considerably smaller in the treated plot. The larger pre-heading accumulation of carbohydrates in the culm must be primarily responsible for this increased yield, but at the same time it is quite possible that not only the size of hulls but also the effectiveness of the conductive tissue facilitated the translocation of carbohydrates to the grain.

Table 11-5—Effect of "deep-layer-application" of nitrogen on dry weight increase and grain yield of rice (Matsuura et al., 1969)

Plot	Dry weight increase		Total available carbohydrates in culms at heading	Yield of brown rice
	Before heading (July 4 - July 31)	After heading (July 31 - Sept 16)		
	g/m²	g/m²	% dry wt	ton/ha
Control	736	454	6.6	6.80
"Deep" 1	755	480	8.9	6.88
"Deep" 2	944	290	8.6	7.12
"Deep" 3	1,052	170	12.5	7.51

Note: Plots are the same as in Table 11-1.

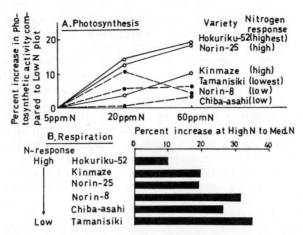

Fig. 11-19—Promotion of photosynthetic and respiratory activity by high nitro-
nitrogen supply in rice varieties differing in nitrogen response (Osada, 1966).
Photosynthetic rate was measured under a saturating light intensity and normal
CO_2 conc., using excised leaves, and respiratory rate is based on values of CO_2
mg/g dry wt of the whole shoot at 28C, both at heading stage of water-cultured
plants.

F. Nitrogen Response of Varieties

According to the results of Osada and Murata (1962, 1965) and
Osada (1964, 1966), high nitrogen-response varieties of rice show,
under heavy nitrogen application, a larger promotion in photosynthetic
activity, but a smaller promotion in respiratory activity, than do low
response varieties (Fig. 11-19). Reflecting these characteristics, the
P/R ratio, on a field-area basis, is larger in high response varieties
than in low response ones (Fig. 11-20).

Tanaka et al. (1966), on the other hand, have shown that shortness
of culm is essential for high nitrogen response from the standpoint of
avoiding lodging, but that it is also important in that it decreases the

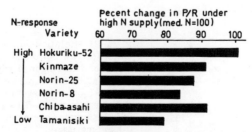

Fig. 11-20—Changes in the ratio of total photosynthesis to respiration of population (P/R) by increasing nitrogen supply in rice varieties differing in nitrogen
response (Osada, 1966). Nitrogen supply: High N, 150 kg/ha; med. N, 75 kg/ha.

portion of respiration which is not directly effective for grain production. Takahashi, Iwata, and Baba (1959) showed that high response varieties accumulated, under heavy nitrogen supply, more carbohydrates than low response varieties, while nitrogen absorption at early stages of growth was more active in low response varieties than in high response ones. Tanaka et al. (1964) have proved that even low response varieties can produce a high grain yield if grown in an environment where nitrogen supply is restricted or photosynthesis is enhanced.

From these results it may be concluded that high nitrogen-response varieties tend to have higher ability for carbon assimilation in comparison to the ability for nitrogen assimilation and growth, while low response varieties tend to be superior in the ability for nitrogen assimilation and growth but somewhat inferior in their ability for carbon assimilation.

Baba (1961) mentioned, as one of the important characteristics of high response varieties, their comparatively high grain/straw ratio under heavy nitrogen supply. In relation to this problem, the speaker has very recently found an interesting phenomenon from Osada's data (1966): As shown in Fig. 11-21, there is a very clear, positive correlation between the panicle/straw ratio and the $P_0 \cdot S/A$ ratio, where P_0 denotes the average photosynthetic activity, during the filling period of individual varieties; S, the number of spikelets per unit area, and A, the LAI at heading stage, respectively. Here, S/A represents the important morphological characteristics expressing the yield "capacity" relative to the thickness of the stand, as was mentioned before (c.f. Fig. 11-3). The relationship shown in Fig. 11-21 indicates that the larger the ability for carbon assimilation and the spikelet number, and/ or the smaller the LAI, the higher is the panicle/straw ratio.

Recently Ogata and Ishizuka (1967a,b,c) have studied the genetics of nitrogen-response in potato, using a cultivated species, a wild species, their hybrid, and the progeny of the second backcross to the cultivated species. As is shown in Fig. 11-22, the closer the relationship to the cultivated species, the larger is the amount of dry matter production, the growth of tubers, and chlorophyll concentration, under high nitrogen supply. However, chlorophyll concentration under low nitrogen supply was higher in the wild species. It was also found that the closer the

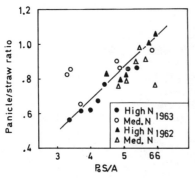

Fig. 11-21—Relationship between the panicle/straw ratio and P_0S/A in rice varieties differing in nitrogen response (Calculated from the data of Osada, 1966). P_O = photosynthetic activity of leaf during grain-filling period. S = spikelet number per area, and A = LAI at heading stage.

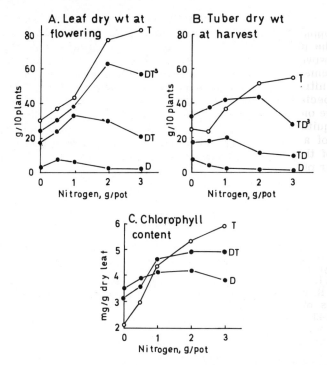

Fig. 11-22—Changes in the dry weight of leaves and tubers and chlorophyll concentration in the leaf in relation to nitrogen supply in cultivated, wild, and their hybrid potatoes (Ogata and Ishizuka, 1967). T = cultivated species, Solanum tuberosum; D = wild species, S. demissum forma atrocyaneum; DT = their hybrid; and, DT^3 = two-time backcross.

relationship to the wild species, the lower was the apparent photosynthetic rate and more photosynthates were turned into amides and organic acids, whereas in the cultivated species more of the photosynthates were held as compounds soluble in hot alcohol.

One may conclude that in the case of potato, the wild species is lower than the cultivated species, not only in the ratio of carbon assimilation to nitrogen assimilation, but also in the absolute level of both types of assimilation. In the case of rice varieties, on the other hand, it seems that the assimilation of both carbon and nitrogen has been greatly improved in the process of breeding, while the ratio has been left unchanged in low nitrogen-response varieties, which are useful under low nitrogen conditions.

VI. CONCLUSION

The speaker has shown, in a limited way, the outline of the knowledge we have at present on how nitrogen affects the processes of yield formation of crop plants, using the rice plant as an example. During the analyses, it has been pointed out that the way in which nitrogen affects the development of an organ always follows the same principles, however morphologically different the organs may be, but that there seems to be some difference in the degree of interdependence between nitrogen metabolism and carbohydrate metabolism among different species. Also we have recognized how limited is our present knowledge on such a field of study as, for example, on the harvest index which is quite important in relation to economic yield, both as a characteristic of a genotype and as a comprehensive expression for the response of the plant to an environment. The speaker feels that in the future our physiological knowledge should be greatly extended into such field.

LITERATURE CITED

Adegbola, A. A., and C. M. McKell. 1966. Effect of nitrogen fertilization on the carbohydrate content of coastal bermudagrass (Cynodon dactylon). Agron. J. 58:60-64.

Auda, H., R. E. Blaser, and R. H. Hageman. 1966. Tillering and carbohydrate contents of orchardgrass influenced by environmental factors. Crop Sci. 6:139-143.

Baba, I. 1961. Mechanism of response to heavy manuring in rice varieties. IRC News Letter 10:9-16.

Baba, I., and K. Tajima. 1962. Physiological studies on the root of crop plant. III. Proc. Crop Sci. Soc. Japan 31:11-14.

Beevers, L., L. E. Schrader, F. Flesher, and R. H. Hageman. 1965. The role of light and nitrate in the induction of nitrate reductase in radish cotyledons and maize seedlings. Plant Physiol. 40:691-698.

Biddulph, O., and R. Cory. 1965. Translocation of C^{14}-metabolites in the phloem of bean plant. Plant Physiol. 40:119-129.

Bonner, J. 1952. Plant biochemistry. Academic Press, New York.

Bourdu, R., Marie-Louse Champigny, M. Lefort, R. Remy, and A. Moyse. 1965. Structure and activities of the photosynthetic apparatus of Bryophyllum daigremontianum leaves in terms of their growth, nitrogen deficiency and nutrition. I. Physiol. Vegetale 3:305-327.

Bourdu, R., Marie-Louse Champigny, M. Lefort, M. Maslow, and A. Moyse. 1966. Ibid. II. Physiol. Vegetale 3:355-392.

Chernavskaya, N. M., and A. A. Nichiporovich. 1966. Hormonious combination of illumination and nitrogen nutrition. In A. A. Nichiporovich (ed.) Photosynthesis of productive systems. Academy of Sci. USSR (English translation, by Kaner and Monteith, 1967).

Chibnall, A. C. 1954. Protein metabolism in rooted runner-bean leaves. New Phytol. 53:31-37.

Colby, W. G., Mack Drake, D. L. Field, and G. Kreowski. 1965. Seasonal pattern of fructosan in orchardgrass stubble as influenced by nitrogen and harvest management. Agron. J. 57:169-173.

Fujiwara, A. 1965. The specific roles of nitrogen, phosphorus, and potassium in the metabolism of the rice plant, 93-105. In The mineral nutrition of the rice plant, IRRI, Johns Hopkins Press, Baltimore.

Fujiwara, A., K. Ohira, K. Otsuki, and S. Narita. 1951. Studies on the nitrogen nutrition of crops. I. J. Sci. Soil and Manure, Japan 22:91-96.

Griffith, W. K., M. R. Teel, and H. E. Parker. 1964. Influence of nitrogen and potassium on the yield and chemical composition of orchardgrass. Agron. J. 56:473-475.

Hageman, R. H., and D. Flesher. 1960. Nitrate reductase activity in corn seedlings as affected by light and nitrate content of the nutrient media. Plant
physiol. 35:635-641.

Hageman, R. H., D. Flesher, and A. Gitter. 1961. Diurnal variation and other
light effects influencing the activity of nitrate reductase and nitrogen metabolism in corn. Crop Sci. 1:201-204.

Harper, J. E., and G. M. Paulsen. 1967. Changes in reduction and assimilation
of nitrogen during the growth cycle of winter wheat. Crop Sci. 7:205-209.

Hoshino, T., S. Matsushima, and A. Matsuzaki. 1969. Analysis of yield-determining process and its application to yield prediction and culture improvement of lowland rice. 94. Proc. Crop. Sci. Soc. Japan 38:   (in press).

Ishizuka, Y., and A. Tanaka. 1956a. Studies on ecological characteristics of
rice plant grown in different localities, especially from standpoint of nutrio-
physiological characters of plant. Part I. J. Sci. Soil and Manure, Japan
27:1-6.

Ishizuka, Y., and A. Tanaka. 1956b. Nutrio-physiological characteristics of
growth process of rice plant in different localities. Ibid. 27:95-99.

Ito, S., and S. Sakamoto. 1942. Studies on rice blast. Report for 1941. Min. of
Agr. and Forestry, Tokyo.

Izawa, G., Y. Ohi, and S. Okamoto. 1966. Utilization of nitrate nitrogen in higher
plant. Part 2. J. Sci. Soil and Manure, Japan 37:558-562.

Knipmeyer, J. W., R. H. Hageman, E. B. Earley, and R. D. Seif. 1962. Effect of
light intensity on certain metabolites of the corn plant (Zea mays L.). Crop
Sci. 2:1-5.

Kumura, A. 1956a. Studies on the effect of internal nitrogen concentration of
rice plant on the constitutional factor of yield. Proc. Crop Sci. Soc. Japan
24:177-180.

Kumura, A. 1956b. Studies on the production and behavior of carbohydrates in
rice plant. III. ibid. 24:324-330.

Matsushima, S. 1957. Analysis of developmental factors determining yield and
yield-prediction in lowland rice. Bull. Nat. Inst. Agr. Sci. Japan, Ser. A,
5:1-271.

Matsuura, K., T. Iwata, and T. Hasegawa. 1969. Studies on the effect of deep-
layer application of fertilizers in rice plant. I. Proc. Crop Sci. Soc. Japan
38: (in press).

McKee, H. S. 1962. Nitrogen metabolism in plants. Clarendon Press, Oxford,
London. 728 p.

Menke, W. 1966. The structure of the chloroplasts, p. 3-18. In T. W. Goodwin
(ed.) Biochemistry of chloroplasts. Vol. I. Academic Press, London and New
York.

Mitsui, S., and T. Ishii. 1938. Effect of differences in three major elements
supply quantity on the efficiency of carbon assimilation of the young rice plant.
J. Sci. Soil and Manure, Japan 12:287-289.

Mitsui, S., and T. Ishii. 1939. Effect of nitrogen topdressing. J. Sci. Soil and
Manure, Japan 13:309-313.

Monsi, M., und T. Saeki. 1953. Über den Lichtfaktor in den Pflanzengesellschaften und seine Bedeutung für die Stoffproduktion. Jap. J. Bot. 14:22-52.

Mothes, K., und L. Engelbrecht. 1956. Über den Stickstoffumsatz in Blattsteck-
lingen. Flora 143:428-472.

Murata, Y. 1961. Studies on the photosynthesis of rice plants and its culture
significance. Bull. Nat. Inst. Agr. Sci. Japan, Ser. D,9:1-169.

Murata, Y. 1965. Photosynthesis, respiration and nitrogen response, p. 385-
400. In The mineral nutrition of the rice plant. IRRI, Johns Hopkins Press,
Baltimore.

Murata, Y., J. Iyama, M. Himeda, S. Izumi, A. Kawabe, and Y. Kanzaki. 1966.
Studies on the deep-plowing, dense-planting cultivation of rice plants from the
point of view of photosynthesis and production of dry matter. Bull. Nat. Inst.
Agr. Sci. Japan, Ser. D,15:1-53.

Murata, Y., J. Iyama, and T. Honma. 1965. Studies on the photosynthesis of rice plants. XIII. Proc. Crop Sci. Soc. Japan 34:148-153.

Murayama, N. 1967. A discussion on the leveling-off trend of rice yield in Japan and measures to level it up. J. Jap. Soc. Plant Physiologists 6:25-32.

Murayama, N., M. Yoshino, M. Oshima, S. Tsukahara, and Y. Kawarazaki. 1955. The process of carbohydrate accumulation associated with growth of rice plants. Bull. Nat. Inst. Agr. Sci., Japan, Ser. B,4:123-164.

Navasero, S. A., and A. Tanaka. 1966. Low-light induced death of lower leaves of rice and its effect on grain yield. Plant and Soil 14:17-31.

Ogata, S., and Y. Ishizuka. 1967a. Variation of nutrio-physiological characters of crops in the process of their crossing. Part 1. J. Sci. Soil and Manure, Japan 38:79-84.

Ogata, S., and Y. Ishizuka. 1967b. Variation of nutrio-physiological characters of crops in the process of their crossing. Part 2. J. Sci. Soil and Manure, Japan 38:131-134.

Ogata, S., and Y. Ishizuka. 1967c. Variation of nutrio-physiological characters of crops in the process of their crossing. Part 3. J. Sci. Soil and Manure, Japan 38:466-468.

Ojima, M., J. Fukui, and I. Watanabe. 1965. Studies on the seed production of soybean. II. Proc. Crop Sci. Soc. Japan 33:437-442.

Okajima, H. 1960. Studies on the physiological function of the roots system in the rice plant, viewed from the nitrogen nutrition. Bull. Inst. Agr. Res. Tohoku Univ. 12(1):1-146.

Oritani, T. 1963. The role of root in nitrogen metabolism of crop plants. Proc. Crop Sci. Soc. Japan 31:277-283.

Oritani, T., and R. Yoshida. 1967. Studies on nitrogen metabolism in crop plant. II. Proc. Crop Sci. Soc. Japan 36:509-513.

Oshima, M. 1962. Studies on the nitrogen nutrition of plant. J. Sci. Soil and Manure, Japan 33:243-246.

Osada, A. 1964. Studies on the photosynthesis of indica rice. Proc. Crop Sci. Soc. Japan 33:69-76.

Osada, A. 1966. Relationship between photosynthetic activity and dry matter production in rice varieties, especially as influenced by nitrogen supply. Bull. Nat. Inst. Agr. Sci. Japan, Ser. D,14:117-188.

Osada, A., and Y. Murata. 1962. Studies on the relationship between photosynthesis and varietal adaptability for heavy manuring in rice plants. I. Proc. Crop Sci. Soc. Japan 30:220-223.

Osada, A., and Y. Murata. 1965. ibid. III. Effects of photosynthetic characteristics on dry matter production and ripening of rice varieties. Proc. Crop Sci. Soc. Japan 33:460-466.

Ota, Y., and N. Yamada. 1965. Studies on sterility of indica rice. Part 2. Jap. J. Trop. Agr. 9:76-79.

Pate, J.S. 1966. Photosynthesizing leaves and nodulated roots as donors of carbon to protein of the shoot of the field pea (Pisum arvense L.) Ann. Bot. (London) 30:93-109.

Sato, K. 1956. Studies on the starch content in the tissues of rice plant. II. Proc. Crop Sci. Soc. Japan 24:154-155.

Shimizu, T. 1967. Processes of yield-formation in rice plants from the point of dry matter production. Matter Production in Crops 4:12-26.

Soga, Y., and M. Nozaki. 1957. Studies on the relation between seasonal changes of carbohydrates accumulation and the ripening at the stage of generative growth in rice plant. Proc. Crop Sci. Soc. Japan 26:105-108.

Stansel, J. W., C. N. Bollich, J. R. Thysell, and V. L. Hall. 1965. The influence of light intensity and nitrogen fertility on rice yield and components of yield. Rice J. 68:34-35.

Takahashi, J., M. Yanagisawa, M. Kono, F. Yazawa, and T. Yoshida. 1955. Influence of the amount of application of nitrogenous fertilizer upon the composition of paddy rice plants. Bull. Nat. Inst. Agr. Sci. Japan, Ser. B,4:85-122.

Takahashi, Y., I. Iwata, and I. Baba. 1959. Studies on the varietal adaptability for heavy manuring in rice. I. Proc. Crop Sci. Soc. Japan 28:22-24.

Takeda, T. 1961. Studies on the photosynthesis and production of dry matter in the community of rice plants. Jap. J. Bot. 17:403-407.

Tanaka, A. 1958. Studies on the physiological characteristics and significance of rice leaves in relation to their position on the stem. XI. J. Sci. Soil and Manure, Japan 29:327-333.

Tanaka, A., K. Kawano, and J. Yamaguchi. 1966. Photosynthesis, respiration, and plant type of the tropical rice plant. Int. Rice Res. Inst. Tech. Bull. 7:1-46.

Tanaka, A., S. A. Navasero, C. V. Garcia, G. T. Parao, and E. Ramirez. 1964. Growth habit of the rice plant in the tropics and its effect on nitrogen response. Int. Rice Res. Inst. Bull. 3:1-80.

Thomas, M. D., and G. R. Hill. 1949. Photosynthesis under field condition, p. 19-52. In J. Franck and W. E. Loomis (ed.) Photosynthesis in plants. Iowa State Coll. Press, Ames, Iowa.

Thorne, G. N. 1965. Physiological aspects of grain yield, p. 89-105. In F. L. Milthorpe and J. D. Ivin (ed.) The growth of cereals and grasses. Mutterworths, London.

Togari, Y., and Y. Kashiwakura. 1958. Studies on the sterility in rice plant induced by superabundant nitrogen supply and insufficient light intensity. Proc. Crop Sci. Soc. Japan 27:3-5.

Togari, Y., Y. Okamoto, and A. Kumura. 1954. Studies on the production and behavior of carbohydrates in rice plant. I. Proc. Crop Sci. Soc. Japan 22:95-97.

Togari, Y., and K. Sato. 1954. Studies on the production and behavior of carbohydrates in rice plant. II. Proc. Crop Sci. Soc. Japan 22:98-99.

Togari, Y., and T. Oritani. 1960. The role of root in nitrogen metabolism of crop plants. Proc. Crop Sci. Soc. Japan 29:71-74.

Tokitsu, T., Y. Muraoka, and M. Oka. 1957. On the functional differentiation of taproots and adventitious roots in tobacco. Proc. Crop Sci. Soc. Japan 26:53-54.

Tsuno, Y. 1968. Analysis of dry matter production in high yield rice. Proc. JIBP-PP-Photosynthesis Symposium on comparative studies on the primary productivity in terrestrial plant community.

Tsuno, Y., and K. Fujise. 1965. Studies on the dry matter production of sweet potato. Bull. Nat. Inst. Agr. Sci. Japan, Ser. D,13:1-131.

Wada, G. 1969. Influence of nitrogen fertilizer on the yield and yield components in rice plants. Bull. Nat. Inst. Agr. Sci. Japan, Ser. A,16:27-167.

Wada, G., and S. Matsushima. 1962. Analysis of yield-determining process and its application to yield prediction and culture improvement of lowland rice. LXIII. Proc. Crop Sci. Soc. Japan 31:23-26.

Wada, S., and T. Kudo. 1965. Varietal difference of yield of rice plants in response to the direct supply of fertilizers to the rhizosphere of the growing plants. I. Proc. Crop Sci. Soc. Japan 34:425-430.

Yamada, N. 1963. Ecology of rice plants, p. 1-122. In Y. Togari (ed.) Crop plants. Yokendo, Tokyo.

Yamada, N., Y. Ota, and K. Kushibuchi. 1957. Studies on ripening of rice. I. Proc. Crop Sci. Soc. Japan 26:111-115.

Yanagisawa, M., and J. Takahashi. 1964. Studies on the factors related to the productivity of paddy soils in Japan with special reference to the nutrition of the rice plants. Bull. Nat. Inst. Agr. Sci. Japan, Ser. B,14:41-171.

11...DISCUSSION

RICHARD H. HAGEMAN

University of Illinois
Urbana, Illinois

May I congratulate you, Dr. Murata, for a very thorough and well documented presentation on the physiological responses of rice to nitrogen.

I would like to recapitulate several points from your manuscript that illustrate the importance of nitrogen on morphology, physiology, and yield components of rice:

It was shown that there was a linear relationship of nitrogen content or supply with: (i) leaf area expansion rate, (ii) total leaf area development, (iii) tiller number, (iv) number of spikelets initiated/hill, (v) number of spikelets/hill, (vi) number of spikelets/m^2, and (vii) photosynthetic activity. In addition, it was stated that the nitrogen supply must be adequate to maintain the photosynthetic apparatus during the grain-filling period. It would appear that nitrogen exerts a direct and positive effect on several of the critical yield components.

Nitrogen was shown to have certain adverse effects, as excessive amounts were associated with spikelet sterility and pollen viability. These adverse effects were enhanced by low light intensities. It was also shown that nitrogen can promote vegetative growth which results in competitive plant shading that adversely affects yields. Varietal types with minimal canopy would tend to negate this aspect. In summary, it appears that high levels of ammonical salts supplied without regard to the carbohydrate status of the plant could adversely affect yield.

Because ammonium ions are the principal form of nitrogen available to paddy rice and as such are toxic to many metabolic systems, rice must maintain an adequate supply of carbohydrates (presumably keto acids) to insure prompt conversion to amino acids. It is possible that spikelet degeneration could be due to excess free ammonia in the spikelets rather than the lack of carbohydrates in the whole plant as suggested (a negative correlation between carbohydrate content and spikelet degeneration, Fig. 11-8, Murata, this book). Since neither carbohydrate nor nitrogen content of the degenerating spikelet per se was determined, it can be postulated that neither was the causal factor and that metabolite deficiency or hormonal imbalance are responsible. This suggestion is prompted by the work of E. Insleberg (Ph.D. thesis, University of Illinois, Urbana, 1956) who found that although there was no difference in levels of various sugars, nitrate accumulated in the nondeveloping ear of a three-eared corn hybrid (Zea mays L.). The other two ears developed normally. The accumulation of nitrate in the presence of adequate sugars indicates that metabolism was arrested.

In contrast, nitrate is the principal form of nitrogen available to the major cereal crops grown in the USA. Nitrates can be and are accumulated in the vegetation without known detriment to the plant. Recent work in our laboratory (Lowell Klepper, Ph.D. thesis, University of Illinois, 1969) has suggested that carbohydrates, specifically 3-phosphoglyceraldehyde is the energy source (NADH produced by its oxidation) for the NADH-dependent nitrate reductase. The carbohydrate product this oxidation, 1-3-diphosphoglycerate can be further transformed by the glycolytic enzymes to provide pyruvate to the Krebs cycle, thus insuring the input of a carbohydrate skeleton for amino acid formation for each molecule of nitrate reduced. This is partially illustrated in the following diagram.

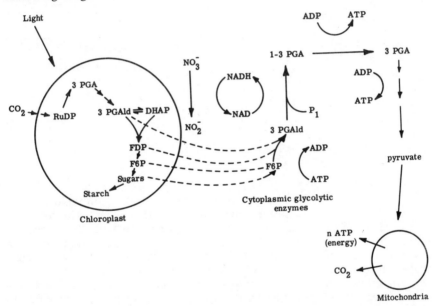

The glycolytic enzymes in the cytoplasm are capable of metabolizing any of the sugar phosphates, that enter from the chloroplast, to pyruvate and at the same time generating the NADH required for reduction of nitrate to nitrite. It is suggested that this system provides a "safety factor" that explains why nitrates are "safer" fertilizers than ammoniacal salts.

In green tissue nitrite reduction is considered to occur in the chloroplast. This is based on the observations that nitrite reductase is localized with or within the chloroplast and that ferredoxin, an intermediate of the electron transport pathway of the chloroplast, is considered the electron donor for nitrite reductase. Reduced ferredoxin can also generate NADPH (via NADP reductase), which is used to reduce fixed-CO_2. It appears that if reduction of nitrite and reduction of fixed-CO_2 are in competition for light energy as suggested by A. Moyse (Plant Physiol., Russian, 6, 287, 1959) that ferredoxin is the point where competition occurs. In this vein it is interesting to speculate as to the proportion of light energy used directly for reduction of nitrite. Assuming that at certain stages in the development of the plant that the C/N ratio of the plant is 4 and that respiration utilizes 50% of the photosynthetic product, the reduction of nitrite to ammonia would utilize 15% of the incident light. In mature plants the C/N ratios ranging from 15:1 to 20:1 have been reported.

Beyond these differences it is visualized that the influence of nitrogen on morphology, physiology and yield components of the other cereal crops are very similar to those recorded by Dr. Murata for rice.

11... DISCUSSION

AKIRA TANAKA

Hokkaido University

Sapporo, Japan

The economic yield of small grains at a high grain yield level is the function of the dry matter production after flowering. The total dry matter production does not necessarily correlate with the economic yield. How to improve the dry matter production after flowering is the key for a high economic yield. Thus, discussions should be concentrated on the status of the plants at and after flowering.

An increased supply of nitrogen in the soil to a crop causes an increased uptake of nitrogen by the crop, depending upon the capacity to absorb nitrogen. Increased nitrogen uptake may result in

1) expansion of leaf area,

2) increase in nitrogen content of the leaves, and

3) increased capacity of ears as the sink to accumulate photosynthetic products of the leaves (the yield-container).

At low nitrogen levels, frequently (3) is the most dominant factor in increasing yield and analysis of the yield components has an important meaning. However, under such conditions a high yield is impossible.

With an ample supply of nitrogen it is not a difficult task to increase the size of the yield-container. For this reason, the importance of studies on the size of the yield-container may diminish if we aim at a high grain yield with heavy nitrogen application.

At high nitrogen levels where maximum yield may be obtained (1) may have a dominant role. Frequently excess leaf area caused by a heavy nitrogen application results in a decreased grain yield due to mutual shading of the leaves. This can be overcome by employing varieties with desirable plant types combined with improved cultural methods. Excessive nitrogen content of leaves seldom adversely affects active photosynthesis. However, generally (1) and (2) take place simultaneously, thereby complicating the situation.

The degree of response to increased nitrogen uptake in the direction of (1) or (2) depends upon climatic conditions, the timing of nitrogen application, and also on varietal characters. If one can increase nitrogen content of the leaves while keeping an optimum leaf area, a high grain yield will be obtained. At high nitrogen levels, the leaf area frequently exceeds the optimum. The increased nitrogen content of the organs also results in accelerated photosynthetic potentiality and the respiratory rate. Mutual shading of the leaves increases as does respiration of the organs which are not directly associated with grain production. These upset the balance between photosynthesis and respiration. This situation is generally discussed in terms of nitrogen and carbohydrate balance. To obtain maximum grain yield nitrogen application should be made to balance (1) and (2). How to apply nitrogen to have adequate leaf area with high nitrogen content is important in obtaining a high grain yield.

Dr. Murata discussed the point that the dry matter production is the balance between photosynthesis and respiration, and accelerated respiration has a negative effect in increasing the grain yield. However, it should be noted that there is no production of substances if there is no respiration from which energy needed for the production of substances is generated. Thus, critical studies on the efficiency of respiration in dry matter production are indispensable to evaluate the significance of increased uptake of nitrogen in producing higher grain yield. As a parameter to express the efficiency of respiration the growth efficiency, which is the efficiency of photosynthetic products in producing dry matter, seems to be a useful tool to elucidate the relationships among photosynthesis, respiration, and dry matter production, and, therefore, grain production. Growth efficiency may be associated with the morphology of plants as well as with the chemical nature of respiration which are governed by environmental conditions and by genetic factors.

Considering these points, I believe that cooperation of crop physiologists with plant breeders is indispensable for maximizing crop yield.

12

Plant Morphology and Stand Geometry in Relation to Nitrogen

ROBERT F. CHANDLER, JR.

International Rice Research Institute
Manila, The Philippines

I. INTRODUCTION

During the past decade, the importance of plant morphology and spacing in relation to nitrogen responsiveness in terms of crop yield has been increasingly recognized, particularly in the case of the cereal grains.

It is the purpose of this paper to present examples of experimental results obtained by rice research workers which support certain significant principles. Although this treatise will be confined to the rice plant (Oryza sativa L.), as Wittwer (1968) points out, the principles elucidated are applicable to many other crops, and particularly to the small grains, such as wheat (Triticum aestivum L.), oats (Avena sativa L.), barley (Hordeum vulgare L.), and rye (Secale cereale L.).

In preparing this paper, the writer, although aware that certain other topics assigned for the symposium (Engineering for Higher Yields, Chapter 2; Productivity and the Morphology of Crop Stands, Chapter 3; and Cultural Manipulation for Higher Yields, Chapter 14, for instance) offered opportunities for covering much of the same ground as he contemplated, could not know beforehand the content of other presentations and hence avoid duplication. In any case, the necessary and thus intentional limitations of any one paper reduce the likelihood of totally excessive and unredeeming coverage. This paper, for example, will deal only with the above-ground plant components, although roots are an equally essential morphological structure of all higher plants.

The morphological concept of the rice plant as described by Ishizuka and Tanaka (1963) is helpful in understanding and interpreting the response of the crop to its environment. This concept is that the developing rice plant should be considered as a body of many units of different ages. The unit out of which the plant is constructed is repeated at each node and consists of a leaf, a tillering bud, a root, and an internode. (There are, of course, other minor structures which have little bearing on the life processes of the plant.) If any one of these construction units is separated from an individual plant and given the appropriate environment, it can develop into a separate and entire plant. Each tillering bud stimulated into growth develops a culm with a series of nodes and accompanying structures; and, of course, each tiller has the potential of producing a panicle at the uppermost internode of the stem. Environmental and physiological factors, as well as the genetic constitution of the plant, determine whether tillering buds develop and, if they do, whether they bear panicles. Furthermore, these same factors determine the number of spikelets, the size of grain, the size and shape of leaves, and the degree of elongation of the internodes.

The topic is a complex one, much work having been devoted to its various phases. It is not the object of this paper, however, even to approach a literature review; rather, it is to bring out what, in 1969, is known about the relationships between the morphology of the rice plant and its management, with particular reference to nitrogen and spacing.

II. MORPHOLOGICAL CHARACTERISTICS ASSOCIATED WITH RESPONSIVENESS TO NITROGEN

A. Length and Thickness of Culm

Undoubtedly, no factor is more important in determining the nitrogen responsiveness of a rice plant than the length and stiffness of its culm. This is because the tall, weak-strawed varieties lodge early and severely at high nitrogen levels; and lodging decreases the rice yield. So well established is this fact that it needs no further verification. Good examples of experimental evidence, however, can be found in Chang (1964), Jennings and Sornchai (1964), Singh and Takahashi (1962), Umali, Castillo, and Castillo (1956), and Basak, Sen, and Bhattacharjee (1962).

The only successful approach to the attainment of consistently high yields in rice has been to develop, through plant breeding, varieties that have an inherent morphological makeup which permits their thick planting and heavy fertilization without subsequent lodging.

The most important single morphological character affecting lodging resistance is plant height, which is largely the summation of the elongated internodes. This is readily seen in Fig. 12-1, which is a photograph of the culms and panicles of three rice varieties grown on the same soil at a high fertility level. The nodes from the base of the panicle on down have been connected by strings to show the differences in elongation. Note that there are six elongated internodes in each specimen. The three lower internodes had a total length of only 14 cm on both 'IR8' and IR532, while the corresponding figure for 'Peta' was 70 cm.

Peta, which is one of the parents of IR8 and was strongly involved in the breeding of IR532 (actual designation, IR532E576), is a tall, lodging-susceptible variety. IR8, a cross between Peta and 'Deo-geo-woo-gen,' is highly lodging-resistant and nitrogen responsive. IR532, at the time of the writing of this article, was the selection most likely

Fig. 12-1—Photograph of culms and panicles of IR532, IR8, and Peta varieties of rice, with leaf sheaths removed and with the nodes connected by strings to show varietal differences (height in centimeters). Peta is highly susceptible to lodging, IR8 is highly resistant, and IR532 is intermediate.

to be named a variety by the International Rice Research Institute, for it is short and high yielding, has good grain quality, and possesses a high degree of resistance to several important diseases and insects. Its only significant defect is that it is not so resistant to lodging as is IR8.

As Fig. 12-1 shows, the basal internode elongation of IR532 is essentially the same as that of IR8, and the three upper internodes are only slightly longer. The cause of the weak straw seems to lie in the thickness of the stem (the difference between the outer and inner diam-

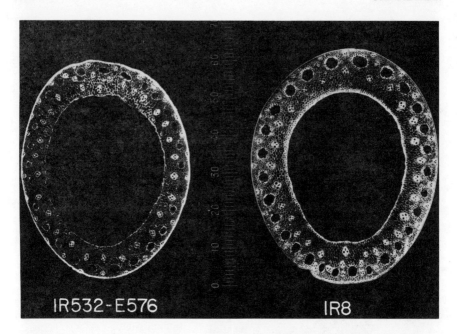

Fig. 12-2—Photograph of cross sections of the 2nd basal elongated internode of
IR532E576 and of IR8. Note the thinner culm in the somewhat lodging-susceptible IR532.

eters of the culm). This is clearly shown in Fig. 12-2. In further support of this fact, De Datta calculated the lodging resistance of IR8,
IR532E576, and Peta, grown during the monsoon season of 1968, at three
levels of nitrogen. The data are presented in Table 12-1.

The P/E ratio (defined in Table 12-1) is positively correlated with
lodging resistance (International Rice Research Institute, 1964). Table
12-1 clearly shows that IR532E576 has a much lower resistance to lodging than does IR8, but that it is quite superior to Peta. Since the value
for L of IR532 is essentially the same as for IR8, its calculated lodging
susceptibility must be connected with its thin culm. As would be expected, the application of nitrogen increased the lodging susceptibility
of all varieties.

Another factor which appears to contribute to the stem weakness of
IR532 is that it matures much more quickly after flowering than does
IR8. As these two varieties approached maturity, the lower leaves and
leaf sheaths of IR532 had died completely, leaving an average of 1.3
green leaves per stem. IR8, by contrast, had an average of 3.3, the
tightly wrapped, living leaf sheaths having helped support the culms.

The detailed description of the culm characteristics of IR8 and
IR532E576 was given here to demonstrate that plant height, when considered alone, can be misleading in predicting lodging resistance. In
fact it is likely that this one weakness may prevent IR532E576 from
becoming a named variety.

The evidence given for IR8, IR532, and Peta is supported by Chang

Table 12-1—The interaction of variety and nitrogen application on lodging resistance (S. K. De Datta, 1968. Unpublished data obtained at the International Rice Research Inst., Manila, Philippines)

Variety	Nitrogen applied kg/ha	P/E values*	
		Leaf sheath included	Leaf sheath removed
IR8	0	92	19
	40	82	15
	80	83	15
IR532E576	0	46	9
	40	31	6
	80	28	6
Peta	0	11	4
	40	8	2
	80	8	2

* P = Critical straw strength. E = Modulus of elasticity; and P/E = $[.121 (d_2{}^4 - d_1{}^4)]/L^2$. where, D_2 = outer diameter of stem in mm with leaf sheath included; d_1 = inner diameter of stem in mm; and L = length of culm (cm). All measurements were made at maturity, and figures are averages of 50 tillers from each of three replicates of each treatment.

(1967), who states that although height is the predominant factor determining lodging resistance, other important factors include the tightness of the leaf sheath, the length of the two basal elongated internodes, and the thickness and compactness of the stem at the basal elongated internodes.

Another important characteristic of nitrogen-responsive varieties is that internode elongation, after heavy applications of nitrogen are made, is relatively less than in the case of nonresponsive varieties. Fig. 12-3, from the International Rice Research Institute (1965a), shows the internode elongation of 'Taichung Native 1' (a half-sister of IR8) and of Peta under low and high nitrogen levels. The much greater increase in elongation of the upper internodes of the Peta variety, when 120 kg/ha of nitrogen was added, is clearly indicated by the steeper slopes of the dotted lines connecting the nodes. Taichung Native 1, representative of the short-statured varieties, is resistant to lodging even at high nitrogen levels, while Peta, as mentioned above, is typical of nonresponsive, lodging-susceptible tropical varieties.

This supports Chang's (1967) conclusion that the lodging-susceptible varieties are characterized by an elongation of the two basal internodes beyond 4 cm, when grown at high fertility levels.

B. Width, Thickness, Length and Uprightness of Leaves

In addition to the culm characteristics of the rice plant, the properties of the leaves influence its yielding capacity and responsiveness to nitrogen.

It is a known fact that small, erect leaves are essential for high yield response to nitrogen. Since rice leaves have greater variation in length than in width, leaf size is determined more by the former than by the latter (Tanaka, Kawano, and Yamaguchi, 1966).

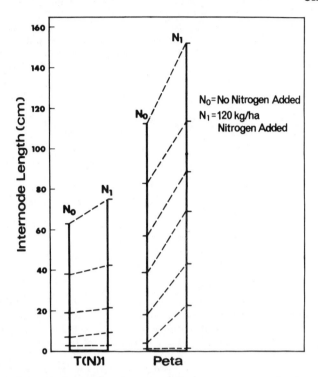

Fig. 12-3—Schematic drawing to show the difference in internode elongation when nitrogen is added to a nitrogen-responsive variety (Taichung Native 1) as compared with a low-responder (Peta).

Although plant breeders frequently mention the advantage of narrow leaves in developing high-yielding, nitrogen-responsive varieties, good experimental evidence to support this contention is difficult to find. Nevertheless, since no exceptionally high-yielding varieties of rice have been developed with wide leaves, it can be assumed that medium-wide leaves are more advantageous than wide ones. Beachell (1968) indicates that extremely narrow leaves tend to be weak and to bend readily, a condition which, of course, is detrimental. (H. M. Beachell, 1968. Personal communication.)

As is true for leaf width, it is difficult to obtain clear-cut evidence from the literature on the importance of leaf thickness. Tsunoda (1965) gives a good discussion of the subject and concludes that varieties suitable for heavy fertilization and low planting density should have thin leaves, but varieties adapted to both heavy fertilization and high planting density should have thick leaves.

The literature abounds in evidence showing that short leaves promote nitrogen responsiveness in rice. This fact is clearly demonstrated in Fig. 12-4, taken from Tanaka et al. (1966).

Inclination of leaves is a highly important factor in determining the degree of response to nitrogen. Rice varieties that show no grain yield

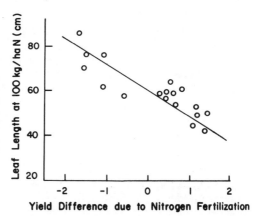

Fig. 12-4—Relationship between leaf length and grain yield. Note that varieties with leaf lengths greater than 65 cm gave a negative response to the addition of 100 kg/ha of nitrogen. (Yield differences expressed in metric tons per hectare.)

response (or, often, a negative response) to heavy nitrogen applications usually have not only long, but drooping leaves that make a wide angle with the stem. Such characteristics may be an advantage when leaf area index is restricted by low fertility levels but are a distinct disadvantage when maximum yields are being attempted at high fertility levels. Leaf angle is associated with the efficient utilization of solar energy, erect leaves favoring the deep penetration of light with a minimum of mutual shading, even at high leaf area index values. To put it in terms commonly used in interpreting light penetration and utilization in a plant stand, the greater the spread of the leaves, the higher the light extinction coefficient (K) and the lower the light transmission ratio (LTR). Of course, leaf spread and leaf length are associated, long leaves tending to spread and bend.

The leaves of the rice plant are usually more erect at low nitrogen levels than at high. Table 12-2 gives some data on this point, obtained by S. Yoshida (International Rice Research Institute, 1968). Yield data obtained over several seasons with these four varieties have consistently shown that total grain yields under heavy nitrogen applications are highest with IR8, followed in decreasing order by '81B-25,' Peta, and 'Hung.' Thus, yield is inversely correlated with leaf angle at high nitrogen levels.

Rice plants vary, not only in the erectness of the leaves in relation to the culm, but also in the spread of tillers originating from the base of the plant. Tsunoda (1965) and Tanaka et al. (1966) examine this point

Table 12-2—Mean leaf openness[*] of four varieties of rice at three nitrogen levels

Nitrogen supply (ppm in culture solution)	81B-25	IR8	Peta	Hung
5	10.3	11.2	13.2	65.1
20	20.6	18.9	34.7	78.3
200	25.8	22.4	48.7	149.2

[*] Leaf openness, in this case, is defined as the angle between the leaf tip and the stem. Thus it includes both leaf angle at the stem and leaf bending.

well and present evidence that open-tillered varieties yield better than upright-tillered ones at low nitrogen levels, whereas at high fertility levels the reverse is true.

More recent but unpublished information from the International Rice Research Institute indicates that if the tillers are extremely erect and crowded, there may be a reduction in yield at high fertility levels due to excessive mutual shading. The openness exhibited by the variety IR8 seems to be optimum.

C. Tillering Capacity

The number of tillers on a rice plant is strongly influenced by both heredity and environment, nitrogen supply being among the most important environmental factors. Let us look first at heredity, however. That varieties differ greatly in their tillering capacity is a well-established fact. S. Yoshida (International Rice Research Institute, 1968) and L. Johnson (International Rice Research Institute, 1966) have used as an indicator of the inherent tillering capacity the number of panicles per hill, when rice is widely spaced at high nitrogen levels. Merely to demonstrate the range that exists, some of Yoshida's data are reproduced in Table 12-3.

Among the environmental factors influencing the tillering of the rice plant, one of the most important is the nitrogen supply in the soil. This is a widely recognized fact and the literature presents no conflicting evidence. As an example, data accumulated in 1968 at the International Rice Research Institute by S. Yoshida are presented in Table 12-4.

These results clearly show that nitrogen level and amount of tillering are highly and positively correlated and that tillering ceases earlier at low nitrogen levels. Naturally, any factor influencing the growth (to be covered later), the deficiency of other mineral nutrients, and water supply and depth would be among the more important.

It is generally conceded that the traditional tall tropical varieties are usually heavy tillering. In the earlier variety fertilizer-interaction studies conducted at the International Rice Research Institute, as well as elsewhere, these highly vegetative varieties were compared with the medium-tillering, but shorter ponlai varieties, which responded much better to heavy applications of nitrogen. The conclusion was rightfully

Table 12-3—The number of panicles per plant for several varieties when widely spaced and heavily fertilized[*]

Variety or genetic line	No. of panicles per plant[†]
Century Patna 231	30
IR154-34-1-3-3	48
IR165-34-22	58
IR154-18-2-1	94
IR262-A43-8-11-3-5	121
Taichung Native 1	126

Spacing = 100 × 100 cm, with one seedling per hill.   Nitrogen added = 150 kg/ha.
[*] Because of wide spacing, panicle number at harvest time was only slightly lower than total tiller number.   [†] One plant per hill.

Table 12-4—The effect of the nitrogen content of the culture solution on the number of tillers per plant at 3, 8 and 10 weeks after transplanting (IR8 variety)

Nitrogen content of substrate, ppm	Number of tillers per plant* at different ages		
	3 weeks	8 weeks	10 weeks
0	1.0	3.5	3.7
5	1.7	13.3	12.8
25	2.5	22.6	31.8
50	4.2	42.7	48.6
100	4.8	44.7	56.6

* 1 seedling per pot of 4-liter capacity.

reached from these studies that a medium-tillering variety should be sought and that too heavy tillering would result in excessive mutual shading within each hill, even at fairly wide planting distances (Tanaka et al., 1966).

By 1966, a number of short, upright-leaved, heavy-tillering indica varieties, or stable genetic lines (of the plant type of IR8), had been

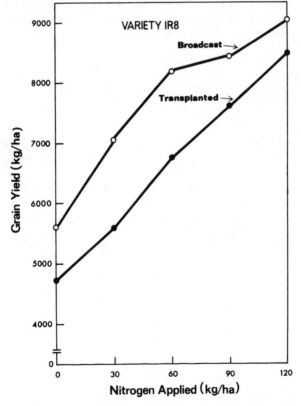

Fig. 12-5—Nitrogen response of the IR8 variety of rice under two methods of planting. (The transplanting distance was 20 by 25 cm and the seeding rate for the broadcast plots was 100 kg/ha.)

developed and tested. It now appears that plant breeders need not fear introducing too much tillering capacity into their varieties, provided, of course, that the other important morphological characters are included in the new varieties.

The statement presently appears in the literature that varieties developed for direct seeding, e.g., the USA varieties, are inherently low tillering, the implication, at least, being that this characteristic would ensure high yields at thick planting densities. This conclusion is based on the assumption that if heavy tillering varieties are direct seeded, lodging will occur at high fertility levels. This would certainly be true for many heavy-tillering varieties that are medium-tall to tall or that have inherently weak stems.

S. K. De Datta and J. C. Moomaw, working at the International Rice Research Institute, have accumulated much information on the performance of short, stiff-strawed, early-maturing, upright-leaved tropical varieties under direct-seeded (broadcast) and transplanted conditions.

Figure 12-5, from unpublished data by De Datta, shows the grain yield of IR8 grown during the 1968 dry season at applied nitrogen levels ranging from 0 to 120 kg/ha of N. In one set of plots, the seed was broadcast, and, in the other, 12-day-old seedlings were transplanted at 20 by 25 cm spacing. Note that the broadcast plots somewhat outyielded the transplanted ones at all nitrogen levels. The conclusion, however, should not be that direct-seeded generally outyields transplanted rice. The reverse tends to be true under farm conditions, where the water- and weed-control facilities at the disposal of the farmer are inadequate for the requirements of direct-seeded rice. Furthermore, even under experimental conditions, a consistent and statistically significant yield difference between direct-seeded and transplanted rice has not yet been established.

The tiller number and various yield component data for the same experiment are presented in Table 12-5. It is evident from these data

Table 12-5—Tiller number and certain yield components of the IR8 variety of rice when differentially fertilized with nitrogen

Applied nitrogen	Tillers	Panicles	Panicle weight	Filled grains	Unfilled grains	1,000 grain weight
kg/ha	—— no. /m² ——		g	—— no. /panicle ——		g
			Broadcast†			
0	624	609	1.22	54	5.8	27.6
30	676	618	1.38	51	11.2	29.0
60	644	630	1.44	64	8.5	28.5
90	644	619	1.55	66	10.5	28.2
120	691	672	1.51	64	9.5	29.6
			Transplanted*			
0	290	283	1.88	69	10.2	26.1
30	392	321	1.87	72	17.2	27.8
60	361	353	1.96	74	12.0	28.1
90	381	372	2.06	76	12.0	30.2
120	437	422	2.12	84	10.2	28.3

* Planting distance = 20 × 25 cm.   † Seeding rate = 100 kg/ha.

that the number of panicles per unit of land area increased greatly when the seed was broadcast, but that the panicle size was less than when the rice was transplanted. With heavier nitrogen applications, however, there was a marked increase in panicle number and a small but consistent increase in panicle weight. The data show that this increase in panicle weight is primarily associated with a larger number of filled grains, although there was a slight tendency, also, for the 1000-grain weight to increase. These findings are in accord with those of others (Tanaka et al., 1966; Matsushima, 1966; Yoshida, 1968).

Yoshida (1968) makes the point that the short, sturdy-strawed varieties that are heavy tillering and have short, upright leaves, also have a higher optimum leaf area index (LAI) for dry matter production than do the taller varieties. Figure 12-6 shows his data for IR8, representing the improved plant type, and for Peta, a typical tall variety.

The relationship between LAI and grain yield has not shown a true optimum in the case of IR8 and similar varieties. Yoshida's data on the subject are presented in Fig. 12-7. Note that Peta shows a distinct optimum LAI value between 5 and 6, whereas the curve for IR8 remains more or less flat from an LAI of 6 through 10. These data were obtained in the cloudy monsoon season, yet mutual shading was not severe enough to decrease yields.

All of this indicates the importance of heavy tillering capacity in the improved plant types. As Tanaka et al. (1966) states, the number of leaves per stem or tiller at flowering time usually averages about four, so that any increase in LAI must come about from more tillers per unit area of land.

A further advantage of heavy tillering—but short—varieties is that if skips occur in either the transplanted or direct-seeded fields, the

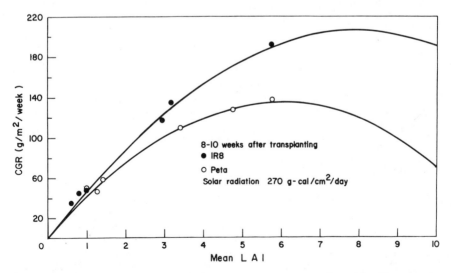

Fig. 12-6—Relation between mean leaf area index (average value at booting stage) and crop growth rate (grams of dry matter per square meter per week—in this case for the 2 weeks before heading) for IR8 and Peta varieties of rice.

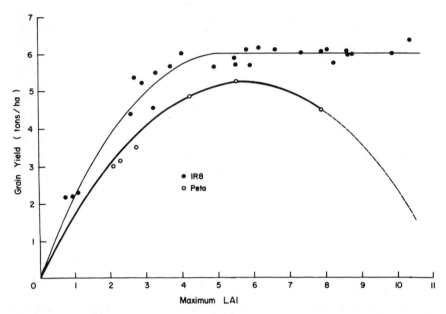

Fig. 12-7—Relation between maximum leaf area index (maximum value between booting and heading stages) and grain yield of IR8 and Peta varieties of rice. (The unusually high yields for Peta are due to the fact that the plants were tied up to prevent lodging.)

plants adjacent to the open spaces will tiller more and tend to fill in the gaps, and thus maintain a high concentration of panicles per hectare.

D. Panicle Weight

Grain yield is a function of the number and weight of the grains. As stated above, panicle number in a given variety is almost a direct function of tiller number, which in turn is strongly influenced by the nitrogen supply. The weight of the panicle is essentially determined by the number of filled spikelets and by the size of the grain. As was pointed out earlier, in the explanation of Table 12-5, the main influence of nitrogen is on the number of spikelets formed and on the number of filled grains.

Matsushima (1966) has made a thorough examination of the impact of nutrient level, at different stages of the developing rice plant, on spikelet number and on grain filling. Among many other experiments, he grew rice plants in pots with nutrient solution at one-fifth the normal concentration. At 10-day intervals he raised the solution to the normal concentration for 10 days and then returned the plants to cultures at one-fifth the normal concentration. The control plants were those that were grown throughout their life in the full-strength culture solution. He found that increasing nutrient supply for 10 days, beginning 33 days before heading, resulted in a significant increase in spikelet number.

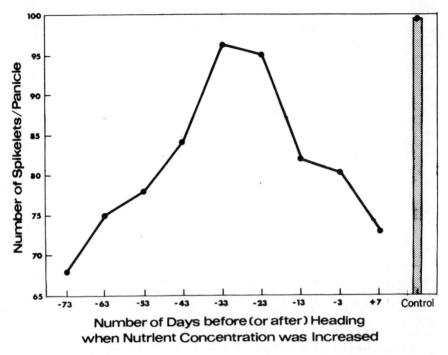

Fig. 12-8—Relation between nutrient supply and number of spikelets per panicle.
(See text for explanation.)

Later applications did not change the spikelet number but did have a
strong influence in preventing spikelet degeneration, or conversely, in
increasing the number of filled grains. In Fig. 12-8, one of Matsushima's graphs from the above-described study is reproduced. He
states that nitrogen application at 33 days before heading corresponded
to the neck-node differentiation stage, and suggests that this should be
the real guide for timing nitrogen applications in rice varieties. Indeed,
the rice plant develops so much faster in the tropics that only the physiological stage can be used as a guide. There is considerable evidence
to indicate that, under field conditions, topdressing with nitrogen just
previous to the panicle initiation stage increases the number of spikelets and thereby, ultimately, the yield. (Hall and Tackett, 1962; Hall
and Railey, 1964; Evatt, 1965; Togari, 1968; and Mikkelsen, Finfrock,
and Miller, 1958).

E. Grain-Straw Ratio

No discussion of plant morphology and nitrogen responsiveness
should omit mention of grain-straw ratio. The traditional rice plant of
the tropics has a grain-straw ratio ranging between 0.3 and 0.6, while

Table 12-6—Grain-straw ratios for selected varieties

Class	Variety		Grain-straw ratio
Highly nitrogen responsive	IR8		1. 15
	Chianung 242		1. 14
	Taichung Native 1		1. 20
	Tainan 3		1. 23
	IR5		0. 95
		Mean	1. 13
Low or negatively responsive to nitorgen	Hung		0. 60
	Peta		0. 60
	Nang Mong S4		0. 49
	Puang Nahk 16		0. 40
	H-4		0. 58
	Sigadis		0. 69
		Mean	0. 56

the modern rice plant with short stems and erect leaves has a ratio between 0.9 and 1.3.

Table 12-6 gives the grain-straw ratios for selected varieties in two groups--those that are nitrogen responsive and those that tend to have either a low or a negative response to nitrogen under field conditions. These data were obtained by various scientists at the International Rice Research Institute and can be found in the Annual Reports between 1963 and 1968.

It is obvious from these data that of the total dry matter produced, the nitrogen-responsive varieties put twice as much into grain production as do the low nitrogen responders. This appears to be due principally to two factors: (i) Although the tall tropical varieties produce many tillers at high nitrogen levels, many of them are ineffective (bear no panicles) because of intense mutual shading; and (ii) the better plant types tend to continue to grow (that is, to produce dry matter) after flowering, while the leafy nonresponsive types show little increase in total dry matter after flowering. Hence, in the latter type grain filling results to quite a degree from carbohydrates previously stored in other parts of the plant (Tanaka et al., 1966; Togari, 1968).

In general, grain-straw ratios decrease with increasing nitrogen applications, and the change is most pronounced in the low-response varieties. Furthermore, the ratio is highest when solar energy is high. For example, in the Philippines, Peta can give a ratio as low as 0.28 during the cloudy, monsoon season and as high as 0.90 during the sunny, dry season.

III. STAND GEOMETRY AND NITROGEN

A. Spacing-Nitrogen-Variety Interactions

The problems of spacing are closely related to the morphological characteristics of the rice plant, particularly to such features as tillering capacity, plant height, and leaf and tiller erectness.

Table 12-7—Number of panicles per square meter, average panicle weight, and grain yield for two rice varieties grown at different spacing[*]

Spacing	IR154-45-1-3-3 Low-tillering variety			IR8 High-tillering variety		
	Panicles	Panicle weight/ plant	Grain yield	Panicles	Panicle weight/ plant	Grain yield
cm	no./m²	g	kg/ha	no./m²	g	kg/ha
10 × 10	350	2.25	5,744	340	2.02	6,119
20 × 20	194	3.47	5,533	250	2.97	6,444
30 × 30	140	3.92	4,494	198	3.54	5,733
40 × 40	96	3.79	3,474	167	3.36	4,816
50 × 50	70	4.29	2,803	141	3.43	4,649

* Wet season data, and 100 kg/ha of N applied to all plots.

Let us examine the variety-spacing interaction in relation to yield. Data obtained by Yoshida and published by the International Rice Research Institute (1968) are reproduced, in part, in Table 12-7. Both of these varieties were short and sturdy and no lodging took place at any spacing. The principal contrast was in the tillering capacity, IR154 being low and IR8 high. At 10 by 10 cm spacing there were only small varietal differences with respect to panicle number, panicle weight, and total grain yield, but as the spacing interval was increased the panicle number and yield went down rapidly in the case of the low-tillering variety, while the high-tillering variety maintained a rather high yield

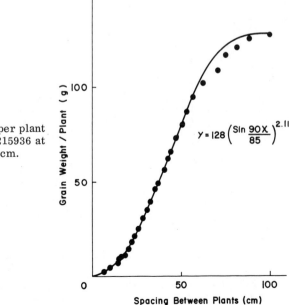

Fig. 12-9—Grain weight per plant of the rice variety PI 215936 at spacings from 7 to 100 cm.

$$y = 128 \left(\frac{\sin 90X}{85} \right)^{2.11}$$

up to a spacing of 30 by 30 cm. As expected, the decreases in panicle
number were partially offset by increases in panicle weight.

A thorough and careful study by Johnson (International Rice Research Institute, 1965b) using a medium-tillering, nitrogen-responsive
ponlai variety, revealed the relation between spacing and both grain
yield per plant and yield per hectare. Two of his charts are reproduced
in Fig. 12-9 and in Fig. 12-10. His conclusions from these data are that
the modern rice plant can be transplanted at any distance from 10 to 35
cm without significant differences in yield, and that direct seeded rice
can have densities up to 200 seedlings/square meter without loss.

Naturally, there is an optimum spacing for any variety and at any
nitrogen level, but the short, erect-leaved, heavy-tillering varieties
now being developed in Southeast Asia can be transplanted at distances
ranging from 10 by 10 to 30 by 30 cm without any significant change in
yield, provided other cultural practices are ideal.

The tall tropical varieties respond best to nitrogen at wide spacing,
and optimum yields may occur at spacings as great as 50 by 50 cm, de-

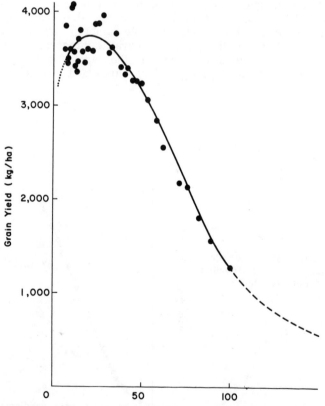

Fig. 12-10—Grain yield per hectare of the rice variety PI 215936 at spacings
from 7 to 100 cm.

pending on solar radiation intensity and soil fertility levels (Tanaka et al., 1964).

IV. GENERAL CONSIDERATIONS

This paper has analyzed the various morphological characters of the rice plant in relation to performance, principally as separate entities. Obviously, it is the summation of all the characteristics and environmental factors that determine yield. For example, a medium-tall variety may have stiff enough straw to offset the detrimental effect of its height and thus yield the same as a shorter, somewhat weaker strawed variety.

The new rice plant that has been developed and recognized in the tropics during the past few years has a combination of characteristics that give it unusual yielding ability. New high-yield records have been obtained by IR8, or by equivalent plant types, in all the major rice-producing countries of the tropics where it has been adequately tested. This is not a chance happening but is related to the morphology and physiology of the plant itself. An additional analysis of the combined morphological characteristics seems appropriate here.

Figure 12-11 is a photograph of an IR8 stand ready for harvest in

Fig. 12-11—Typical stand of IR8, in the dry season in the Philippines, showing its excellent plant type.

Table 12-8—The model yield components of IR8 in the cloudy wet season and in the sunny dry season

Component	Wet season	Dry season
Panicle number per m²	250	375
Grains per panicle (No.)	100	100
Total number of grains per m²	25,000	37,500
Filled grain, %	85	85
1,000 grain weight, g	29	29

Expected grain yield in wet season = 6,163 kg/ha.
Expected grain yield in dry season = 9,244 kg/ha.

the dry season in the Philippines. One plant per hill was transplanted at a spacing of 25 by 25 cm. Note the heavy tillering, the sturdy straw, and the uprightness of the leaves, including the flag leaf. The average height of these plants is just under 100 cm, and the yield of this particular stand was 8,500 kg/ha.

Yoshida (1968) has listed the model yield components of IR8 during the wet and dry seasons under the typical monsoon climate of Southeast Asia. His analysis is reproduced in Table 12-8. Figure 12-12 shows that the expected yields are being approached in the wet season and are being realized in the dry season. This figure gives the average yields over a 3-year period for IR8 and Peta, in both the wet and dry seasons, when differentially fertilized with nitrogen. Experience indicates that as the disease resistance of this new plant type is increased, wet season yields will equal those of Yoshida's model rice plant. IR8 is susceptible to both bacterial leaf blight and bacterial leaf streak, which are more prevalent in the rainy season than in the dry.

From the standpoint of morphology, IR8 seems ideal. In the light of present knowledge it is difficult to conceive of ways of improving it.

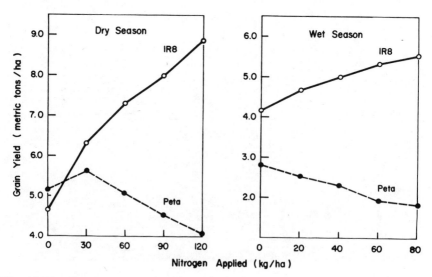

Fig. 12-12—The responsiveness to nitrogen of IR8 and Peta rice varieties in the dry and wet seasons in the Philippines.

It has the ability to tiller and grow fast early in its life; yet, unlike Peta and other tall tropical varieties, it continues to grow well through the ripening stage. Its straw is sturdy, its leaf sheath is well wrapped around the stem, its tillers form a sufficient angle from the vertical to utilize sunlight well, yet are not too spreading. Its short, upright leaves shed rain water quickly, admit sunlight to the lower leaves, and more efficiently utilize solar energy, particularly when it is needed for grain production during the last 40 to 45 days that the crop is in the field. Its crop duration of about 125 days (from seed to seed) is satisfactory under most circumstances. Its lack of photoperiod sensitivity allows it to be planted at any date during the year at latitudes from about 17 degrees north or south of the equator (IR8 does not have cold tolerance and hence its maturity is severely delayed when planted during the winter months at latitudes greater than 17 or 18 degrees).

IR8 needs improvement in grain type and in its disease resistance, and soon it will be obsolete. Also its rate of senescence during ripening should be decreased and its leaves should be toughened to better withstand heavy winds. Its plant type, however, as far as can be predicted now, is here to stay. In fact, there are those who believe that this plant type will spread into the temperate zone to replace the japonicas of Japan and the USA varieties. Naturally this will require alteration in grain type and in cold tolerance, but there are no known genetic barriers to these accomplishments.

That each of the morphological characters of IR8 is important is continually being revealed as new genetic lines are developed and tested. For example, at the International Rice Research Institute a new line was developed from a cross between a dwarf line known as CP 231 × SLO 17 and an Indonesian variety named 'Sigadis.' The plants were short, stiff-strawed and nitrogen-responsive, but had superior grain quality and disease resistance as compared to IR8. It yielded well when closely planted and well tended. However, when planted under less than favorable conditions, its tillering capacity was too low and yields decreased. Under the same circumstances, IR8 would have given a satisfactory yield because of its vigorous tillering habit.

As related earlier in this paper, IR532E576 looked highly promising. It has tillering capacity, short stature, excellent grain quality and high resistance to insects and diseases, but its culm weakness will probably disqualify it for general release.

Tropical rice breeders all over Asia, and now in Latin America as well, are using the dwarfing gene, obtained from Dee-geo-woo-gen or I-geo-tse in Taiwan, to shorten the tall, tropical rice varieties to give them nitrogen responsiveness and yet retain disease resistance and other characters essential for high yield. The future for rice production, as is true for wheat and other cereal grains, is brighter than ever before. Man now has at hand the tools and the knowledge to engineer, biologically, super-cereals to feed the world.

V. CONCLUSIONS

This paper presents examples of experimental evidence, derived from rice research, to support the more important relationships among plant morphology, stand geometry and nitrogen. Interpretation of the data would seem to warrant the following statements:

1) Culm length is the most important single factor affecting lodging resistance and nitrogen responsiveness.

2) Culm strength is associated not only with the length but also with the thickness of the culm and with the tightness and durability of the leaf sheath that wraps the stem.

3) Nitrogen-responsive varieties show less relative internode elongation when heavily fertilized than do the unresponsive varieties.

4) Short, erect leaves of medium width are associated with high yielding capacity and nitrogen responsiveness.

5) The tillering of the rice plant is strongly influenced by genetic factors and by the nitrogen level in the soil.

6) When varieties are short (100 cm or less) and have erect leaves and sturdy stems, inherent high tillering capacity seems to be a distinct advantage. There is no evidence in the literature that grain yield in such plant types is decreased by a too-heavy tillering capacity, and no optimum and specific leaf area index has yet been identified for maximum yield.

7) Nitrogen levels in the soil greatly influence the number of panicles per square meter and, to a lesser degree, the number of spikelets per panicle and the number of filled grains. The influence on 1000-grain weight is negligible.

8) The newly created, nitrogen-responsive tropical varieties have a grain-straw ratio of about 1.1, whereas the traditional tall, leafy varieties average about 0.55, depending upon the individual variety and upon the environmental conditions under which it is grown.

9) The new, heavy-tillering, short, erect-leaved, nonlodging varieties, such as IR8, show essentially no change in yield when direct sown (thus, in a dense stand) or when transplanted at distances from 10 by 10 to 30 by 30 cm, and in some cases up to 35 by 35 cm if excellent cultural practices are followed.

10) The low-tillering to medium-tillering varieties, if short and stiff-strawed, yield best at close spacing at all nitrogen levels.

11) The traditional tall, leafy, tropical rice varieties generally yield best at wide spacing (50 by 50 cm), when grown at high fertility levels and when solar radiation is low. If sunlight is plentiful and nitrogen is more limiting, they yield better at somewhat closer spacing.

12) The point is emphasized that the combined morphological characters of the new plant type exemplified by the IR8 variety are so important that they will be incorporated in all future rice varieties in the tropics which are developed for use under conditions of reasonably good water control. Furthermore, it is possible that this plant type may even gradually replace the conventional, but improved, rice varieties now used in the temperate zone.

VI. ACKNOWLEDGMENTS

The writer wishes to express his appreciation to Dr. Shoichi Yoshida and to Dr. S.K. De Datta for their advice in selecting some of the data used in this paper and for making available certain of their yet unpublished experimental results. He is grateful, also, to Dr. B. S. Vergara and to Miss Genoveva Loresto for their assistance in preparing the materials for the photographs appearing in the first two figures.

LITERATURE CITED

Basak, M. N., S. K. Sen, and P. K. Bhattacharjee. 1962. Effect of high nitrogen fertilization and lodging on rice yield. Agron. J. 54:477-480.

Chang, T. T. 1964. Varietal differences in lodging resistance. Int. Rice Comm. Newsletter. 13(4):1-11.

Chang, T. T. 1967. Growth characteristics, lodging and grain development. Int. Rice Comm. Newsletter. Special Issue. p. 54-60.

Evatt, Nathan S. 1965. The timing of nitrogenous fertilizer applications on rice, p. 243-254. In The mineral nutrition of the rice plant. Johns Hopkins Press. Baltimore.

Hall, V. L. and D. L. Tackett. 1962. Growth and nutritional balance of Nato rice as influenced by time of nitrogen fertilization and water management. Arkansas Agr. Exp. Sta. Bull. 662, p. 31.

Hall, Vernon L., and Robert M. Railey. 1964. Timing nitrogen fertilization of rice with morphological development of the plant. Rice Journal 67(1):6-9.

International Rice Research Institute. 1964. Annual report for 1963. Agricultural engineering section. p. 135-146.

International Rice Research Institute. 1965a. Annual report for 1964. Varietal improvement section. p. 13-48.

International Rice Research Institute. 1965b. Annual report for 1964. Agricultural engineering section. p. 185-194.

International Rice Research Institute. 1966. Annual report for 1965. Agricultural engineering section. p. 267-288.

International Rice Research Institute. 1968. Annual report for 1967. Plant physiology section.

Ishizuka, Y. and A. Tanaka. 1963. Nutriophysiology of the rice plant. Yokendo Press. Tokyo. 307 p.

Jennings, P. R. and S. Sornchai, 1964. The influence of lodging on rice yields. Int. Rice Comm. Newsletter. 13(3):10-21.

Matsushima, Seizo. 1966. Crop science in rice. Fuji Publishing Co., Ltd. Tokyo. p. 365.

Mikkelsen, D. S., D. C. Finfrock, and M. D. Miller. 1958. Rice fertilization. Calif. Agr. Exp. Sta. Leaflet 96.

Singh, J. N. and J. Takahashi. 1962. Effect of varying dates of topdressing nitrogen on plant character leading to tendency to lodging in rice. Soil Sci. Plant Nutr. 8(5):169-176.

Tanaka, A., S. A. Navasero, C. V. Garcia, F. T. Parao, and E. Ramirez. 1964. Growth and habit of the rice plant in the tropics and its effect on nitrogen response. The Int. Rice Res. Inst. Tech. Bull. 3.

Tanaka, A., K. Kawano and J. Yamaguchi. 1966. Photosynthesis, respiration and plant type of the tropical rice plant. Int. Rice Res. Institute. Tech. Bull. 7. 46 p.

Togari, Yoshitsugu. 1968. Photosynthesis of rice plant related to high yield (1). Farming Japan 1(3):5-12.

Tsunoda, S. 1965. Leaf characters and nitrogen response, p. 401-418. In The mineral nutrition of the rice plant. Johns Hopkins Press. Baltimore.

Umali, D. L., E. S. Castillo and P. S. Castillo. 1956. The effect of time of lodging on the yield and other agronomic characteristics of rice. Philippine Agriculturist. 40(4):178-184.

Wittwer, S. H. 1968. Approaching maximum capacity in production—Biological limits of productivity. Mich. Agr. Exp. Sta. Journal article 4176. 98-123.

Yoshida, Shoichi. 1968. From data yet unpublished but to appear in the 1968 annual report of the International Rice Research Institute.

12 ... DISCUSSION

PETER R. JENNINGS

Centro Internacional de Agricultura Tropical
Colombia, South America

Dr. Chandler's paper succinctly summarizes much of the evidence on the direct causal relationship of rice morphology to nitrogen responsiveness and grain yield.

Application of the concept of plant type to rice improvement during the period 1962 to 1966 resulted in dramatic changes in national yields in the tropics. Nitrogen responsive, high-yielding varieties are rapidly replacing the vast numbers of narrowly adapted, old tropical varieties having limited nitrogen responsiveness and grain productivity.

The crop physiology and breeding work done during the period cited resulted in a doubling to trebling of experimental and commercial grain yields. Since 1966 when IR8 was released, little or no further progress has been made. This questions the continued usefulness of the concept of plant type if another yield doubling is the breeder's objective. It appears difficult to visualize means by which the morphology of IR8 could be improved further to achieve continued significant advance in nitrogen responsiveness or grain production.

The application of the principles of plant type to other largely unimproved plant types in the tropics, namely maize (Zea mays L.) and soybean (Glycine max L.), however, would appear to offer the most logical approach to achieve rapid improvement of economic production of these species.

Recent work at IRRI with photosynthetic rates per unit leaf area may offer a new approach to rice breeders. Large varietal differences in photosynthetic rate appear to be unrelated to plant type. It remains to be determined whether high rate per unit leaf area combined with ideal plant type will show prolonged, high photosynthetic activity in field populations.

Regardless of the approach taken by rice workers to continue the recent advances in nitrogen responsiveness and grain yield, it is essential that breeders and crop physiologists cooperate closely.

Plant morphology is directly related to nitrogen responsiveness and grain yield. Desirable plant types in rice are poor competitors so that competitive ability is inversely related to agronomic worth. The tropical environment abhors nitrogen responsiveness for nitrogen-responsive, high-yielding types are rapidly purged from mixed or segregating populations.

Appreciation of this negative relationship is critical to the selection process. Breeders correctly state that large nitrogen applications should be supplied populations where nitrogen responsiveness is a breeding objective. However, added nitrogen and close spacing, two practices required for maximum varietal yield, greatly intensify the competitive disadvantage of desired plant types. This can be remedied only by removal of competitive, undesirable plants from heavily fertilized segregating populations at early flowering.

The tentative conclusions from the negative association of competitive ability with yield and nitrogen responsiveness are:

1) The unrestricted bulk breeding method is futile when used for improved plant morphology, nitrogen responsiveness, and increased yield.

2) Perhaps in other crops as maize and soybean, breeders select plants which produce more seed through competitive advantage and reject the adversely affected phenotypes suffering from competitive disadvantage. These latter plants might be the most productive when grown in pure stand under optimum agronomy.

12...DISCUSSION

WERNER L. NELSON

American Potash Institute
West Lafayette, Indiana

Dr. Chandler has outlined some excellent relationships between certain morphological characteristics of rice and response to nitrogen. Nitrogen-responsive rice varieties show less relative internode elongation when heavily fertilized than do the unresponsive varieties. Short, erect leaves of medium width are associated with high yielding capacity and nitrogen responsiveness. A grain-straw ratio of about 1:1 is characteristic of these varieties.

It would appear that these relationships might well be considered carefully in our research with corn (Zea mays L.) particularly in reference to breeding efforts to construct a more efficient corn plant.

A few points will be brought out using corn as an example.

It is well known that with "adequate" amounts of other nutrients, additional nitrogen makes a bigger corn plant. With other nutrients inadequate or becoming unbalanced, additional nitrogen may make a smaller plant. This was shown for corn in the first part of the growing period in Wisconsin on a soil medium in phosphorus and potassium (Liebhardt and Murdock, 1965).

In this same study lodging was affected by nutrient balance:

N		P		K		Lodging
lb/acre	(kg/ha)	lb/acre	(kg/ha)	lb/acre	(kg/ha)	%
0		0		0		2
160	(179)	0		0		38
160	(179)	0		133	(149)	3
160	(179)	70	(78)	0		78
160	(179)	70	(78)	133	(149)	10

With nitrogen alone in this particular situation there was considerable parenchyma breakdown in the brace roots and lower stalk by late summer and early fall (Liebhardt and Murdock, 1965; Liebhardt et al., 1968).

In the Corn Belt in the USA one of the outstanding research developments in recent years has been the positive effect of early planting on corn yields. Early planting produces a shorter corn plant and a higher grain-stover ratio. Work by Jordan et al. (1950) in Mississippi indicated that with no nitrogen added the grain-stover ratio was 1:4.7 while with 134 kg of N/ha (120 lb/acre) the ratio was 1:1.

Nitrogen response is greater with early planting (Mulvaney et al., 1968).

Planting date	Nitrogen used, lb N/acre (kg/ha) (1966-67 Dekalb, Illinois)								
	0		80	(89.6)	160	(179.2)	240	(268.8)	Response
	Yield, bushels/acre (kg/ha)								
	bu	(kg/ha)	bu	(kg/ha)	bu	(kg/ha)	bu	(kg/ha)	bu (kg/ha)
May 2	117	(7,336)	146	(9,154)	161	(10,095)	166	(10,408)	49 (3,072)
May 14	122	(7,649)	148	(9,280)	160	(10,003)	159	(9,969)	37 (2,320)
May 24	123	(7,712)	146	(9,154)	152	(9,530)	153	(9,593)	30 (1,881)
June 5	97	(6,082)	113	(7,085)	114	(7,148)	113	(7,085)	16 (1,003)

The interaction of plant population and nitrogen rate is well-known. The response to higher rates of nitrogen is more likely with higher populations (Mulvaney et al., 1968).

N rate		Plants/acre (plants/ha) (1966-67, DeKalb, Illinois)					
		16,000	(39,536)	22,000	(54,362)	28,000	(69,188)
		Yield, bushels/acre (kg/ha)					
lb/acre	(kg/ha)	bu	(kg/ha)	bu	(kg/ha)	bu	(kg/ha)
0		84	(5,267)	81	(5,079)	80	(5,016)
80	(89.6)	114	(7,148)	127	(7,963)	120	(7,524)
160	(179.2)	126	(7,900)	136	(8,527)	145	(9,092)
240	(268.8)	130	(8,151)	142	(8,903)	156	(9,781)
Response		46	(2,884)	61	(3,825)	76	(4,765)

The effect of nitrogen on root development has received limited attention. However in general, plants responding to applied nitrogen show an increase in top-root ratio.

LITERATURE CITED

Jordan, H. V., K. D. Laird, and D. D. Gerguson. 1950. Growth rates and nutrient uptake by corn in a fertilizer-spacing experiment. Agron. J. 42:261-268.

Liebhardt, W. C., and J. T. Murdock. 1965. Effect of potassium on morphology and lodging of corn. Agron. J. 57:325-328.

Liebhardt, W. C., P. J. Stangel, and J. T. Murdock. 1968. A mechanism for premature parenchyma breakdown in corn (Zea mays L.). Agron. J. 60:496-499.

Mulvaney, D. L., L. V. Boone, and R. E. Bell. 1968. The Northern Illinois Agronomy Research Center—Report of research results. AG-1942. Dept. of Agronomy, Univ. of Illinois, Urbana.

13

Development, Differentiation, and Yield

JOHN HESLOP-HARRISON

University of Wisconsin
Madison, Wisconsin

I. INTRODUCTION: FEATURES OF THE DEVELOPMENTAL PROCESS IN PLANTS

The task of reviewing some of the ways development and differentiation may act as determinants of economic yield would be much simpler had knowledge advanced to a point where the basic principles concerned in the control of these processes in eukaryotic organisms were clear. Unfortunately, this stage has not yet been reached. There is no shortage of schemes and hypotheses to set beside a mountain of observational and experimental data, but the unifying thread which might allow us to pick out the significant and reject the irrelevant in any particular context is still lacking. What is incontestable is that development and differentiation are manifestations of gene function, so the fundamental problem can at least be defined: it is to understand how gene action is governed in ontogeny so as to give orderly expression to the potentialities attained during the evolutionary history of a species, producing an organism that is harmoniously coordinated both within itself and with the environment. I will begin by considering some general aspects of this problem as it applies to higher plants.

It is sometimes didactically convenient to separate the concepts of growth, differentiation, organogenesis and development; yet the processes to which we apply these terms are in no sense independent in the life of the plant. Development is the progression through time of organogenetic events, and the ontogeny of each organ is based upon particular patterns of cell and tissue differentiation. Growth, in the sense both of increase of cell number and of cell size, is an inevitable accompaniment throughout.

What we witness is, of course, the working out of the potential present in the genome of the zygote. According to present understanding, the two functions of the gene as a stretch of DNA are to replicate and to direct the synthesis of proteins of specific amino acid sequence through the intermediacy of mRNA. All manifestations of gene action, morphological and functional, have therefore to be traced back to the activities of specific proteins; and differentiation in cells and tissues is to be interpreted as the outcome of qualitative and quantitative changes in protein complements, and of the modulation of the functional activities of proteins in enzymatic and other roles by various endogenous and exogenous agencies.

Given that differentiation is of this nature, regulation could obviously be applied at different points in the causational chain. We have just passed through a period when the most popular view has been that control is mostly imposed at the level of the gene itself, determining whether it should be transcribed or not in individual nuclei in accordance with the circumstances of the cell. In so far as protokaryotic microorganisms may be said to show differentiation, it may well be that it is at this level that its regulation is largely effected; but with eukaryotes it is looking more and more likely that much of the control of gene expression is exerted at later links in the chain (Cline and Bock, 1966). It is unnecessary to review this aspect here, but in the context of higher plants it is noteworthy that the presence of molecules with cytokinin activity in tRNA (review, Helgeson, 1968) at least suggests the possibility that they may be concerned in regulating translation, while schemes have been offered imputing to auxins a role at this same level (Armstrong, 1966).

There are certainly very good circumstantial reasons for supposing that control is imposed at several levels in the growth and differentiation of higher plants. Competence phenomena in general point to this: whenever a tissue or an organ shows temporal variation in its capacity to react to a stimulus, the conclusion is unavoidable that it is passing through states of "cryptic" differentiation. The attainment of competence in some tissues may represent the completion of a transcriptional step; the later, overt, differentiation could then be the consequence of activation at translational or later points. This is evidently so in seeds, where the mRNA concerned with the early protein synthesis associated with germination is present in masked form during dormancy (Waters and Dure, 1966; Chen et al., 1968).

On the other hand, it can hardly be assumed that differences in the competence of specific tissues to respond to hormonal and other stimuli always depends upon variation in pre-existing mRNA populations. In many cases the response to the inducing stimulus itself involves the synthesis of RNA. An example pertinent is the grass Lolium temulentum. The genotype of this grass used by Evans (1964) initiates an inflorescence in response to a single inductive long day; actinomycin D applied the morning following this experience suppresses the response, suggesting that this is a critical period for the synthesis of an RNA fraction specifically associated with flowering. In Lolium, as in spicate grasses generally, the formation of spikelets begins in specific sites on the flanks of the shoot apex, axillary to the leaf primordia. These sites represent islets of "competent" tissue, which have attained their potential for reacting to the inductive stimulus by some prior process of differentiation, probably each at the time of initiation during successive plastochron cycles (Knox and Evans, 1966).

Some other features of flowering merit attention. Flower initiation always follows a period of vegetative growth, and the event may be viewed as a transition by apical meristems from leaf production to the sequential formation of floral parts. Where the terminal meristem is converted in this manner, the product is a single flower, and when the first or later order axillary buds are so transformed, the result is an inflorescence. The balance between vegetative growth and flowering is thus between the factors tending to direct appendicular structures into pathways of differentiation characteristic of leaves, and those selecting instead the pathways leading to perianth, stamens and carpels. Lang (1965a) has provided a very thorough review of the role of environmental factors in controlling this balance. Some of the responses observed in experiment appear to point to the existence of a positive, switch-like mechanism, but in most species the environmental control is no more than modulating, affecting the rate of progression from vegetative to reproductive growth, but not determining in any absolute sense whether it occurs or not. The implication of this is that the transition to flowering is part of a rather inflexible developmental program, governed in its essentials by autonomous controls (Nougarède, 1965; Heslop-Harrison, 1969). It is unfortunate that the concentration of photoperiodic research on a few rather exceptional plants has helped to conceal this point by over-emphasizing the more superficial, rate-modulating aspect of the control mechanism.

What, then, can be said about the nature of endogenous controls of gene expression in development? Some examples seem to indicate that an intrachromosomal regulatory mechanism is at work, exposing genes for transcription according to predetermined programs. An example from the work of Hotta and Stern (1965) on the pollen mother cells of lily (Lilium sp.) illustrates this, and shows that programed gene action in development is not a matter of substrate-induction. During one specific period in the life of the anther, the enzyme thymidine kinase is produced, and its activity subsequently decays. The enzyme can be induced by exogenously-supplied thymidine during only a short interval of time, and this interval begins just before thymidine kinase appears naturally. This result suggests that the locus concerned is made accessible just as its transcription is required in the general developmental program.

Sequential gene "exposure" can be referred to the operation of unknown, time-related controls at the chromosomal level, but it is more plausibly interpreted as resulting from the working of a kind of relay system, where the functioning of each gene group is contingent upon the work of the preceding, and leads in turn to the activation of the next (Stern, 1964). A model of this kind has some attraction in seeking to explain the behavior of the plant apex (Heslop-Harrison, 1963), but there is as yet little to substantiate it. What evidence there is relates to the "determination" of lateral appendages during vegetative growth (Cutter, 1965). Operative experiments (Wardlaw, 1949; Sussex, 1954, 1955) and organ culture (Steeves, 1962) suggest that the fate of a primordium initiated on a flank of the apical meristem is affected by influences—presumably chemical in nature--reaching it from the apical dome itself, and by interaction with other, neighboring primordia. Thus the youngest prospective leaf primordia produce centric structures when isolated from the growth cone; but later, after some decisive event or events occurring over a definable period of time, changes occur in the primordia which constrain them to develop in a leaf-like manner, expressing dorsiventral symmetry. This kind of evidence suggests that there are short-range humoral agencies in the apex concerned with the selection of prospective developmental pathways for the primordia as they originate. These, then, would be the agencies responsible for imposing the condition of competence referred to in previous paragraphs.

These considerations show that there is an urgent need for plant physiologists to come to grips with the neglected problem of the metamerism of the shoot system so characteristic of higher plants. The growth of the plant is open-ended, in the sense that apices are persistently meristematic and continuously concerned with organogenesis. They are engaged in an endless succession of cycles, but in each they are laying out a sequence of comparatively few structures. Each cycle represents the definition of a "phytomer" in the terminology of classical structural botany, and the phytomer is never seen to better advantage than in the corn plant (Zea mays L.) (Arber, 1934; Galinat, 1959). Now the circumstance that has its morphological expression in the sequence: node, root site, leaf, axillary bud, internode, must be physiological at base. In the terms of the preceding discussion, there must be some cyclical regulatory mechanism operating through each plastochron to determine the potential of different cell lineages according to the times they are initiated. With the move towards reproduction, more potentialities are laid out, to be realized or not according to the general hormonal situation in the plant as a whole (Fig. 13-1).

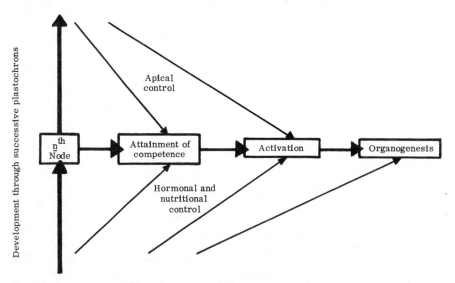

Fig. 13-1—Events leading to organogenesis in the shoot system. At each node, cell lineages are defined which attain competence for certain types of differentiation. Whether the selected pathway is entered depends upon whether or not activating stimuli are received; if they are, organogenesis proceeds. The potential pathways available at each node change as development progresses.

As we have seen, the experiments of Evans (1964) and others do strongly suggest that the potentiation of particular tissues in the neighborhood of the apex is not itself the completion of transcription. The alternative is that the determining act is the exposure of part of the genome for transcription; or, stated negatively, the blanking off of those parts not to be read in the cell, tissue or organ concerned. This would seem to be the deduction from the experiments of Huang and Bonner on the synthesis of the storage protein of the pea cotyledon (Pisum sp.) (Bonner, 1965). RNA was synthesized when isolated chromatin from the young cotyledons was provided with polymerase and substrates, and this RNA, supplied in turn with messenger-free ribosomes, appropriate co-factors and substrates, supported the synthesis of the storage globulin, recognized in the experiment by its immunological properties. When chromatin from vegetative buds was tested, it was found to be less effective in directing these same syntheses by a factor of up to eight. The interpretation given to these results by Huang and Bonner was that different constellations of genes are open for transcription in the chromatin from the two types of tissue, and they supported the view that the "blocking" agent is the chromosomal histone.

A difficulty lies in understanding how predifferentiations, if they do depend upon differing states of gene accessibility, can be transmitted through cell lineages (Heslop-Harrison, 1967). Clearly, if the transmitted changes depend upon permanent gene inactivation, they are mutations, not differentiations in the normal sense. Regenerative experiments, now performed for almost all plant organs, show that organ determination is not of this character. Knowledge of mitotically transmissible, specific, reversible "gene-blocking" agents is very hazy for higher organisms, if it can be said to exist at all. The histone hypothesis has not yet been developed to a point where it offers a satisfactory explanation of the specificity observed in differentiation, nor of the transmissibility apparent in so many examples of development and differentiation. There remains the possibility that controls of gene expression of the operon type are responsible (Jacob and Monod, 1963). These could be envisaged as carrying repressed states through mitotic cycles because of the persistence of extranuclear elements of the circuit through mitotic contraction, or as cooperating in maintaining common conditions of partial differentiation in tissues by the transfer of repressors between cells. The operon scheme therefore can offer some useful models, but there is no unequivocal evidence yet of the existence of such control circuits in higher organisms.

Once a primordium or a volume of axial tissue has been committed to a particular developmental pathway by virtue of its time of initiation and position relative to the apex, whether its potential is realized or not depends on the working of a further superstructure of control, that embodied in the general hormonal and nutritional milieu of the whole plant. At this level, also, control may be imposed so positively as to amount effectively to a "determination," as in the suppression of axillary bud development by a strongly dominant apex. Figure 13-2 is a chart of some of the alternative developmental pathways open during the growth of the corn plant. At the "switch" points marked, development can be deflected in the directions shown by photoperiodic, temperature or

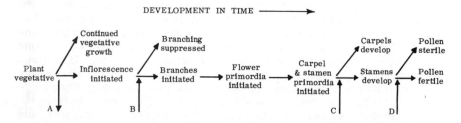

Fig. 13-2—Alternative pathways in the flowering of Zea mays. The axial sequence represents the route leading to a fertile male inflorescence in a normal
annual cycle of growth. At A, B, C and D the developmental pathway can be
deflected in the direction indicated by short-day experience. From Heslop-
Harrison (1961).

chemical treatments (Heslop-Harrison, 1961; Moss and Heslop-Harrison,
1968). Once made, the decision at each of these points is in effect irreversible, so that they represent commitments yet more extreme than
axillary bud inhibition. The specificity is strikingly illustrated in the
growth of the individual flower primordium in corn. All primordia, in
tassel and ear, pass through a primitively monoclinous condition. Then,
according to the position in the plant and prior temperature and photoperiodic experience, stamen growth is suspended in the ears and gyno-
ecial growth in the florets of the tassel. It can be shown that each floret
passes through a phase of sensitivity during which sex determination
takes place, and there is circumstantial evidence to show that the decisive events are local ones, not engaging all the tissues of the inflorescence (Heslop-Harrison, 1961). Once complete, this determination is
certainly irreversible, since the primordia of the alternate sex atrophy.
Similar evidence exists for sex determination in the monoecious cucurbits, where the early lability of the bud primordium and its sensitivity
to control by auxins and gibberellins has been demonstrated in culture
in vitro (Galun, Jung, and Lang, 1962).

Even though differentiation continues to present so many enigmas,
the foregoing paragraphs show that it is possible to distinguish a hierarchy of control levels in higher plants. In the following section, some
features of storage organ formation are examined in the light of this
fact.

II. STORAGE TISSUES: CHARACTERISTICS AND DEVELOPMENT

Recent reviews of the morphology and cytology of storage organs
include those of Weber (1958a,b) and Wanner (1958). The characteristic cytological features of storage tissues are associated with the kinds
of reserves accumulated, and not with the nature of the storage structure in organographic terms. This means that the differentiations concerned with the acquisition of the storage function can be superimposed

upon those undergone in the normal course of organogenesis. These differentiations may involve no more than trivial changes in cell organization, as is often found when soluble compounds are stored, or they may demand far-reaching structural modifications, particularly in organelles. In starch-storing tissues, proplastids may develop directly into amyloplasts and pass through no stage where an extensive lamellar system is formed, or, as in the storage stems of Pellionia, amyloplasts may be formed from previously functional chloroplasts by the regression of the lamellar system. Plastids may also undergo radical structural reorganization for the storage of lipids and proteins. However, lipid reserves more commonly accumulate in spherosomes, which according to one current view are derived from embayments of the endoplasmic reticulum. Some types of protein inclusions, both amorphous and crystalline, appear to have a similar origin, although there is much yet to be found out about the ontogenetic derivation of many classes of reserve proteins.

In some tissues, specialization for a storage function may represent a terminal differentiation; in others it clearly does not. Although the state of endopolyploidy has yet to be established for many types of storage organs, it is probable that the chromosome number does often increase in the cells during differentiation (d'Amato, 1964), and it is likely that the chromosomes of some become polytenic. These are devices serving to increase the number of functional loci, and they are characteristic of glandular and other types of tissue where rapid synthesis of a few products is required over a comparatively short period of time. Highly endopolyploid or polytenic cells probably never revert to division and growth in the natural tissue. Storage may also culminate in irreversible damage to organelles, as seems to be true of amyloplasts in endosperm (Badenhuizen, 1958); again, it would seem improbable that cells modified to this extent could revert to a meristematic state.

On the other hand, some metabolic activity must be resumed in storage structures connected with perennation, even if only for the purpose of mobilizing the reserves, and extensive "re-differentiation" may follow, as when storage cotyledons become photosynthetic during germination. In climacteric fruits, the truly terminal differentiation is that which leads to the climacteric itself, as in the banana (Musa sp.) (Sacher, 1967). Right up to this time, banana fruit tissue can be caused to resume growth, to lose starch content, and to produce a callus of actively proliferating cells (Mohan Ram and Steward, 1964). The many similar demonstrations that the storage tissues of fruits, tubers, rhizomes, corms, and storage roots can be caused to proliferate in culture in vitro and even to regenerate plants proves that at least some cells have retained totipotency, and perhaps more importantly, genomic balance. These experiments also cast light on some of the reasons for the metabolic inactivity of mature storage tissues, since the induction of growth uniformly requires that auxin and cytokinin should be supplied from exogenous sources. Growth induction involves an initial lag phase, during which many syntheses are resumed with concomitant far-reaching changes in organelles (Israel and Steward, 1966).

A. Biological Role of Storage Organs

In general, storage tissue serves either to provide incentives for animal collaboration in haplophase or diplophase dispersal, or to carry reserves accumulated in one season through a period inimical to growth for use in organogenesis, or for some reproductive purpose, in the next. Fleshy fruits are the prime examples of the first function; endosperm and all types of storage structures derived by the modification of vegetative organs characterize the second. The biological significance of storage organs is thus to be understood first in ecological terms— specifically, in relation to adaptation to climate and particular types of biota. Plant survival in any habit but the most uniform depends upon the acquisition of a developmental cycle fitting growth and reproduction to the annual march of the seasons. For annuals, this will mean an adjustment of the relative durations of seed dormancy, vegetative growth, flowering, seed maturation, and fruit set to optimize the opportunities for dispersal and establishment each year. For perennials the survival of the individual will require the accumulation of reserves in vegetative organs and a strict regulation of growth periodicity and bud dormancy.

For each different climatic complex and each habitat or microhabitat, natural selection will determine what life forms will dominate, and will further ensure the continuous adjustment and readjustment of the developmental cycles of species populations to maintain optimum "fit" to the seasonal cycle. This serves to emphasize the time-keeping aspect of developmental processes, and to bring out the fact that where accurate temporal regulation of periodicities is essential for survival, selection will favor the adoption of reliable environmental "clocks" for the purpose. Here, then, lies the significance of the photoperiodic reaction, and of the temperature responses controlling seed and bud dormancy and vernalization.

The specific effects of light and temperature upon developmental periodicities are all of the inductive type, in the sense that the perception of the stimulus over one period determines behavior at some future time—often, in terms of a growing apex, many cell generations later (Lang, 1965a). This device provides the element of anticipation necessary for survival in climates with seasons inimical to growth. An important point is that the activating signals are not necessarily related directly to the environmental conditions that will prevail when the response is executed. This is obvious enough for the examples of flowering and control of winter dormancy just mentioned; but the principle applies, mutatis mutandis, with all adaptively significant developmental periodicities, including the differentiation of vegetative storage tissues. So it may be concluded that the stimuli potentiating tissues for storage and launching the growth of storage organs will normally act earlier than, and not be identical with, those later to be concerned with the synthesis and translocation of the reserves themselves. This proposition, justified here from theoretical considerations, is of course well enough substantiated from observation. Bulbing, tuberization, corm formation are all typically responses to photoperiod and inductive temperature experience, sharing many of the characteristics of the flowering response (Gregory, 1965; Nitsch, 1966).

B. Development of Storage Structures

It is usually possible to distinguish three phases in the development of a vegetative storage structure after its initiation, (i) an early period of increase in cell number leading to, or overlapping with, (ii) a period of cell expansion and reserve accumulation, which gives place in turn to (iii), a period of relative metabolic inactivity, amounting often to dormancy. These phases vary in their duration, and may occur cyclically. Leading from the arguments of preceding paragraphs, the sequence of events is as in Fig. 13-3. This scheme postulates that the potentiation of the tissue for storage depends upon endogenous controls, modulated to some degree through the general hormonal milieu of the plant. The initiation of growth in competent tissue is represented as being primarily dependent upon general hormonal control, whereas size and storage capacity must necessarily be related, as shown, to availability of mineral nutrients, water and photosynthate. A feed-back loop, discussed in more detail below, is shown as influencing translocation,

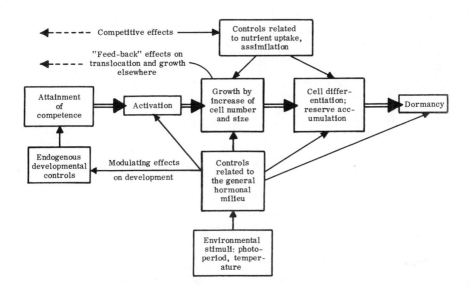

Fig. 13-3—Scheme for the differentiation of a vegetative storage structure. The axial sequence begins at a time when a volume of tissue competent to differentiate for the storage function has been defined. Activation is shown as being primarily under hormonal control, and also the ultimate passage into dormancy. Growth and reserve accumulation are governed both nutritionally and hormonally.

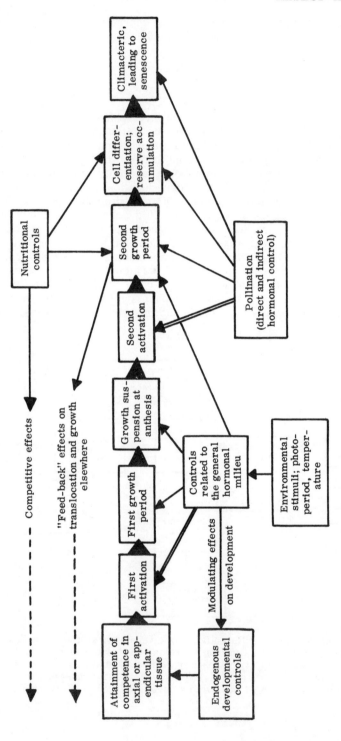

Fig. 13-4—Scheme comparable with that of Fig. 13-3 for the growth of a climacteric fruit. Activation is here in two steps, the second depending upon pollination and its after effects.

and another as affecting growth elsewhere in the plant. The control of the onset of dormancy is imputed to hormonal control from outside of the developing organ, again allowing for time-regulation through photo-period.

A similar scheme can be drawn up for fruits, but it must neces-sarily take into account other strata of control. An outline is given in Fig. 13-4. The first activation phase is initiated with the onset of flower formation; the resulting growth is arrested or drastically re-duced around the time of anthesis. The second activation phase depends on the consummation of pollination. The stimulation here may be three-fold: through the growth substances borne by the pollen itself; through the activation of growth-substance synthesis in ovary tissues by cofac-tors brought in by the pollen tube, and, later, through growth substances released from the developing embryos and endosperms after the suc-cessful completion of fertilization. Again, nutritional control enters as a determinant of size, and there are feed-back effects on the translo-cation system. The culmination of the pathway in many fruits is entry into the climacteric, which is probably timed both by local controls and the general hormonal environment of the plant.

A third scheme, Fig. 13-5, relates to the development of seed re-serves. Here five organisms are involved: the parental sporophyte, the female gametophyte, the male gametophyte, the diploid embryo and the triploid endosperm (the justification for regarding the endosperm as a separate organism is primarily genetical, but the concept also has its physiological usefulness). To simplify this scheme, the time se-quence is started at the point where the female gametophyte is already differentiated: the antecedent circumstances would be those leading to flowering, carpel activation, meiosis, and megaspore germination. There are some plants where meiosis and embryo-sac development are contingent upon pollination, but this seems rare, and in general it is the further development of the egg and the primary endosperm nucleus that demands the stimulus of pollination—or, more specifically, fertilization. As in the examples of vegetative storage organs, the duration of growth before dormancy is governed in part from without, although here it is a question of a teleonomic influence of one generation upon another.

It is worth noting in passing that fruit and seed development offer excellent models for the interplay of competent-tissue and activating-stimulus which elsewhere has to be inferred from experiment with iso-lated organs and tissues, since one link in the natural control pathway lies outside of the plant. Growth of the ovary is arrested at anthesis; but ovary tissues are competent to respond to the stimuli accompany-ing, and generated by, pollination. Similarly, egg and primary endo-sperm nucleus are blocked unless further development is promoted by fertilization. In both of these examples, the requirement for the exog-enous stimulus is bypassed in certain genotypes, so that the fruit devel-ops parthenocarpically, or the egg and endosperm parthenogenetically.

C. The Hormonal Factors

The schemes discussed above help to direct attention to various persistent lacunae in our knowledge of hormonal function in the control

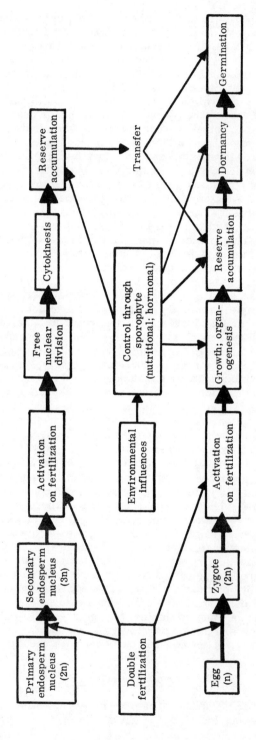

Fig. 13-5—Scheme comparable to Fig. 13-3 for seed formation. The two axial sequences refer to the endosperm and the embryo, beginning with the parental nuclei in the female gametophyte. Fertilization is shown as having dual effects: providing two male nuclei for the two fusions, and activating the DNA synthesis leading to the first divisions of the zygote and secondary endosperm nuclei. Control by the sporophyte is comparable with that exerted by a host upon a parasite, and is both nutritional and hormonal.

of differentiation and development. A conspicuous example is the absence of any comprehensive explanation for the way environmental influences, particularly photoperiod, affect the transition to flowering. The perceptive mechanism in the leaf patently involves phytochrome, and there are cogent reasons for supposing that there is a transmitted stimulus (Salisbury, 1963; Hillman, 1962; Lang, 1965b). Yet in spite of the great body of data at hand, there is so far no unequivocal indication of its nature, nor of the precise functions other growth substances, notably the gibberellins, discharge in the photoperiodic response (Chailakhyan, 1967, 1968). The physiology of flowering-plant reproduction remains therefore a most challenging field for research, and obviously one of considerable practical importance if we are ever to achieve the ability to manipulate flowering with precision for breeding and production.

Essentially the same comments can be made about the control of tuberization, bulbing, and similar processes. The resemblance between tuberization and flowering in manner of control has been mentioned above. Since the work of Zimmermann and Hitchcock (1936), it has been clear that shoot-generated stimuli pass to the potential tuber sites in subterranean organs, and control by photoperiod and temperature has been adequately demonstrated experimentally (Went, 1957; Chapman, 1958; Madec, 1963; Slater, 1963; Gregory, 1965). As with the flowering stimulus, it is possible that the transmissible agent is nonspecific. Nitsch (1966), for example, has shown that the shoot of Helianthus annuus, a species genetically incapable of tuberization, will nevertheless act as a photoperiodic receptor for a grafted root system of artichoke, Helianthus tuberosus, and transmit the tuber-activating stimulus. Wareing et al. (1967) have reported that tuberization in Solanum andigena, a species setting tubers in short days, can be promoted in long days by foliar sprays of abscisic acid (dormin). These authors suggest that this effect could be an indirect one resulting from retardation of shoot growth, but the possibility remains that the transmissible stimulus is indeed abscisic acid (Nitsch, 1966); if so there is a glimpse of a unifying principle, since tuberization is normally associated with increasing inactivity of vegetative apices. However, the hormonal control system is undoubtedly complex. Abscisic acid depresses levels of endogenous gibberellins in some tissues (Thomas, Wareing, and Robinson, 1965), and exogenous GA3 can inhibit tuberization (Tizio, 1964). During the early period of tuberization there is active cell division and growth, and this suggests cytokinin activity. It is therefore significant that cytokinins have been found in the young potato tuber (Tizio, 1966), and that the tuberization of the artichoke (Cynara scolymus) in vitro is promoted by kinetin (Courduroux, 1966). In the interplay of the different classes of growth substances in natural tuberization, it could be that the effect of the mobile stimulus, should this be abscisic acid, is to change the balance between other physiologically active substances in the target tissue. If so, precise observation of time-related changes in the responding sites will be needed to elucidate the sequence of events and evaluate their meaning for the differentiation of storage tissue and the subsequent passage into dormancy (Burton, 1963).

D. The Nutritional Factors

There is the further question of the part played by nutrients in the control of development and differentiation. Theories current 30 or 40 years ago attributed roles in the control of development to carbon/nitrogen ratios, and correlations can often be observed between measure of nutrient status like this and developmental state. Apart from the problem of what is cause and what effect here, it is now apparent that in so far as the environment does affect flowering, tuberization and other comparable developmental events, it is through specific timekeeping stimuli which do not impinge directly on nutrient status. This conclusion seems in conflict with much earlier work where nitrogen nutrition, in particular, was thought to be an important factor in the control of flowering. Various chapters in The Induction of Flowering, edited by L. T. Evans, shortly to be published, show what is evidently the true situation. In species where the photoperiodic or thermal control of flowering is rather positive, nitrogen nutrition affects initiation very little, but in plants where these controls are less effective, nitrogen status may modify the time of initiation, and does commonly affect the abundance of flowering. Nitrogen availability may be a factor in controlling the balance of vegetative and reproductive growth through its effect on leaf senescence, a point mentioned further below.

Nevertheless, we are not well informed on the specificity of nutritional effects in development. No particular chemical connotations attach to the concept of a hormone, and there are situations where a constituent normally classed as a nutrient fulfills what is essentially a hormonal role. This may be of considerable importance when interrelationships between assimilation, differentiation, and storage are in question. Specificity has certainly been revealed in some experiments and two examples will serve to show that both organogenesis and differentiation at the cellular level may be subject to control by nutrient factors. Sexuality in Arisaema japonica is determined, as in corn, by the activation of carpels or stamens in any one inflorescence and the concomitant suppression of organs of the alternative sex. The plant is perennial, and the sexuality in any one year is closely related to corm size. Below a critical size there is no flowering; above this level, a male inflorescence is formed, and with a yet larger corm there is a transition to femaleness. Cutting the corm so as to reduce the reserves available causes a putatively female inflorescence to differentiate as a male one, or to form flowers of both sexes (Maekawa, 1927). The effect here is undoubtedly teleonomic and it is quite specific. The agency in this example of the control of flower morphogenesis has not been identified, but it is possible that it is the concentration of sucrose in the vicinity of the developing inflorescence. Specific control of cell differentiation by sucrose was demonstrated by Wetmore and Rier (1963), who were able to show that the development of vascular nodules in a block of lilac callus could be controlled by adjusting the balance between an auxin, α-naphthalene acetic acid, and sucrose diffusing into the block from a localized source. Jeffs and Northcote (1967) have confirmed that the effect of sucrose is indeed highly specific in this system, and have used labelled sucrose and auxin to give quantitative estimates of the relative concentrations required for the induction.

III. GROWTH, DIFFERENTIATION AND TRANSLOCATION

Translocation has been given princely treatment in other contributions to this symposium, and I shall accordingly restrict my remarks to the aspects most closely connected with growth and differentiation. One familiar relationship is seen in the effects of growing structures on the capacity of the transport system. The translocating tissues, xylem and phloem, are themselves the product of cell differentiation, and the establishment of conducting strands is as much subservient to the general developmental controls within the plant as any other histogenic event. In primary growth the tendency is for the demands of an organ to be nicely balanced against the capacity of the conducting channels leading into it, and it has to be supposed that this relationship depends upon the working out of a pre-established program of cell differentiation, providing for some anticipation of the ultimate requirements of the organ. This is well seen in the differentiation of the leaf, where the number of veins initiated in the primordium is related not to the size of the primordium but to the ultimate area of the lamina.

Demands rising later in life are met by secondary growth in the vascular system, and this is ordinarily effected by cambial activity. The cambium is under hormonal control, and its activities are related to the demands of the remote site because the hormonal flow from that site is related to the growth being accomplished there. The growth of massive fruits presents a model system (Nitsch, 1952). Pollination promotes auxin synthesis in the ovary tissue and ultimately in the developing seeds, and in consequence of the enhanced auxin flow through the pedicel, the growth of vascular tissue is promoted. This in turn facilitates the flow of water and nutrients into the fruit, and increases its competitive power in relation to other organs of the plant. There can thus be a kind of positive feed-back loop operating through control of the capacity of the translocation system. There are similar effects in the development of vegetative storage organs, and the control pathway is indicated in Fig. 13-3.

Growing tissues have also more immediate effects on transport. Loomis (1953) drew special attention to the sequestering effect developing storage structures have on assimilates, and Aronoff (1955), commenting on the movement of ^{14}C-labelled photosynthate, concluded that no physiological condition approaches growth as a causative agent for the direction and magnitude of translocation. Some recent observations cast light on the nature of the influence that meristematic and growing tissues have on the movement of nutrients and metabolites. It is usual to look upon the translocation stream as a flow of materials between source and sink, and it has been widely accepted that the gradient is maintained by the continuous removal of compounds at the receiving end by incorporation into insoluble fractions in the cells. However, some evidence now indicates that the conducting system itself actively directs assimilates into the growing zones, and that the process is under hormonal control (Kursanov, 1963, Edelman, 1963). The striking experiments of Mothes and collaborators (Mothes, 1964) show that accumulation and retention need not only be due to consumption of the translocated compounds. When the synthetic cytokinin, kinetin, is applied in a spot on one-half of the lamina of a detached tobacco leaf (Nicotiana tabacum L.), amino acids and other substances move to the site of application, and are held there. This is true even for amino acids which are not incorporated into protein; these accumulate in soluble state at the kinetin site. The applied kinetin does promote synthesis and retard senescence, but this effect can be separated from that on transport, since RNA and protein synthesis can be blocked with inhibitors without preventing the movement of metabolites to the kinetin-treated area. In pointing out that these cytokinin effects must involve a form of "active" transport since movement can occur against a gradient of a soluble substance, Mothes suggests that the key lies in a change in the capacity of the receiving cells to capture and retain low molecular weight substances and to prevent their rediffusion. This interpretation accepts the proposition that the intensity and direction of movement depend on the capacity and location of the sink. However, the experiments of Pozsár and Király (1964) permit a different conclusion—namely that the effect is on the transport system itself. In intact plants of Phaseolus vulgaris, the movement of labelled phosphate, glucose, and cysteine from a site of application on an old leaf was principally to the growing point and the younger leaves. When the excised bud was replaced by a kinetin source, the normal pattern of movement was restored, and upper leaves became receptors. Here there is no question of competitive growth at the cytokinin site because the accumulation was measured in adjacent leaves. This effect is evidently one on the polarity and activity of the conducting tissues.

In some systems, auxins reveal what is evidently a similar capacity to direct translocation. Loomis (1953) pointed to the possibility that the auxins of developing seeds may be concerned in their capacity for inducing movement of metabolites, and Booth et al. (1962), Davies and Wareing (1965), and Wareing and Seth (1967) have described experiments in which applied auxins produce effects on movement of nutrients very like those recorded for cytokinins. Indeed, Wareing and Seth (1967) record that IAA applied to the cut peduncle of Phaseolus vulgaris after removal of the developing fruit induced a greater movement of ^{32}P as phosphate into the peduncle stump than either kinetin or gibberellic acid. The most effective treatment in these experiments was the application of IAA, gibberellic acid and kinetin together, when the movement was more than four times that induced by IAA alone. This suggests that any one of the three classes of compound would stimulate movement when applied exogenously were its natural counterpart to be at a relative minimum in the tissue.

The implications of these results for future study of the movement of translocated materials into storage structures is indeed far-reaching. As Mothes has said, kinetin in his experimental systems is a model for those substances which cause storage organs to fill in the natural growth of the plant; and the natural cytokinin, zeatin, offers an even better model (Engelbrecht, 1967). It cannot be fortuitous that compounds having the capacity to provoke cell proliferation in undifferentiated tissues and to induce growth in dormant buds—and known also to be concerned in the growth of seeds and fruits and other storage organs—should also have specific effects on translocation.

IV. DIFFERENTIATION AND THE COMPONENTS OF YIELD

My purpose in this section is to consider some of the practical implications of the facts, ideas and speculations of the foregoing paragraphs, albeit very briefly and inadequately, taking into account the scope of the topic. We may begin with the commonplace proposition that yield in a crop plant is related both to total assimilation and nutrient uptake achieved during a growing season and to the way the material acquired is partitioned between harvestable storage structures and the rest of the plant. This directs attention immediately to the possibility that where the differentiation of storage structures is an alternative to vegetative growth the timing of the transition from one to the other will be a factor in determining yield, and the certainty that such factors will be found among those governing the numbers of storage structures and their competitive ability in the accumulation of reserves.

In plants like the cereals with terminal inflorescences, vegetative growth and flowering are strictly alternative processes in any one axis. The timing of the translation of the apex in terms of plastochrons is governed by autonomous controls, modulated by inductively-acting environmental factors such as temperature and photoperiod. It is evident, then, that in so far as assimilatory capacity is related to the number of foliage leaves it will be influenced by the developmental controls concerned with the transition to flowering. How far this will ever be a limiting factor will depend upon other circumstances, including leaf area duration and net assimilation rate. Furthermore, it is now well established that foliage below the flag leaf makes little contribution to grain yield in barley (Hordeum vulgare L.) and wheat (Triticum aestivum L.) (Archbold, 1942; Buttrose and May, 1959; Thorne, 1963, 1965; Kriedemann, 1966), and similarly in corn the contribution of the upper leaves considerably exceeds that of the lower (Allison and Watson, 1966). It would seem, then, that numbers of leaf-bearing nodes is not a highly important factor in itself in cereals, and accordingly that little practical significance attaches to this aspect of the functioning of developmental controls concerned in the transition to flowering. The time of initiation may, however, have some importance, should the correlations of yield with leaf area duration after the beginning of grain development revealed in small-grain cereal experiments (Watson, Thorne, and French, 1963; Welbank, French, and Witts, 1966) prevail with wide variation in relative periods of vegetative and reproductive activity at the apex.

Another component of yield in cereals is the ability of the developing grain to accept assimilate, a factor related both to grain number and individual capacity. Most investigations have shown number of grains set to be a major factor, indeed sometimes a limiting one (Bingham, 1967; Moss, 1962; Asana and Williams, 1965; Nösberger and

Thorne, 1965; Allison and Watson, 1966). If this be indeed a general condition, the circumstances affecting grain set are crucially concerned with yield.

For cereals in general, failure of grain set due to lack of pollination is rarely important, both because of the widespread occurrence of self-ing and the abundance of pollen available in the crop. The limitation of grain number is imposed during ear initiation by the numbers of plasto-chron cycles executed, and in the small grains by the numbers of ear-producing tillers and in corn by the number of axillary ear-shoots be-ginning development. Taking firstly the matter of inflorescence size, it is pertinent to ènquire whether the number of spikelet primordia de-fined before growth at the apex ceases is governed absolutely by influ-ences effective before initiation, or whether the circumstances prevail-ing during the early growth of the inflorescence determine its ultimate size (Ryle, 1966). The question concerns another facet of the control of metamerism discussed above. In cereals, as in most species, there is a sharp decrease in the plastochron with inflorescence initiation. There-after the number of nodes, and accordingly of spikelet primordia de-fined, is given by the duration of growth divided by the new plastochron. Ryle (1965) found that daylength experienced before initiation of the inflorescence determined spikelet number in Lolium perenne, a quanti-tative long-day species, short days increasing the number of primordia formed. A similar response was observed in wheat by Thorne, Ford, and Watson (1968). In corn, a quantitative short-day species, long days experienced before inflorescence initiation increase floret number both in terminal male and lateral female inflorescences (Moss and Heslop-Harrison, 1968). The daylength effect here is specifically a photoperi-odic one, since it was observed in night-interruption experiments when the effective energy content of long and short days was the same. Com-parable results exist for other species, sufficient probably to support the generalization that daylength conditions delaying inflorescence initia-tion increase primordium number.

There is no doubt, however, that the photoperiodic effect is con-founded with a nutritional one in the normal growth of the plant. In corn, long photosynthetic days are more effective than photoperiodically-effective long days given by night interruption (Moss and Heslop-Harrison, 1968) in enhancing the number of female florets formed. Ryle (1963) similarly concluded that although shoot age at the time of initiation was a primary determinant of ear length in Phleum pratense, nutritional factors acting before initiation, including both mineral and carbohydrate availability, affect final inflorescence size, and the same author (1967) noted a marked effect of light intensity during inflores-cence development on floret number in the spike of Lolium perenne and on branch and floret number in the panicle of Festuca pratensis. In this symposium, Dr. Murata (see Chapter 11, this book) has mentioned the effects nitrogen nutrition may have on spikelet number in rice during certain developmental periods.

Nevertheless, for many species with determinate spicate inflores-cences like the cereals, potential inflorescence size in normal light and nutritional conditions would seem to be established for all practical purposes before the actual translation of the apex. This must mean that where the potential yield ceiling is governed by grain number, this too is set before the beginning of flowering. Conditions after initiation may act to lower fertility by causing floret abortion, but never to raise it by inducing a resumption of spike extension (Heslop-Harrison, 1961; Thorne, Ford, and Watson, 1968). This would seem to be an important conclusion, and for this reason some effort should be devoted to reinforcing and generalizing it and to the further analysis of the relative importance of developmental and nutritional controls in the preinitiation period.

The other factor contributing to grain set per plant is the number of contributing inflorescences. In the small grain cereals this is determined by tillering; in corn by the number of potential ear sites activated. Here again the evidence shows that the ultimate potential is governed by determinations made early in the life of the plant. For the small grain cereals no generalizations beyond this seem yet feasible, because of the complexity of temperature, daylength, and nutritional interactions, and the existence of species and varietal differences (Aspinall, 1961; Friend, 1965; Thorne, Ford, and Watson, 1968). There is also here the problem of competitive effects between tiller initials, and in regard to yield in a field crop the significance of tillering has to be considered in relation to plant density (Thorne, 1966). With corn, on the other hand, where the ear is a condensed lateral structure, modifying ear number is not a matter of altering the number of complete foliated axes, but rather of changing the number and distribution of assimilate sinks on the one axis. Ear primordia are initiated at many successive nodes, yet in most cultivars all but one or two fail to develop and then abort. One may note that the archaeology of corn shows that man has willed it to be like this, through selection for cob size and the concomitant changes in plant architecture this has brought about (Mangelsdorf, MacNeish, and Galinat, 1964). The activation of some primordia and the decisive suppression of others takes place early in development, although probably not immediately after inception. There is a photoperiodic element in the control, long days increasing the number of ears developing (Moss and Heslop-Harrison, 1968), and probably a less specific nutritional element (e.g., Andrew, 1967). The suppression of the supernumerary axillary inflorescences has some of the characteristics of correlative bud inhibition, and growth can be provoked by removing competing inflorescences if the excision is made at an early enough stage; yet, later in development, the suppression becomes irreversible (some aspects of the competition between inflorescences have been considered by Moss, 1962). There is an obvious invitation here for fuller investigation, since it should not be too difficult to discover more about the factors controlling the relative activity of the ear primordia, and to explore the possibility of control of inflorescence number by chemical means. Furthermore, it is evident that this particular characteristic of the corn plant would yield readily to manipulation by breeding, reversing the trend hitherto under domestication. This might be one way to alleviate any limitation of yield due to lack of grain capacity, and there are other reasons for rethinking the corn plant along these lines (Army and Greer, 1967).

In systematically-flowering species grown for fruit or seed and in plants producing vegetative storage organs, storage and vegetative growth are competing rather than alternative processes. The great diversity of crop plants in these categories prevents generalization, but again a principle of wide validity is that the distribution of resources during the main period of assimilation is according to a program determined quite early during growth, largely by photoperiod and temperature. These factors may govern not only the timing and localization of flowering and storage-organ inception, but also the competitive ability of apical buds.

A recession in shoot growth is a common concomitant of the beginning of tuberization (Milthorpe, 1963), and in part this reflects competition for assimilate. However, the more specific developmental control is revealed by experiments like those of Nösberger and Humphries (1965) with the potato (see also Goodwin, 1963). When tubers were removed during the filling period, some apices responded by a resumption of growth, but others remained inhibited. These potential sinks were never reactivated, even although a high credit balance of carbohydrate was established in the shoot. Comparable observations have been made with other tuberizing species; for example, in the Jerusalem artichoke short days induce tuberization and stop shoot growth, and thereafter the apical bud remains firmly inhibited, even if the tubers are removed (Edelman, 1963).

These findings have to be considered in relation to the general phenomena of bud inhibition and apical dominance—phenomena, unfortunately, not yet fully understood. While the nutritional status of the shoot does affect the strength of apical dominance—as revealed, inter alia, by the experiments of Gregory and Veale (1957) on flax (Linum usitatissimum)—the control is mediated through the hormonal milieu of the plant. The classical view attributes control to the auxin stream from the dominant apex (Thimann and Skoog, 1934), and recent work on the effects of exogenously supplied kinetin on lateral bud inhibition in peas has led to the proposition that it is the interaction of auxins from this source and the natural cytokinins at the bud site that determines whether growth will occur or not (Wickson and Thimann, 1958). Among other factors to be taken into consideration are the effects on the nutrient status and capacity for growth of the differentiation of vascular tissue at the bud base (Audus, 1959), and the important possibility that correlative bud inhibition, like bud dormancy, may depend upon inhibitors (Wareing et al., 1967). Dörffling (1966, 1967) has shown that inhibitors are present in lateral buds of pea suppressed by apical dominance, and has demonstrated the existence of abscisic acid in this plant. It would seem very likely, then, that at least three hormonal factors interact in the control of bud dormancy. It may be that the tuberization response in the potato is but one part of a syndrome of effects arising from an increase of abscisic acid levels in inductive environments—taking into account the findings of Wareing et al. (1967)—others being the suppression of shoot growth and the reinforcement of the correlative inhibition of lateral buds.

This would mean that the partitioning of assimilate and nutrients between aerial parts and tubers is not governed simply by competition between two sites with the shoot system gradually losing, but by a regulated shift of growth activity related to an innate developmental program, itself keyed to time-keeping agencies in the environment. The existence of some form of teleonomic control even over the relative growth rates of tubers of the same potato plant is shown by the work of Moorby (1968). According to Moorby, the tubers grow in turn, each receiving the greater part of the available substrate during its active periods. There is no indication that tubers at particular sites gain and retain growth advantage, as might be expected were there to be severe competition. The observed phasing could be due, as suggested by Moorby, to the tubers possessing different sources of assimilate supply, but it may also be interpreted as further evidence of the working out of a hormone-mediated developmental program.

The preceding discussion has been mainly focussed upon the relationships between vegetative growth and storage-structure formation; but there is still another factor to be considered, the influence of reproduction, tuberization and similar activities on the photosynthetic capacities of the mature parts of the plant. Two aspects of this concern the longevity of leaves and direct effects of assimilate "sinks" on net assimilation rate.

It has long been appreciated that the initiation of storage structures, whether related to sexual reproduction or perennation, not only reduces shoot growth, but accelerates leaf senescence (Murneek, 1926; Milthorpe, 1963). The trend can be slowed, or even reversed, by removal of the storage structures. Walkley (1940) showed that barley leaves which had lost up to half of their protein content could be induced to resume protein synthesis by removing the upper part of the shoot, and Wareing and Seth (1967) have similarly recorded that removal of the seed from the developing pods of Phaseolus vulgaris not only delays loss of chlorophyll and protein from the leaves but causes a substantial rise in these constituents over control levels for a period of 5 or 6 weeks. Again it might be asked whether effects like these are essentially aspects of competition (Molisch, 1938), or whether the senescence is a controlled event, representing yet another manifestation of the working out of a genetically determined developmental program, as envisaged by Leopold (1961). It is noteworthy that the latter view was supported by most of the authors who touched on the topic in the 1967 symposium of the Society for Experimental Biology on the biology of aging.

Annual and biennial crop plants show the type of senescence Osborne (1962) or (1967) has termed sequential, the older leaves senescing first. Discussing possible explanation of this kind of leaf aging, Simon (1967) stated the view that the principal factor is the rate of translocation of metabolites, particularly amino acids, from the leaf. The argument is that a fraction of the leaf protein is turning over, so that a drain of amino acids would lower the available pool for resynthesis, resulting in a progressive net loss of protein from the leaf. This would mean that control over leaf senescence resides mainly in the factors determining the direction and magnitude of the translocation of nitrogenous and other metabolites in the plant. Since it implies that the nitrogen pool could be a limiting factor, it also offers an explanation for the effects of high nitrogen nutrition in extending leaf life.

An alternative possibility considered by Simon (1967) was that leaf senescence is due to a decay in protein synthesis through the cessation or reduction of mRNA production (Osborne, 1962). The experiments of Mothes' group mentioned above indicate that both of these explanations are likely to be correct. Cytokinins like kinetin not only redirect the flow of amino acids in the leaves, but enhance RNA and protein synthesis at the site of application. According to Wollgiehn (1965, 1967) all RNA fractions increase in kinetin-treated tobacco leaves, including a rapidly labelled fraction with some characteristics of mRNA. Similar observations have been made by Carpenter and Cherry (1966) for the cytokinin, benzyladenine, applied to peanut cotyledons, and Osborne (1967) has shown that the action of kinetin in delaying leaf-senescence in Xanthium involves an actinomycin-D sensitive RNA synthesis.

These observations have led to the hypothesis that natural control resides in cytokinins. It has been suggested that cytokinins from the the root system act as leaf hormones (Wareing and Seth, 1967; Wollgiehm, 1967), and that the effect of competing fruits, seeds and other storage structures may be to divert these from the leaves, so promoting premature senescence. However, no overall explanation can yet be given for the control of leaf senescence, since in no species have all the interactions between hormonal, or quasi-hormonal, factors been worked out. Various synthetic auxins simulate the cytokinin effect by maintaining greenness in leaf tissues, and Osborne (1967) has offered a scheme according to which leaf cells in treated areas induce senescence in neighboring cells by stimulating the formation of a senescence factor. She has indicated further that abscisic acid possesses some of the properties postulated for this factor (see also Wareing et al., 1967). This does not exhaust all the possibilities, since a role for ethylene in leaf senescence is suggested by the work of Burg and Burg (1966, 1968), and it is a moot point where gibberellins, known to affect leaf growth (Humphries and Wheeler, 1963) fit into the picture.

The possible practical significance of leaf senescence naturally lies in the effect loss of metabolic activity in the leaf may have on the availability of assimilate for growing storage structures. The conclusion from cereal experiments such as those of Watson, Thorne, and French (1963) already mentioned has been that yield is closely correlated with leaf area duration after the beginning of grain development. Leaf area duration is related to leaf initiation, growth in area and senescence. Since in cereals leaf initiation is terminated in any one axis at the time of flowering, and since the final leaf area is fixed soon after, the time of leaf senescence is the main determinant of leaf area duration after flowering. Nutritional manipulation. particularly affecting nitrogen availability, can delay leaf senescence, but there is the further question whether any advantage would lie in attempting to extend leaf-life by chemical means. This is problematical. After their photosynthetic function is complete, leaves are drawn upon by storage structures for metabolites other than carbohydrates; for example, for the amino acids released by protein breakdown. It may be that in the evolution of each species a compromise has been achieved between these two roles of leaves, and that to disturb this by delaying senescence and protein breakdown would destroy the adjustment of the growth pattern to the seasonal cycle. Yet for a cultivated species where ecological adjustment is not necessarily an over-riding consideration one might contemplate protracting the photosynthetic function of leaves, taking as a "penalty" a higher retention of leaf protein and minerals at the end of the growing season. But the chain of effects leading from delayed senescence could be far-reaching, and lead to disastrous consequences even in cultivated species. If the leaves are the source of controlling signals for events later in the lives of storage structures and seeds—for example, in the imposition of dormancy—radical alteration of the aging process in leaves could upset this coordination. In the potato, were the leaves to remain exporters of gibberellins, there is no doubt that the normal processes of tuber maturation would be upset (Claver, 1960).

We come to another somewhat equivocal area in turning to the effects of storage structure-growth on net assimilation rate. The common pattern in observations in many experiments has been that removal of developing storage organs—seeds, fruits, tubers—leads to a fall in net assimilation rate (e.g., for cereals, Kiesselbach, 1948; Moss, 1962; for fruits, Maggs, 1963; for tubers, Burt, 1964; Nösberger and Humphries, 1965), and this has been taken to mean that size of the sink for photosynthate may in some conditions determine photosynthetic rate. This view has been supported by the demonstration that net assimilation rate increases in spinach beet tops (Beta sp.) when they are grafted on to sugar beet roots (Beta vulgaris L.) (Thorne and Evans, 1964), and Humphries (1963) has argued that the increased photosynthesis observed in detached leaves when roots differentiate from the petiole points in the same direction. Some experiments do not seem to have shown an effect of sink size on net assimilation rate, however; thus Nösberger and Thorne (1965) found that removing florets had little effect on photosynthetic rate in barley, although it did increase leaf area and greatly modified the movement of carbohydrate.

Evidently there could be several explanations for the results of experiments where sink size does seem to influence net assimilation rates. The formation of roots from the petioles of detached leaves retards leaf senescence, and enhances DNA, RNA and protein synthesis, evidently largely in the plastids (Böttger and Wollgiehn, 1958). In this case the increase of net assimilation rate accompanying rooting could be due to rejuvenation and enlargement of the photosynthetic apparatus. The effect can be mimicked with cytokinins, and for this reason it has been supposed that the leaf rejuvenation is due to the flow of a cytokinin-like hormone from the new roots (Böttger and Lüdemann, 1964).

The situation would seem to be quite different where the presence of storage organs seems to maintain a certain net assimilation rate which diminishes upon their excision. As we have seen, removal of storage structures can retard leaf senescence; it acts, then, like root development on the detached leaf. Yet photosynthetic efficiency is apparently lowered, not enhanced. Since the surplus carbohydrate accumulates in stems and leaves (corn, Moss, 1962; potato, Nösberger and Humphries, 1965), the effect here may be a direct one on the photosynthetic carbon pathway (Went and Engelsberg, 1946).

Considering the overall picture, the many interactions between leaf and storage structure would seem to point to the presence of several compromises; and others are apparent when the relationships between shoot and root (not discussed here) are taken into account (Loomis, 1935). Beyond the compromise mentioned above between the different roles of leaves, in some species yet a further balance must be achieved between the leaf-senescence inducing effect of storage-structure differentiation and the influence these structures have on photosynthetic efficiency. Stated tersely, the circumstance of grain or tuber set may be regarded as ensuring that leaves have a short life but an active one. Again, this is only to be expected as consequence of the selective molding of the developmental cycle to the march of the seasons. It would be quite wrong to suppose that the network of reciprocally-acting controls linking the different parts of the plant has any appreciable accidental element—that, for example, the effect of storage organs on leaf efficiency or senescence is just some sort of mischance unavoidable for some obscure physiological reason. There will undoubtedly be real adaptive advantage to these relationships where they exist—probably along the lines mentioned above, namely that the leaves are not only sources of photosynthate, but convenient reservoirs from which mineral nutrients can be withdrawn at appropriate times during the growth of perennating organs and seeds. This argument does not imply that the adjustments are always perfect; patently they are not. It does mean, however, that in plants in general the genetic control of the whole system of interactions is likely always to be quite flexible, otherwise adaptation to different lengths of growing season would never have been possible. The genetic basis probably always lies in polygenic systems, or in some other mechanism permitting quantitative gradation, such as the serial replication of cistrons. The implication of this in turn is that it should be within the capacity of man to adjust, through breeding, any part of the control network, and so to tailor whatever pattern of developmental cycle he should wish.

V. THE OUTLOOK

I began this review by commenting on the wide gaps in our knowledge of the control of differentiational and developmental processes in plants, and the point will have been underlined by a great deal of what I have said in the preceding paragraphs. Yet much of the phenomenology must be regarded as being tolerably well understood. Certainly this is true of many kinds of environmental response, and notwithstanding the complex and confusing situation with endogenous hormones, there is now a very substantial mass of reliable information concerning plant responses to chemical and other treatments affecting development.

There is a continuing challenge to apply this knowledge in the search for increased yield and production efficiency. In a sense, of course, much of crop husbandry is already concerned with the manipulation of plant development for these ends, but in the present context the problem refers more pertinently to the use of knowledge about the ways patterns of growth are governed in plants to take control yet more completely into human hands. As a botanist I am very reluctant to speculate much on this matter in the presence of so many distinguished agronomists, even although my brief contained an injunction to do so. Still, a comment or two may be admissible. There is no doubt that in the generality of cases the most effective way to obtain a growth pattern efficient in a given environment for a particular purpose is to breed a genotype for the job, but there is no shortage of examples of deliberate manipulation of development in field crops to achieve like ends. The most massive operation was probably grain vernalization in Russia, and no one can have failed to have been impressed by what we have heard here from Dr. H. F. Clements (see Chapter 14, this book) concerning the precise and skillful programming of development practiced with the pineapple and sugar cane crops in Hawaii. Contemplating these trends and those to be seen in horticulture, it seems certain that the manipulation of development in field crops by chemical and other means will become increasingly important in the future. One obstacle is the practical difficulty of regulating treatments on the scale required and fitting them to different climatic contexts and the vagaries of the weather. Yet, again, the trend already seen in disease and weed control and in nutrition towards more and more precise regulation of treatments is indicative. It may not be too long before it becomes feasible to apply on a field scale complicated manipulative procedures which can now be managed only in controlled environments or small experimental plots. In any event, it would seem mistaken to plan on the assumption that this could never become possible however much ingenuity were to be applied. In the long run, the real problem probably concerns the desirability of this kind of intervention rather than the practicability. Judgments on this will require very much more knowledge about the detailed nature of developmental limitations to yield in the major crop plants and about the ways they can be alleviated.

For the immediate future, it seems evident that it is in the realm of plant breeding that the greatest rewards from new knowledge of developmental processes in plants are to be found. Breeding plants for the future is being treated in other contributions, and I am relieved of the need for extensive comment here. However, I would emphasize one point that has become obvious now: whereas hitherto much breeding has perforce taken as a measure of progress the attainment of yield itself, a new approach has opened up where knowledge of the components of yield is permitting a more rational and direct attack on individual limiting factors (Bell and Kirby, 1966). Developmental plant physiology is likely to have an increasing contribution to make here, since many of these limiting factors will undoubtedly turn out to be concerned one way or another with differentiation and development.

It is perhaps unnecessary to stress the contribution to breeding technique physiological manipulation can make: for some 40 years now advantage has been taken of the control available over developmental periodicity through temperature and photoperiod in the breeding of crops ranging from sugar beet to fruit trees. But some comment is due concerning the increasing openings in breeding work for the application of chemical means of manipulating differentiation and morphogenesis. Some remarkable examples are already available, such as the production of gynoecious cucumber lines by Peterson (Peterson and Ahnders,

1960; Peterson, 1960). Here the fact that sex expression can be regulated by manipulating the auxin-gibberellin balance was pressed into service to breed for extreme femaleness, pollen being induced in female individuals when required for a cross by treatment with endogeous gibberellin. With increasing knowledge of the ways flowering, sex expression, and pollen fertility can be influenced chemically, there is a real hope that many of the serious practical problems of breeding work can be reduced or eliminated altogether, and the hazards and tedium of such routine tasks as emasculation removed. Similarly, impediments to breeding arising from intra- and interspecific incompatibility and embryo-endosperm disharmony should become less significant as it becomes possible to control the detailed events of reproduction more and more effectively. I do not think it is pressing the point too far to suggest that one of the vital yet time-consuming tasks of breeding, final seed multiplication, could be revolutionized by the development of methods of mass cloning of desirable genotypes using dissociated-cell technique. The way has already been marked out by Steward and his collaborators (e.g., Steward et al., 1964) with the carrot (Daucus carota L.). On appropriate media in culture, isolated cells of the carrot seedling will differentiate embryoids, each of which has the potentiality of developing into a plant. So far the method has met with success with umbelliferous species, but there is no reason to suspect any basic taxonomic limitation on the technique. Tissue culture may prove to be of great value to plant breeding in other ways; Nitsch and Nitsch (1969), for example, have shown how haploid plants can be derived in great numbers from the pollen grains of Nicotiana species. Should the method prove widely applicable, it has the makings of a practical tool for obtaining one-step homozygosity, since colchicine already offers a method for producing polyhaploids.

LITERATURE CITED

Allison, J. C. S., and D. J. Watson. 1966. The production and distribution of dry matter in maize after flowering. Ann. Bot. 30:365-382.

d'Amato, F. 1964. Endopolyploidy as a factor in plant tissue development. Caryologia 17:41-52.

Andrew, R. H. 1967. Influence of season, population and spacing on axillary bud development of sweet corn. Agron. J. 59:355-358.

Arber, A. 1934. The Gramineae. Cambridge University Press, New York.

Archbold, H. K. 1942. Physiological studies in plant nutrition. XIII Experiments with barley on defoliation and shading of the ear in relation to sugar metabolism. Ann. Bot. 6:487-531.

Armstrong, D. J. 1966. Hypothesis concerning the mechanism of auxin action. Proc. Nat. Acd. Sci. USA 56:64-66.

Army, T. J., and F. A. Greer. 1967. Photosynthesis and crop production systems, p. 321-332 In A. San Pietro, F. A. Greer and J. J. Army (ed.) Harvesting the sun. Academic Press, New York and London.

Aronoff, S. 1955. Translocation from soybean leaves. Plant Physiol. 30:184-185.

Asana, R. D. and R. F. Williams. 1965. The effect of temperature stress on grain development in wheat. Aust. J. Agr. Res. 16:1-13.

Aspinall, D. 1961. The control of tillering in the barley plant. I. The pattern of tillering and its relation to nutrient supply. Aust. J. Biol. Sci. 14:493-505.

Audus, L. J. 1959. Correlations. J. Linn. Soc. Bot. 56:177-187.

Badenhuizen, N. P. 1958. Structure, properties and growth of starch granules. Encyclopedia of plant physiology 6:137-153.

Bell, G. D. H., and E. J. Kirby. 1966. Utilization of growth responses in breeding new varieties of cereals, p. 308-319. In F. L. Milthorpe and J. D. Ivins (ed.) The growth of cereals and grasses. Butterworths, London.

Bingham, J. 1967. Investigations on the physiology of yield in winter wheat, by comparisons of varieties and by artificial variation in grain number per ear. J. Agr. Sci. Cambridge 68:411-422.

Bonner, J. 1965. The template activity of chromatin. J. Cell. Physiol. 66:77-90.

Booth, A., J. Moorby, C. R. Davies, H. Jones and P. F. Wareing. 1962. Effects of indolyl-3-acetic acid in the movement of nutrients within plants. Nature 194:204-205.

Bottger, I. and I. Ludemann. 1964. Uber die Bildung einer stoffwechsel-aktiven Ribonucleinsaurefraktion in isolierten Blattern von Euphorbia pulcherrima zu Beginn den Wurzel-regeneration. Flora 155:331-340.

Bottger, I. and R. Wollgiehn. 1958. Untersuchungen uber den Zusammenhang zwischen Nucleinsaure-und Eiweissstoffwechsel in grunen Blattern hoheren Pflanzen. Flora 146:302-315.

Burg, S. P. 1968. Ethylene, plant senescence, and abscission. Plant Physiol. 43:1503-1511.

Burg, S. P., and E. A. Burg. 1966. The interaction between auxin and ethylene and its role in plant growth. Proc. Nat. Acad. Sci. USA 55:262-266.

Burt. R. L. 1964. Carbohydrate utilization as a factor in plant growth. Aust. J. Biol. Sci. 17:867-877.

Burton, W. G. 1963. Concepts and mechanisms of dormancy, p. 17-23. In J. D. Ivins and F. L. Milthorpe (ed.) The growth of the potato. Butterworths, London.

Buttrose, M. S., and L. H. May. 1959. Physiology of the cereal grain. I. The source of carbon for the developing barley kernel. Aust. J. Biol. Sci. 12:40-52.

Carpenter, W. J. G., and J. H. Cherry. 1966. Effects of benzyladenine on acculation of ^{32}P into nucleic acids of peanut cotyledons. Biochim. Biophys. Acta 114:640-642.

Chailakhyan, M. K. 1967. The role of gibberellins in photoperiodism and vernalisation processes of plants, p. 569-576. In Wachstumsregulatoren bei Pflanzen. Gustav Fischer Verlag, Jena.

Chailakhyan, M. K. 1968. Internal factors of plant flowering. Ann. Rev. Plant Physiol. 19:1-36.

Chapman, H. W. 1958. Tuberisation in the potato plant. Physiol. Plant. 11:215-224.

Chen, D., S. Sarid, E. Katchalski. 1968. Studies on the nature of messenger RNA in germinating wheat embryos. Proc. Nat. Acad. Sci. US 60:902-909.

Claver, F. K. 1960. Efetos del acido giberelico y de la hidrazida maleica sobre la tuberizacion de la papa. Phyton 15:29-35.

Cline, A. L. and R. M. Bock. 1966. Translational control of gene expression. Cold Spring Harb. Symp. Quant. Biol. 31:321-334.

Courdurox, J. C. 1966. Le mechanisme de la tuberisation chez le topinambour. Bull. Soc. Franc. Physiol. Veget. 12:213-232.

Cutter, E. 1965. Recent experimental studies of the shoot apex and shoot morphogenesis. Bot. Rev. 31:7-113.

Davies, C. R. and P. F. Wareing. 1965. Auxin directed transport of radiophosphorus in stems. Planta 65:139-156.

Dorffling, K. 1966. Weitere Untersuchungen uber korrelative Knospenhemmung. Planta 70:257-274.

Dorffling, K. 1967. Blattfallbeschleunigende Eigenschaft zweier "Hemmstoffe" aus Erbsenpflanzen. Nachweis von (+)-Abszisin II (Dormin), p. 673-674. In Wachstumsregulatoren bei Pflanzen. Gustav Fischer Verlag, Jena.

Edelman, J. 1963. Physiological and environmental aspects of carbohydrate metabolism during tuber growth, p. 135-147. In J. D. Ivins and F. L. Milthorpe (ed.) The growth of the potato. Butterworths, London.

Engelbrecht, L. 1967. Die Bedeutung vershiedener Cytokinine fur die Uber-
windung der apikaler Dominanze bei Nicotiana glauca, p. 647-649. In Wachstumsregulatoren bei Pflanzen. Gustav Fischer Verlag, Jena.

Evans, L. T. 1964. Inflorescence initiation in Lolium temulentum L. VI. Effects
of some inhibitors of nucleic acid, protein and steroid biosynthesis. Aust. J.
Biol. Sci. 17:24-35.

Friend, D. J. C. 1965. Tillering and leaf production in wheat as affected by
temperature and light intensity. Can. J. Bot. 43:345-353.

Galinat, W. C. 1959. The phytomer in relation to floral homologies in the American Maydeae. Bot. Mus. Leafl. Harvard Univ. 19:1-32.

Galun, E., Y. Jung, and A. Lang. 1962. Culture and sex modification of male
cucumber buds in vitro. Nature 194:596-598.

Goodwin, P. B. 1963. Mechanism and significance of apical dominance in the
potato. In J. D. Ivins and F. L. Milthorpe (ed.) The growth of the potato, Butterworths, London.

Gregory, F. G., and J. A. Veale. 1957. A re-assessment of the problem of
apical dominance. Soc. Exp. Biol. Symp. 11:1-20.

Gregory, E. E. 1965. Physiology of tuberisation in plants. Encyclopedia of
Plant Physiology 15:1328-1354.

Helgeson, J. 1968. The cytokinins. Science 161:974-981.

Heslop-Harrison, J. 1961. The experimental control of sexuality and inflorescence structure in Zea mays. Proc. Linn. Soc. 172 Session: 108-123.

Heslop-Harrison, J. 1963. Sex expression in plants. Brookhaven Symp. in Biol.
14:109-122.

Heslop-Harrison, J. 1967. Differentiation. Ann. Rev. Plant Physiol. 18:325-348.

Heslop-Harrison, J. 1969. The state of the apex and the response to induction
in Cannabis sativa. In G. Bernier (ed.) Cellular and molecular aspects of
floral induction. (In press)

Hillman, W. S. 1962. The physiology of flowering. Holt, Rinehart & Winston,
New York.

Hotta, Y., and H. Stern. 1965. Inducibility of thymidine kinase as a function of
interphase stage. J. Cell. Biol. 25:99-108.

Humphries, E. C. 1963. Dependence of net assimilation rate on root growth of
isolated leaves. Ann. Bot. 27:175-182.

Humphries, E. C., and A. W. Wheeler. 1963. The physiology of leaf growth.
Ann. Rev. Plant Physiol. 14:385-410.

Israel, H. W., and F. C. Steward. 1966. The fine structure of quiescent and
growing carrot cells, and its relation to growth induction. Ann. Bot. 30:63-80.

Jacob, F., and J. Monod. 1963. Genetic repression, allosteric inhibition and
cellular differentiation, p. 30-64. In M. Locke (ed.) Cytodifferentiation and
macromolecular synthesis. 21st Symp. Society for the Study of Development
and Growth. Ronald Press, New York.

Jeffs, R. A., and D. H. Northcote. 1967. The influence of indol-3/yl acetic acid
and sugar on the pattern of induced differentiation in plant tissue culture.
J. Cell Science 2:77-88.

Kiesselbach, J. 1948. Endosperm type as a physiological factor in corn yields.
J. Amer. Soc. Agron. 40:216-236.

Knox, R. B., and L. T. Evans. 1966. Inflorescence initiation in Lolium temulentum L. VIII. Histochemical changes at the shoot apex during induction. Aust.
J. Biol. Sci. 19:233-245.

Kriedemann, P. 1966. The photosynthetic activity of the wheat ear. Ann. Bot.
30:349-364.

Kursanov, A. L. 1963. Metabolism and the transport of organic substances in
the phloem, p. 209-278. In R. D. Preston (ed.) Advances in botanical research,
1. Academic Press, London & New York.

Lang, A. 1965a. Progressiveness and contagiousness in plant differentiation
and development. Encycl. of Plant Physiol. 15:409-423.

Lang, A. 1965b. The physiology of flower initiation. Encycl. of Plant Physiol. 15:1380-1536.

Leopold, A. C. 1961. Senescence in plant development. Science 134:1727-1732.

Loomis, W. E. 1935. The translocation of carbohydrates in maize. Iowa State Coll. J. Sci. 9:509-520.

Loomis, W. E. 1953. Growth correlation, p. 197-218. In W. E. Loomis (ed.) Growth and differentiation in plants. Iowa State College Press, Ames, Iowa.

Madec, P. 1963. Tuber-forming substances in the potato, p. 124-130. In J. D. Ivins and F. L. Milthorpe (ed.) The growth of the potato. Butterworths, London.

Maekawa, T. 1927. On intersexualism in Arisaema japonica. Jap. J. Bot. 3:205-216.

Maggs, D. H. 1963. The reduction of growth of apple trees brought about by fruiting. J. Hort. Sci. 38:119-128.

Mangelsdorf, P. C., R. S. MacNeish, and W. C. Galinat. 1964. Domestication of of corn. Science 143:538-545.

Milthorpe, P. L. 1963. Some aspects of plant growth, p. 7-11. In J. D. Ivins and F. I. Milthorpe (ed.) The growth of the potato. Butterworths, London.

Mohan Ram, H. Y., and F. C. Steward. 1964. The induction of growth in explanted tissue of the banana fruit. Can. J. Bot. 42:1559-1579.

Molisch, H. 1938. The longevity of plants. Science Printing Co., Pennsylvania.

Moorby, J. 1968. The influence of carbohydrate and mineral nutrient supply on the growth of potato tubers. Ann. Bot. 32:57-68.

Moss, D. N. 1962. Photosynthesis and barrenness. Crop Sci. 2:366-367.

Moss, G. I., and J. Heslop-Harrison. 1968. Photoperiod and pollen sterility in maize. Ann. Bot. 32:833-846.

Mothes, K. 1964. The role of kinetin in plant regulation, p. 131-142. In J. P. Nitsch (ed.) Régulateurs Naturel de la Croissance Végétale. Coll. Internat. Centre Nat. Recherche Scientifique No. 123. Paris.

Murneek, A. E. 1926. Effects of correlation between vegetative and reproductive growth in the tomato (Lycopersicon esculentum). Plant Physiol. 1:3-56.

Nitsch, J. P. 1952. Plant hormones in the development of fruits. Quart. Rev. Biol. 27:33-57.

Nitsch, J. P. 1966. Photopériodisme et tubérisation. Bull. Soc. Franc. Physiol. Végét. 12:233-246.

Nitsch, J. P., and C. Nitsch. 1969. Haploid plants from pollen grains. Science 163:85-87.

Nösberger, J., and E. C. Humphries. 1965. The influence of removing tubers on dry matter production and net assimilation rate of potato plants. Ann. Bot. 29:579-588.

Nösberger, J., and G. N. Thorne. 1965. The effect of removing florets or shading the ear of barley on production and distribution of dry matter. Ann. Bot. 29:635-644.

Nougarède, A. 1965. La méristème caulinaire de Angiosperms: problèmes posés par la passage à la phase réproductrice. Bull. Soc. Franç. Physiol. Végét. 11:105-137.

Osborne, D. J. 1962. Effect of kinetin on protein and nucleic acid metabolism in Xanthium leaves during senescence. Plant Physiol. 37:595-602.

Osborne, D. J. 1967. Hormonal regulation of leaf senescence. Soc. Exp. Biol. Symp. 21, 305-321.

Peterson, C. E., and L. D. Ahnders. 1960. Induction of staminate flowers on gynoecious cucumbers with gibberellin A3. Science 131:1673-1674.

Peterson, C. E. 1960. A gynoecious inbred line of cucumbers. Mich. Agr. Exp. Sta. Quart. Bull. 43:40-42.

Pozsar, B. I. and Z. Kiraly. 1964. Cytokinin-like effect of rust infections in the regulation of phloem transport and senescence, p. 199-210. In Z. Kiraly and G. Ubrizsy (ed.) Host-parasite relationships in plant pathology. Pubs. Res. Inst. Plant Protection, Budapest.

320   HESLOP-HARRISON

Ryle, G.J.A. 1963. Studies on the physiology of flowering of timothy (Phleum pratense): III. Effects of shoot age and nitrogen level on the size of the inflorescence. Ann. Bot. 27:467-480.
Ryle, G.J.A. 1965. Effects of daylength and temperature on ear size in S24 perennial ryegrass. Ann. Appl. Biol. 55:107-114.
Ryle, G.J.A. 1966. Physiological aspects of seed yield in grasses, p. 106-117. In F. L. Milthorpe and J. D. Ivins (ed.) The growth of cereals and grasses. Butterworths, London.
Ryle, G.J.A. 1967. Effects of shading on inflorescence size and development in temperate perennial grasses. Ann. Appl. Biol. 60:297-308.
Sacher, J. A. 1967. Studies of permeability, RNA and protein turnover during aging of fruit and leaf tissues. Soc. Exp. Biol. Symp. 21:269-304.
Salisbury, F. B. 1963. The flowering process. Macmillan, New York.
Simon, E. W. 1967. Types of leaf senescence. Soc. Exp. Biol. Symp. 21:215-230.
Slater, J. W. 1963. Mechanism of tuber initiation in the potato, p. 114-120. In F. L. Milthorpe and J. D. Ivins (ed.) The growth of cereals and grasses. Butterworths, London.
Steeves, T. A. 1962. Morphogenesis in isolated fern leaves, p. 117-151. In D. Rudnick (ed.) Regeneration. 20th Symp. Society for the Study of Development and Growth. Ronald Press Co., New York.
Stern, H. 1964. Concepts and mechanisms underlying intracellular regulation, p. 19-21. In J. P. Nitsch (ed.) Régulateurs Naturel de la Croissance Végétale. Coll. Internat. Centre Nat. Recherche Scientifique No. 123. Paris.
Steward, F. C., M. O. Mapes, A. E. Kent, and R. D. Holsten. 1964. Growth and development of cultured plant cells. Science 143:20-27.
Sussex, I. 1954. Experiments on the cause of dorsiventrality in leaves. Nature 174:351-352.
Sussex, I. 1955. Morphogenesis in Solanum tuberosum: an experimental investigation of leaf dorsiventrality and orientation in the juvenile shoot. Phytomorphology 5:286-300.
Thimann, K. V., and F. Skoog. 1934. On the inhibition of bud development and other functions of growth substances in Vicia faba. Proc. Roy. Soc. B. 114: 317-329.
Thomas, T. H., P. F. Wareing and P. M. Robinson. 1965. Action of the sycamore dormin as a gibberellin antagonist. Nature 205:1269-1272.
Thorne, G. N. 1963. Distribution of dry matter between ear and shoot of Plumage Archer and Proctor barley grown in the field. Ann. Bot. 27:245-252.
Thorne, G. N. 1965. Photosynthesis of ears and flag leaves of wheat and barley. Ann. Bot. 29:317-329.
Thorne, G. N. 1966. Physiological aspects of grain yield in cereals, p. 88-105. In F. L. Milthorpe and J. D. Ivins (ed.) The growth of cereals and grasses. Butterworths, London.
Thorne, G. N., and A. F. Evans. 1964. Influence of tops and roots on net assimilation rate of sugar-beet and spinach/beet and grafts between them. Ann. Bot. 28;499-508.
Thorne, G. N., M. A. Ford and D. J. Watson. 1968. Growth, development, and yield of spring wheat in artificial climates. Ann. Bot. 32:425-446.
Tizio, R. 1964. Action de l'acide gibbérellique sur la tubérisation de la pomme de terre. C. R. Acad. Sci. Paris 259:1187-1190.
Tizio, R. 1966. Présence de kinines dans le périderme de tubercules de pomme de terre. C. R. Acad. Sci. Paris 262:868-869.
Walkley, J. 1940. Protein synthesis in mature and senescent leaves of barley. New Phytol. 39:362-369.
Wanner, H. 1958. Physiologie de Speicherung. Encyclopedia of Plant Physiology 6:834-865.
Wardlaw, C. W. 1949. Experiments on organogenesis in ferns. Growth (Suppl.) 13:93-131.

Wareing, P. F., H. M. El-Antalby, J. Good, and J. Manuel. 1967. The possible role and mode of action of abscisin (dormin) in the regulation of plant growth and development, p. 667-672. In Wachstumsregulatoren bei Pflanzen. Gustav Fischer Verlag, Jena.

Wareing, P. F., and A. K. Seth. 1967. Ageing and senescence in the whole plant. Soc. Exp. Biol. Symp. 21:543-558.

Waters, L. C., and L. S. Dure. 1966. Ribonucleic acid synthesis in germinating cotton seeds. J. Mol. Biol. 19:1-27.

Watson, D. J., G. N. Thorne, and S. A. W. French. 1963. Analysis of growth and yield of winter and spring wheats. Ann. Bot. 27:1-22.

Weber, H. 1958a. Morphologisch-anatomische Grundlagen de Speicherung. Encycl. Plant Physiol. 6:817-828.

Weber, H. 1958b. Bedeutung der Speicherung. Encycl. Plant Physiol. 6:829-833.

Welbank, P. J., S. A. W. French, and K. J. Witts. 1966. Dependence of yields of wheat varieties on their leaf area durations. Ann. Bot. 30:291-299.

Went, F. W. 1957. The experimental control of plant growth. Chronica Botanica Co., Waltham, Mass.

Went, F. W., and R. Engelsberg. 1946. Plant growth under controlled conditions. VII. Sucrose content of the tomato plant. Arch. Biochem. 9:187-200.

Wetmore, R. H., and J. P. Rier. 1963. Experimental induction of vascular tissue in callus of angiosperms. Amer. J. Bot. 50:418-430.

Wickson, M., and K. V. Thimann. 1958. On the antagonism of auxin and kinetin in apical dominance. Physiol. Plant. 11:62-74.

Wollgiehn, R. 1965. Kinetin und Nucleinsaurestoffwechsel. Flora 156A:291-302.

Wollgiehn, R. 1967. Nucleic acid and protein metabolism in excised leaves. Symp. Soc. Exp. Biol. 21:231-246.

Zimmerman, P. W., and A. E. Hitchcock. 1936. The localisation of the mechanism which regulates tuberisation in plants. Amer. J. Bot. 23:690-696.

13...DISCUSSION

NORMAN E. GOOD

Michigan State University

East Lansing, Michigan

Since my professional contact with plants is confined to the contemplation of homogenates of spinach leaves (Spinacia oleracea), I am not able to add much to Dr. Heslop-Harrison's very thorough discussion of the role of differentiation in crop production; nothing obliterates the results of differentiation more quickly or more thoroughly than a Waring blender. Therefore, I propose to confine my remarks to a rather general philosophical consideration of the regulation of photosynthesis by factors which reside in the plant itself. The topics I want to touch on briefly are the following:

1) The implications of the "source-sink" conception of the regulation of photosynthesis rates.

2) Differentiation as a factor in determining source-sink relationships.

3) Possible mechanisms of feed-back control of photosynthesis.

There are excellent a priori reasons for expecting photosynthesis to be regulated, in part at least, by the demand of the organism for the products of photosynthesis. Only those machines which use energy for a single purpose can be satisfactorily regulated at the energy input level. Thus an automobile functions adequately with a single control of energy input (the accelerator) because the energy is being used almost exclusively to push the car down the road. But one need only turn to the electrical system of the same car to see how unsatisfactory is control of a multipurpose system at the input. If the battery did not have a very large excess capacity the lights would go out when the windshield wipers were turned on! In the respiration of higher organisms one encounters the same principle. Respiration is normally controlled by the utilization of energy (i.e., the utilization of ATP controls the level of ADP which controls the respiratory rate). Control of respiration at the substrate level is usually a pathological condition known as starvation. It would be surprising indeed if the same principle did not apply to photosynthesis. Indeed it would be intolerable if the plant were unable to shut off photosynthesis when its growth processes can cope with no more photosynthesis products. The plant would no longer have control of its own growth and development.

Fortunately we do not have to rely on this sort of deductive reasoning, which is always somewhat dangerous when we lack even a qualitative knowledge of the processes involved. Abundant direct evidence of the control of photosynthesis by the plant's requirements has been presented in the literature. Many instances have been reported in discussions at this symposium. I would like to add yet another case. One of our hosts, Dr. Daly and his student, Dr. Livne, have reported (Livne and Daly, 1966) on a controlled sink. When a primary leaf of a bean plant (Phaseolus sp.) is infected with rust its photosynthesis falls and and its respiration rises. With progressively more severe infections the leaf is converted from an exporter to an importer, that is from a source into a sink. At the same time the photosynthesis of the uninfected trifoliate leaf above increases, ultimately almost doubling. Not only does this experiment offer a unique opportunity to produce sources and sinks of varying intensity. It also provides considerable quantitative information about one of the roles of disease in determining crop productivity—an aspect of productivity which may not have been considered adequately in our meetings this week.

In spite of the abundant evidence that photosynthesis can be controlled by internal factors (which have been lumped together as "sink size") this concept has not been accepted unanimously. We have heard of experiments which seemingly conflicted with the concept—decreases in yield in spite of an apparent increase in the size of the sink. This conflict of interpretation brings me to my next topic, the role of differentiation in determining source-sink relationships. It seems to me that our thinking on this matter has been distortedly an overly simplistic picture of source-sink relationships. Too often we have been considering two bathtubs connected by a pipe. In reality the "sink" is infinitely complex, consisting as it does of the entire catabolism of the plant. It is an ever-changing network of pathways with ever-changing flows of photosynthetic products directed toward a multitude of sinks, each pathway controlled at different sites by different rate-determining steps. Overall control of this multitude of rate-determining steps is synonymous with differentiation. Consequently source-sink relationships are modified by anything which modifies differentiation—genetics, photoperiods, the form-modifying effects of light and temperature, endogenous and exogenous hormones, etc. Operations such as the removal of plant parts on the stimulation of fruit set may or may not influence the network of pathways of catabolism, and hence the sink size, depending on whether or not such operations affect the control of some rate-determining step in the network. We must not be surprised to find that some induced changes, which on first thought should increase or decrease the sink for photosynthates, do no such thing. No experiment has any relevance to "sinks" unless it is clear that a regulated, rate-determining step has been modified by the operation.

Assuming, as we must, I think, that the control of photosynthesis by internal factors is an established fact, let us now ask some questions about possible mechanisms by which this control might be exercised. What are some of the ways in which photosynthesis could be inhibited when there is a sufficiency of photosynthesis products?

Is there a pileup of intermediates which stop the process by mass action at some reversible step? Or do we have here an analogy to respiration, the supply of some catalytic intermediate decreasing when an acceptor cannot be found? What is the site of inhibition in biochemical terms—that is to say, what accumulates and what decreases, if anything, when plants with full stomachs are enjoying their midday siesta?

Do the stomates close?

Does some sort of message (hormone?) come to the photosynthetic machinery, telling it to slow down? (Herein lies a trap: we must not confuse effects of hormones on differentiation and hence on the sinks for photosynthate with possible direct effects of hormones as coordinators of the source—sink relationship. A hormone could increase photosynthesis by influencing directly the photosynthetic controls but no such interpretation of hormone action is justified or even reasonable until the effects on the demand for photosynthate have been evaluated.)

Does photorespiration increase during siesta? In other words, is net photosynthesis controlled by the magnitude of a back-reaction?

I am sorry to end with many questions and no answers. If the answers to any of them are known, you will have to blame the organizers of the symposium for asking a contemplator of homogenates to comment on differentiation. If, as I suspect, none of the answers are known, we can reasonably hope that some will be supplied at the next symposium on the physiology of crop production.

LITERATURE CITED

Livne, A., and J. M. Daly. 1966. Translocation in healthy and rust-affected beans. Phytopathology 56:170–175.

13...DISCUSSION

WALTER E. LOOMIS

Iowa State University
Ames, Iowa

Dr. Heslop-Harrison, as expected, has covered the topic of Development, Differentiation, and Yield very thoroughly. I will, therefore, limit my remarks to brief discussions of work which supports and illustrates some of the points he has made.

1. Winter Hardiness

Winter hardiness may be taken as a model of cytoplasmic differentiation, directly related to the sugar levels within the tissue, but dependent upon specific genes which control metabolism. In a very cold winter in Iowa, the winter hardy 'Grimm' alfalfa (Medicago sativa L.) survived without injury if the sucrose content of the roots was 4%, fresh-weight, in December, but was injured or killed when the sugar content was lower. 'Kansas Common' did not survive with less than 8% of sucrose and 'Arizona Common' was nonhardy, even with 12% sucrose. Sucrose, we assume, is the differentiation material, but it was effective only when the necessary genes were present. Similar responses are shown in many reactions—in drouth resistance and in the development of some fruit colors for example.

2. Translocation

Translocation is very specifically related to differentiation and embryo development in fruits. When older varieties of maize (Zea mays L.) were grown in single-stalk hills and allowed to develop two large suckers, defoliation of the main stalk 2 days before silking stopped all development of the floral axis and pistillate flowers. The same defoliation 7 days after silking resulted in the production of full-sized ears on the defoliated stalks with translocation from leaves on earless branch stalks 2m away from the ear. Some grain was produced on stalks defoliated 2 days after silking, with the response rising rapidly with the initiation of embryo development in the pollinated grains.

Apples (Malus sylvestris Mill.) show a similar response. Defoliation of a flowering spur shortly before bloom prevents fruit development. Ten days after flowering normal fruits were produced when all leaves were removed within 2m of the fruiting spurs. It is assumed that hormones produced by the developing embryos of seeds and fruits channel food toward these organs.

Rapid translocation of foods occurs into embryonic and young leaves of sugar beet, but is blocked as the leaves approach maturity. If the plant is covered to exclude light, embryonic leaves develop normally, but mature leaves starve quickly in spite of large reserves in the root. Some alteration in the phloem is considered to be responsible.

3. Antihormones as Florigens

Several years ago we discovered at Iowa State University that soybean plants (Glycine max L.) could be forced into flower on days 2 to 3 hours too long for normal flowering by spraying them with nicotine sulfate. This chemical appears to be specific for soybeans. TIBA (2, 3, 5-triiodobenzoic acid) sprays and the removal of young, growing leaves from the upper plant have, however, been even more effective than nicotine sulfate, and both treatments are expected to reduce the auxin content of the plants and thus permit flower-bud differentiation. NAA (naphthalene acetic acid) sprays applied alone on short-day plants have prevented flowering, but when applied hours after TIBA on long-day plants, have increased total bloom, indicating that flower-bud differentiation proceeds rapidly, and that auxin functions in the development of flowers, as opposed to the initial differentiation of buds.

4. Antihormones and Flowering of Apples

TIBA sprays applied just after the time of petal drop can greatly increase flowering on young trees in the next year. Spraying with the growth retardant, Alar (succinamic acid-2, 2-dimethyl hydrazide), can have the same effect. NAA sprays can almost eliminate flowering the next year. Interstem grafts of short pieces of Paradise, "dwarfing" stocks increase subsequent flowering and show antihormone responses.

Antiauxin sprays, interstem grafts with 'Paradise' stocks, or ringing the stem above the roots all greatly increase root sprouting from essentially zero to dozens of sprouts per tree per year. Applying NAA in a lanolin paste on a ringed stem or to the bark in other treatments which increase sprouting, prevents this response. We interpret these responses as indicating that growth hormones can prevent flower-bud differentiation and that treatments which lower the concentration of these substances can initiate flowering and fruiting responses.

14

Cultural Manipulation for Higher Yields

WILLIAM G. DUNCAN

University of Kentucky
Lexington, Kentucky

I. INTRODUCTION

By cultural manipulation we will mean, in a broad sense, everything a farmer might do to increase crop yields per hectare, after he decides what to plant and buys the seed. With this restriction we leave out the agricultural economist and the plant breeder. When we limit our interest to yields per hectare we introduce an element of area. This will include the crop canopy above the surface and the root system below it. Cultural manipulation also includes what the farmer might do to make best use of water, carbon dioxide, nitrogen, and essential mineral nutrients whether they occur naturally or otherwise. We will also include manipulations designed to make the most efficient use of radiant energy during the growing season. Finally, consideration of the length of the growing season introduces the concept of time as one of the objects of cultural manipulation.

This is a vast subject from which we cannot hope to do more than select a few interesting points to discuss. To review the literature we would have to start with the most ancient findings of archaeology when cultural practices were more the concern of priests than of agronomists. Last year a third to a half of the papers published in the area of agronomy would come within our definition so there is still some interest in the subject. Dr. Clements wrote a review in the Annual Review of Plant Physiology recently containing 284 literature citations, one of which I noticed was a review of climatic influences on crop growth that itself contained 10,000 citations. When we speak of cultural practices we are talking about something that is big business in the agricultural field.

II. INTRASPECIFIC COMPETITION

I would like to start by referring to an experiment done in Lexington last summer for the prosaic purpose of evaluating 63 of the corn varieties (Zea Mays L.) most widely used in Kentucky. We will use it

327

as a background to think together about whole plants growing in the field and about how they interact with each other and with their environment.

This corn was planted in a design described in Biometrics (1962) by John Nelder, now occupying the position at Rothampstead made famous by R. A. Fisher. In Kentucky we call it a wagon wheel design for reasons that are obvious when you see it. Each wagon wheel contains 21 4-row plots and all varieties are replicated three times, hence 9 wheels. The corn is planted in rows corresponding to the spokes of a wheel and the plants are set closer together in the row as we move toward the center of the wheel. Each plant is thus essentially in the center of a trapezoid that diminishes in area as we move toward the center of the wheel. The geometry stays constant, only the dimensions change. The planting rates go from 13,000 plants per hectare at the outside rim to a high of 107,000 plants per hectare at the last harvested radius.

A cross section of the planting design is almost a history of corn planting practices. On the outside rim the corn is planted almost like it was 40 years ago when Dr. Kiesselbach was doing such fine pioneering work with corn here at Lincoln and when almost all corn was open pollinated. The population, 13,000 plants per hectare, was close to the average rate used then and the yields are strikingly similar.

As we move toward the inside of the wheel we are progressing through 40 years of change in corn cultural practices. Near the center we reach the present and possibly even the future of corn cultural practices and problems. As planting rates change in our wheel so do the yields. The very best varieties yield 5,000 kg/ha on the outside radius and yields increase toward the center to as much as 15,000 kg/ha somewhere between the extremes of population studied.

Many feel that the major thrust of research toward higher corn yields should be to push the population higher and higher. As we do so the difficulties to be overcome change in nature. It is well to think of the problems of yield in terms of things that occur in the test tube and under the microscope, but it is in the competitive struggle among plants that any changes must operate and survive. It is for this reason that I want to spend some time talking about what happens to plants growing at various positions within our wheel.

As we move from the outside rim of the wheel toward the center, the yield per plant decreases in a very regular manner. Without bothering about a mathematical statement let us just say that if we plot the yield per plant as the ordinate against population per hectare as the abscissa on semilog paper we get a linear regression, a straight line that slopes downward (Duncan, 1958). From such a regression we can calculate the yield per unit of area at any rate of planting. The fact that the regression is linear indicates that there is a plant population at which a maximum yield per hectare would occur and we can of course estimate that maximum grain yield. This is why we plant our variety test in such a bizarre pattern. This is a good way to compare varieties. It lets us compare varieties on the basis of what each is capable of at its optimum population. It raises an interesting question about why the relationship between plant population and yield per plant should behave in such a beautifully mathematical manner, but this is outside the scope for this particular paper.

A. Cooperative Interaction

Instead let us first consider the general height relationship. The height of the corn plants increased with increasing plant population to a maximum and then the average height decreased again. This observation is in agreement with a more general statement by Yoda, Kira, and Hozumi (1957) who observed that "When plants are experimentally exposed to shade, there is usually found a certain light intensity at which the plant attains its maximum (height)"—There were relatively large differences in this among the varieties we tested but all increased in height with increase in mutual shading. First appearance of the tassel and anthesis were observed at about the same time in all populations within most varieties so we can infer that the length of time to attainment of maximum height was not much affected by mutual shading. Thus the taller plants must have elongated at a more rapid rate than the shorter ones.

This tendency of shaded plants to elongate more rapidly than unshaded ones was first reported by Hozumi, Koyama, and Kira (1955) as a result of their observations with corn. They noted that in closely spaced plants, the shorter plants had a higher elongation rate than the taller ones that were shading them. They gave the name "cooperative interaction" to this phenomenon because by reason of it the shorter plants tended to "catch up" in height with the taller ones. The results of this cooperative interaction were readily observable in the wagon wheels. The plant heights were more uniform at intermediate plant populations than at either the highest or lowest populations, and the difference in uniformity was statistically significant.

B. Competitive Interaction

Kira and his associate, however, noted no such tendency for shorter plants to increase faster in weight. It was quite the opposite. Shaded plants, as one would expect, gain weight more slowly than less shaded ones. With corn the effect of height difference on gain in dry weight is closely related to plant density. By use of a modification of the computer simulation program mentioned earlier by Dr. R. S. Loomis (Chapter 3, this book) and using plant descriptions taken from experiments conducted by Williams and Loomis in California, I estimated the effect of difference in height on average daily photosynthesis of corn. A plant 10 cm shorter than those surrounding it would be deficient in the production of dry matter at low populations by about 20%, at high populations by almost 50%. If the difference in height is increased to 30 cm the deficiency in dry matter production would increase to 40 and 80%, respectively.

From this I think we can agree on several general propositions. One is that a corn plant shorter than its neighbors is at a considerable disadvantage. A second is that a difference in rate of elongation such as Kira described that could reduce the height difference would reduce the penalty imposed by overshadowing. A third obvious conclusion is that the higher the population of plants the more severe the penalty imposed by height difference. As we move to higher planting rates, height differences produce larger effects. Another observation by Kira and his associates that is a corollary of the first is that beyond some degree of shading, that produces a maximum height, further shading must result in shorter plants and hence slower elongation rates.

With these relationships in mind let us go back and slowly walk into our wagon wheel starting with our 1928-type plant populations. Here the plants are typically rather short and sturdy with several tillers, or suckers as grandfather called them. The plants are irregular in height and even more in yield of grain. The height irregularity is presumably due to genetic differences and the lack of enough competition to invoke Kira's cooperative interaction to hurry the shorter ones. The plants are irregular in grain yield per plant because some plants have one ear, some two, and some even three or four. In other low-population experiments we have observed that the top or first ear is remarkably uniform from plant to plant within a variety. The difference in yield from plant to plant seems to be due to differences among plants in whatever impulse or stimulant or absence of repression is needed to cause a second or third ear to form. Among varieties the higher yielding at these low populations were those capable of forming the largest or the most ears. This takes us back in memory to the old state fairs in the Cornbelt where the corn shows were the big attraction and the prizes went to the big well-filled ears. These were closely related to yield in the early 1900's. Another characteristic of our low-population corn I hadn't mentioned was that where our chemical weed control broke down, the weeds grew with astonishing vigor. It was easy to look at these and see why corn was cultivated three to five times in those days and checking was the popular way to plant it.

As we move through increasing plant populations we lose the tillers and most of the second ears and weeds are much less aggressive. The plants look uniform in height because of the cooperative interaction and they get taller and ear height increases. This is the 6,000 to 8,000 kg/ha yield level which is easily realized with adequate fertilization and rainfall or irrigation. This is the corn of the late 1940's and early 1950's. The main problems were fertility and water. No one worried much about row widths and barren plants weren't much of a problem. Unfortunately we did not put any of the old open-pollinated varieties in our wheels. I will do so next year and feel reasonably confident that we can get yields in excess of 6,000 kg/ha at these planting rates.

C. Plant Uniformity and Barrenness

As one moves to higher populations still we encounter the problems of the present and get a look at those of the future. Plant heights become less uniform because our cooperative interaction no longer operates. All of the plants are shaded to nearly their maximum height and hence their maximum rate of elongation. A plant that germinates slowly or is slow in getting started is soon shaded beyond its maximum elongation rate. In consequence it grows more slowly than its neighbors. It is soon even more heavily shaded and hence grows more slowly still. It is thus suppressed and becomes a starved, spindly, barren plant.

By doing everything possible to insure uniformity one could probably avoid such suppressed plants, but only up to a point. When the maximum-height shading is reached for all plants the equilibrium becomes unstable. Some plants must be suppressed. As stated by two famous Nebraskans, Clements and Weaver (1929), in their description of an experiment with sunflowers (Helianthus annuus L.), "in a crowded population a difference in height of as little as a millimeter could be decisive if it enabled one plant to get its leaf over its neighbors."

We have stressed the competition for light, but an equally deadly competition must be going on under the soil. Shaded plants have an increased shoot/root ratio. The more shaded plant invests a decreased part of its resources in roots so its root system is smaller and shallower than its more favored neighbors. Moisture or fertility stress can only add to the relative disadvantage and increase the probability of of suppression. The nature of this double competition has been shown in many experiments, but possibly never more clearly than by Donald (1958) in his experiments in the 1950's.

In the 63 varieties we observed, these suppressed plants were almost invariably barren. The ears formed contained only a few scattered kernels if any at all. More interesting was the fact that only plants that would be classified as suppressed by competition were barren. This might not have been the case under more normal field conditions where more reasons for barrenness might exist. In our plots there was ample pollen over a long period of time because of the number of varieties planted together. We also had a very favorable growing season with supplemental irrigation but I feel that the competitive interactions I have described are one of the important causes of barrenness in high-population corn. It has received surprisingly little attention in the agronomic literature.

Barren plants are one of today's serious problems in seeking higher yields and it is one not likely to get less important. A barren stalk intercepting light and using water and nutrients but giving nothing in return cannot but reduce grain yield. It should be pointed out, however, that grain yield in corn reaches a maximum and then declines as population continues to increase whether there are barren stalks or not. The effect of barren plants is to cause the yield maximum to occur at a lower plant population and to accelerate the rate of decrease in yield as populations continue to increase. As might be expected barrenness increases with stress.

It would have been interesting to see what some of the old open-pollinated varieties would have done at these much higher plant populations. Undoubtedly the increased variability among plants would have meant increasing numbers of plants would have been suppressed and hence barren. From this point of view it seems obvious that one advantage of hybrid corn varieties is uniformity that permits higher plant populations. The greater uniformity of single-cross varieties might be one factor in their yield potential.

Dr. Donald has written recently (1968) about the possibility of increasing plant yields by the breeding of crop ideotypes, defined as plants with model characteristics known to influence photosynthesis, growth, and grain production. One basic characteristic he notes is that ideal plants should have weak competitive ability. By this he means they should have characteristics that enable them to make the best possible use of their share of the environment without encroaching on environment allocated to neighboring plants. We will return again to this thoughtful observation but we can see in the tendency of corn plants to elongate when shaded the survival of a trait that in more primitive ancestors represented the thrust of green blades above competitors. In a field of crop plants where all plants have equal value the tendency to try to crowd out neighboring plants is highly undesirable.

In addition to mutual shading this elongation increases plant and ear height and decreases stalk strength. Both make the plant more likely to lodge. It has the less obvious effect of increasing the tendency to suppress individual plants at high plant populations. Elongation at a more rapid rate in response to shading may provide the mechanism for a certain improvement in height uniformity but this is small compensation for the additional stresses it imposes. The fact that there is relatively large variation in this tendency to elongate among varieties we have observed indicates that there is genetic variability for breeders to work with and probably that progress is already being made.

D. Planting Patterns

Our observations have stressed the potential loss of yield caused by lack of uniformity and the need for increased uniformity as plant populations increase. Some preventable causes of nonuniformity are obvious. Seeds should be uniform in germination time and should be planted uniformly.

A more subtle influence on uniformity is in the pattern of planting. In our wheels each plant was in the center of a trapezoid, almost as well separated from neighboring plants as possible for a given planting rate. This deferred competition among plants for light as well as for underground factors as long as possible. At critically high planting rates any lack of uniform plant distribution would mean localized high density areas where plants would be shaded past the point of instability at which some plants must be suppressed no matter how uniform the initial conditions. The adverse effect of any lack of uniformity would be accentuated.

This at least partially explains the current interest in narrow rows. As one decreases the distance between rows to some point, for a given plant population, the distribution of plants becomes more uniform. Our experiments have shown that the higher the plant population the greater the yield advantage of narrower rows. This is the usual conclusion from such experiments.

The high planting rates necessary for higher yields in the future thus require more uniform planting patterns. The best planting pattern for any plant can be shown by rather rigorous mathematics to be equilateral or hexagonal as you choose to look at it. We might assume, therefore, that planting patterns of the future will tend toward this one. The present interest in narrower rows may be taken as a part of this trend. The problem of developing planting equipment that will place seed in a hexagonal pattern does not seem to me to be insuperable. A square pattern is almost as good and this was the common pattern for many years although the spacing was far too wide.

Dr. Daynard and I have also shown by convincing mathematics with the aid of our computer that the worst way to distribute seed within a given area is with multiple seed hills. Quite a number of early experiments compared such hills with row plantings at the same population and usually showed small yield differences in favor of the rows. These were done at far lower than what we now consider high populations. At high rates the differences in favor of the row plantings are quite a bit higher as we learned in a small unpublished experiment 2 years ago. This is not to say that disease or insect control or other considerations might not favor other planting patterns but theory favors the hexagonal design.

E. Tillering

The disturbing fact is that tillering plants such as wheat [Triticum (aestivum L.) sp.] or rice (Oryza sativa L.) are essentially plants growing in multiple-plant hills which is, according to our computer, the worst way. Using somewhat different reasoning, Dr. Donald has selected as his ideotype for wheat a single-culm variety. This is not to say that a tillering plant might not have advantages in specific localities. Dr. Donald mentions the very obvious advantage of a tillering rice plant for Japanese conditions where the individual plants are usually set by hand. Scientists at the International Maize and Wheat Improvement Center in Mexico are interested in the development of a strongly tillering variety of corn which may have great advantage under some conditions. What I am asserting, with Dr. Donald, is that highest yields under very favorable conditions, will probably result from nontillering plants. It is again a matter of plant geometry and of our ability to control it.

F. Leaf Area Index

In summary of this discussion of the problems associated with the best use of space we may ask the question as to why high planting rates are required for high yields and if there is no limit to planting rates. If there is a limit, what determines it? The answer goes back, in part, to some of the points made by Dr. R. S. Loomis (see Chapter 4, this book) and his computer in describing the architecture of plant canopies. Higher plant populations are needed with a plant like corn in order to have high leaf area indices (LAI). Without high LAI values, the useful light cannot be intercepted at efficiently low levels of illumination. There is a limit to this, however, that is set by the leaf angles involved.

With flat horizontal leaves a high LAI is a disadvantage because of excessive self shading. As leaf angle increases so can LAI. The rate of planting required for maximum canopy photosynthetic rate and presumably yield with a given phenotype is set by the leaf area per plant and the angle or aspect of the leaves. There are obviously other considerations but these are fundamental and limiting.

We can think about this in terms of Dr. Donald's idea that the ideal plant should be as noncompetitive as possible. With near vertical leaves it is possible for a plant to intercept light at low levels of illumination and hence more efficiently as far as the use of radiant energy is concerned. With such leaves the shading of neighboring plants is minimal. High yielding crops come from plants that are pacifists; that concentrate on productivity and minimize rivalry.

In this context, a soybean plant (Glycine max L.) might be a good example of a plant with reprehensible social behavior. It has a bush habit of growth that tends toward overshadowing neighboring plants. For many varieties the leaves are large, relatively flat and placed close together. They thus intercept both direct sunlight and skylight at inefficiently high levels of illumination instead of dividing the light flux among many more leaves.

III. NO-TILLAGE PLANTING

Let us continue by considering the underground environment and to some extent the use of water. In Kentucky and adjoining states there is considerable interest in a cultural method called "no-tillage." It is an awkward term to use in writing or speaking but no better one has evolved as yet. This year there were almost 40,000 ha (100,000 acres) planted in Kentucky by this method and more will be planted next year. What has brought it to the front is a better approach to an ancient problem, the control of weeds. The fact that weeds are easier to control in corn than in other crops probably explains why it is in wider use in this crop than others.

Under this concept the grass sod or other ground cover is killed with herbicide mixtures and a 5-cm-wide (2-inch) seedbed prepared with a fluted coulter. Seeds are placed in this strip with only slightly modified planters. Results haven't been free of problems but there is solid reason for encouragement and for thinking it is much more than a passing agricultural fad. One that is most exciting to me is that our corn so planted has shown less wilting under moisture stress than corn in adjoining plots prepared conventionally. Apparently less water is lost from the soil during preparation, during the time when corn is too small to shade the soil surface, and possibly even after this when most visible radiation is being intercepted. There is a favorable effect on infiltration of rainfall also which may be a factor. At any rate, yields for no-tillage corn in Kentucky are as good as conventional tillage under very favorable conditions and consistently higher when there is moisture stress.

While in Davis, California, I audited a class in tropical agriculture taught by Dr. W. A. Williams in which he discussed a comparable planting system in the steep hills of a remote part of Brazil. Here the farmer applied an ancient herbicide, fire, by burning the brush. He then planted his no-tillage corn—by a touch with the tip of his machete that made a mark just large enough to allow him to insert and cover a grain of corn. The farmer didn't know anything about scientific agriculture but he knew that the less he disturbed the surface of the soil the fewer weeds he would have. The process may sound a bit crude but it may embody the fundamental principles of the best cultural manipulation of soil for the future.

As we think about no-tillage systems and see how well they work we must ask the question, why do we plow in the first place? Observations of no-tillage systems suggest to me that what we refer to as soil preparation has little to do with improving the environment for root development. Corn yields without plowing are just as good, usually better, and sometimes quite a bit better than with conventional tillage. Apparently in our part of the country the major reason for plowing is to control weeds. Dr. deWit has told about similar results with crops other than corn in Holland, so it isn't too local a conclusion. A huge tractor pulling four or five bottom plows is a lot of machinery just to kill weeds.

A. Rooting Patterns

One of our exciting observations about no-tillage is that crops seem to improve with successive cropping. Dr. deWit has told me that this seemed to be the case over a 6-year experience in Holland, and he proposes to look under the soil surface to see if there might be some progressive change in rooting habits. It is not unreasonable to think that with time in undisturbed soil there are increased numbers of passages into deeper layers of the soil attributable to old root channels, insect holes, animal burrows, etc. These channels are, to a considerable degree, structured so that roots following them would be led downward, and most such openings would have some degree of permanence. Plowing presumably interrupts and destroys such channels and substitutes for them a non-structured and less permanent porosity.

I can make almost any statements about roots growing in the soil without much fear of contradiction because we know so little about them. They are too hard to dig up. Probably Dr. Weaver and his students here at Nebraska have done more than anyone else to try to find out about roots growing in soil but there is much more we need to know to evaluate the need for plowing.

If I have inspired any of you to take a closer look at roots in the soil, don't go very deeply into it without reading a little paper on root sampling techniques by E. T. Newman (1966) on work done at Duke University. I found out about it from Dr. Torsell, one of Dr. R. O. Slatyer's associates who has used the methods described. It is a real breakthrough in a way to study a difficult subject.

B. Future of No-Tillage

The present interest in and development of no-tillage methods has come from a basic new agricultural tool, modern chemical herbicides. The possibilities for the future depend on further development and perfection of agents for the control of weeds. It is still too early to do away with our tractors and plows and sell stock in companies that manufacture agricultural implements. The ideal herbicide hasn't been developed yet and our techniques for using them will probably seem unbelievably crude as seen through our grandchildren's eyes.

If by remote sensing from airplanes high above the earth we can distinguish between wheat and oats (Avena sativa L.) it should be possible to build a herbicide applicator that can locate and identify general classes of weeds. With such a tool we can apply the best herbicide to control each class of weeds and none at all where no weeds are growing. This will increase effectiveness, decrease cost, and minimize the danger of undesirable contamination of soil and crops.

Planting and fertilizing through masses of organic debris on the surface poses challenging problems. Thus far fertilization has been almost disappointingly simple. Surface application of all nutrients seems to be entirely adequate on the soils we have worked with. Surely this cannot be generally true.

Planting equipment seems crude and awkward for the task. We are still chained to cultivated-field thinking. We must get our engineers to spend some time meditating on the Brazilian farmer tapping the soil with the tip of his machete and dropping the seed into the wound. The need is for a tool that will deposit the seed under the soil with a pecking motion like the beak of a bird, not a device that will prepare even a 5-cm-wide strip down which a conventional planter can be dragged.

Many problems remain to be solved. One interesting one our experimenters ran into in Kentucky was with field mice. When they cultivated a narrow strip and planted seed in an old bluegrass sod they made a mouse freeway studded with refreshment stands. Some plots had to be replanted three times. They also made more than one hurried call for the entomologist to look at insects they had never before recognized as corn pests. It we can send men around the moon, however, we can probably solve problems like these in some way.

I should point out here that results from one state, Indiana, do not agree with other states which have worked with no-till corn. What I have presented is a majority report. The fact that there might be a minority opinion is added reason to learn more about the basic principles involved. Differences in results suggest differences among soils or climates or methods that affect the results.

I haven't mentioned the most obvious reason for interest in no-tillage methods. As we have been made more aware at this conference by Dr. J. G. Harrar's address, there is urgent need for more food production. No-till methods could allow us to bring millions of hectares of sloping land into permanent row cropping thus effectively increasing the acreage available for production of human food. This possibility should give powerful motivation for study of no-till methods.

Research should proceed in steps. The first is to confirm our observations and to be sure of our facts. This is about where we are in no-tillage. The second step is to develop hypotheses to explain what we observe and to reconcile apparent discrepancies. The third step is to design experiments to test our hypotheses. When our hypotheses survive to evolve into theories and stronger we can begin to feel that we understand the problems. This is where we would like to be with no-tillage and as rapidly as possible.

IV. UTILIZATION OF THE GROWING SEASON

The last of our elements of cultural manipulation is time, by which is meant the procedures we may use to make fullest use of the growing season. This is not exclusively a temperate zone problem. Even in the tropics there are often factors that make some part of the year a more desirable growing season than others.

Agronomists in Nebraska do not have the same problems we have in Kentucky with corn. Here they plant early varieties as soon as they can in the spring and spend the summer hoping they will mature before it snows. In Kentucky if we plant corn early it will be mature and dead by the last of August. With really early varieties it will be dead sooner. There is often a month or more of fairly good growing season left unused. The farther south one goes in the United States the more corn growing weather is wasted. Our problem is how to translate the unused season into higher yields. Later varieties grow taller and silk later but there seems to be little increase in the filling time during which grain is produced.

A. Ideotypes

To state the problem in Dr. Donald's terms, we are looking for an ideotype that will be short and hence early with erect leaves and that would have several or very large ears on every stalk. It would silk and tassel early and would spend the remaining growing season filling the kernels pollinated earlier. The time from silking to maturity would not be affected by temperature. With such varieties a farmer could buy seed to suit his planting time and the length of his growing season, and corn yields would increase with the growing time available. The ideal ideotype for high yields would germinate quickly in cool soils and grow off rapidly at low and variable spring temperatures.

Presently we probably sacrifice yield by seeking varieties that mature early enough to dry in the warmer days of fall. It would be better, as far as yield is concerned, to develop varieties with longer filling periods that would mature later. There are other ways of drying corn after harvest than by using solar radiation. Our only energy for growth comes from the sun. We should use as much of it as possible for producing grain, and develop ideotypes that will make full use of it.

B. Double Cropping

Another method for extending the growing season is by using the cooler part of the year to produce crops that do well at lower temperatures and follow or precede them with crops that flourish during the warmer part of the season. Alert farmers in our area are experimenting with various plans for double cropping to accomplish this and our plant breeders are developing early maturing small grains to fit into such plans. Only recently I heard of one of our farmers trying to develop a corn planter to fit under his combine in order to put no-till corn in the clean ground behind the cutter bar to be covered by the straw falling behind the combine. Farmers are alert and thinking along these lines everywhere and they are developing methods that we agronomists must help them with. Another idea that is coming into use is the seeding of small grains in standing soybeans and corn with airplanes. I am sure the birds approve of this, but seeding rates are increased enough to feed them and get satisfactory stands. Yields are as good as, or better than, with conventional seeding. Any improvement in yield probably comes about because earlier seeding is possible rather than because of the method used.

V. FUTURE RESEARCH

Work to improve plant yields through cultural manipulation is probably the most ancient form of agricultural research, but there is still room for improvement. As one new and powerful tool we have the modern digital computer whose speed and memory capacity permit the simulation of complex plant and environment situations. We can begin to fit what we know about the parts of the system together like pieces of a giant puzzle to make model systems we can manipulate in the computer. With such models we can test our ideas in seconds instead of years and without having to worry about droughts and floods and all the other accidents that happen to field experiments. In such models we can test the plant ideotypes Dr. Donald mentions without ever having to produce a seed. We can design plants for specific situations and turn the blueprints over to the plant breeders. We are well on the way toward this.

The greatest present obstacle standing in the way of rapid progress in the development of simulation or systems analysis methods in the agricultural sciences is lack of any way to publish results or methods. Fortran programs make dull reading to the uninitiated and explaining them takes more space than is usually allowed in journals. A further difficulty is that most agricultural journals are frozen to the idea that publishable data comes from physical experiments rather than from sound logic and transistor hookups. As a result there is little opportunity for those working in simulation to exchange ideas. Neither is there an opportunity to show agricultural scientists generally that simulation with modern computers has tremendous potential for solving many complex agronomic problems. Such new scientific developments call for imaginative new ideas in publication.

By whatever the method, the general need in agronomy is more mathematics to aid us in generalizing complex problems. There is no other way we can gain clear understanding of the real nature of the difficult problems involved in cultural manipulation for higher yields. We have improved yields through the centuries by trail and error methods, however, and we can probably continue to make stumbling progress by the same methods. We can attain our ends more rapidly and more surely, however, if our experiments are guided by a higher level of understanding.

LITERATURE CITED

Clements, F. E., J. E. Weaver, and H. Hanson. 1949. Carnegie Inst., Washington, D.C. Publ. no. 398.

Donald, C. M. 1958. Interaction of competition for light and for nutrients. Aust. J. Agr. Res. 9:421–435.

Donald, C. M. 1968. The breeding of crop ideotypes. Euphytica 17:193–211.

Duncan, W. G. 1958. The relationship between corn population and yield. Agron. J. 50:82–84.

Hozumi, Kazuo, Hirosi Koyami, and Tatuo Kira. 1955. Interspecific competition among higher plants. IV. A preliminary account of the interaction between adjacent individuals. J. Inst. Polytechnics, Osaka City Univ. Series D. Vol. 6.

Nelder, J. A. 1962. New kinds of systematic designs for spacing experiments. Biometrics 18:283–307.

Newman, E. T. 1966. Method for estimating the total length of root in a sample. J. Appl. Ecol. 3:139–145.

Yoda, Koyoji, Tatuo Kira, and Kazuo Hozumi. 1957. Interspecific competition among higher plants. IX. Further analysis of the competitive interaction between adjacent individuals. J. Inst. Polytechnics, Osaka City Univ. Series D, Vol. 8.

14...DISCUSSION

HARRY F. CLEMENTS

University of Hawaii
Honolulu, Hawaii

In sugarcane fields (Saccharum officinarum L.) maximum yields are more nearly obtainable when the requirements of the crop are diagnosed and satisfied while the crop grows and all negative factors are neutralized as much as possible prior to the start of the crop. In order that the requirements of the crop be met as they develop, samples of leaf sheaths and blades are collected every 35 days starting at 2-3 months of age and continuing until harvest. All the samples are analyzed for tissue moisture, N, K, and total sugars of the sheaths. Normal levels of sheath moisture and leaf nitrogen for each cane variety for each age are a matter of calculation. Within 48-72 hours after a sampling, the actual levels are obtained, plotted on the log, and, when compared with the "normal," appropriate action can be taken.

Intensive analytical work during the period of maximum growth gives data on all the essential elements, major and minor and SiO_2. Three consecutive samples are so analyzed. Soil pH is also determined for each station. These data provide all the information needed with which to start off the next crop, i.e., not only to provide adequate nutrients but just as important to eliminate toxicities—particularly those associated with poorly aerated, poorly drained acid soils: ferrous iron, aluminum, nickel, excessive amounts of the minor elements, particularly Mn, Zn, and Cu. Crop log data at times are fortified with root data covering the potentially toxic elements. Calcium metasilicate, calcium carbonate, calcium sulfate, or magnesium oxide may be called for and each would be applied at the start of the next plant crop and worked into the soil with deep plowing, discing and/or rotovating.

On irrigated plantations, the moisture regime is checked at each analysis and adjustments made if necessary. Maintaining high tissue moisture levels is a primary requirement for maximum yields. On unirrigated plantations below normal moisture levels during adequate rainfall and fertilization may call for a change in soil preparation techniques.

Blossoming of sugar cane can be completely prevented by imposing a mild moisture stress onto the crop. Withholding one water application between August 4 and September 8 will drop the tissue moisture level to stress levels and prevent flowering.

The last 6 or 7 months of the 2-year cycle crop are given over to deliberate ripening of the crop. Weekly samples of sheath tissue are taken and moisture analyses are made. At the start of the period, tissue moisture should be high—82-84%. And on the day of harvest the level should be 73% which is usually achieved in a series of drought impositions, at first light but progressively more severe. With each drop in tissue moisture, growth is reduced and carbohydrates accumulate. When water is again applied, tissue moisture rises but never to the previous high levels. In this way a very orderly ripening is effected.

In pineapple culture, according to Dr. Wallace Sanford, efforts have been expended to broaden the time of fruit ripening and harvest. If the crops were allowed to differentiate naturally, they would peak at the same time resulting in crowding the canneries for a very short time. To lengthen the harvest and processing, early fruiting is induced by aqueous application of such growth regulators as ethylene, acetylene, sodium naphthalene acetic acid (SNA), and by beta-hydroxyethylhydrazine. Depending on temperature and sunlight, the time of fruit development from induction varies from 6-7 months. With rather precise knowledge for each area and field the canning period is broadened and peak performance is maintained.

Experimentally, flowering has been delayed with SNA if used in large amount but some bad side effects may ensue. Application of beta-naphthoxy-acetic acid or SNA in large amounts 6 to 8 weeks before expected harvest will increase fruit weight by as much as a half-pound and delay harvest 1 to 2 weeks. Moisture levels of the fruits are raised but there is a lowering of sugars, acids, and pigments.

In Hawaii, the flowering of the daylength indifferent lychee (Litchi chinensis) is very uncertain. Work done by Dr. Shigeru Nakata however points up the effective control measures. Although cold nights (14.0-15.6C) during the September to January induction period assures profuse blossoming, as demonstrated in controlled chambers, rarely are our temperatures that low. Abundant carbohydrate accumulation is associated with flower induction. This condition can be induced by imposing a drought either through the cessation of irrigation or by covering of the soil with clear polyethylene sheets. It can also be accomplished by girdling either a branch or the whole trunk, overcoming in this way to some extent at least the tendency toward biennial bearing.

Shipments of papaya (Carica papaya L.) to the mainland United States, an expanding business, are beset by three main problems: fruit fly, fruit rot and a short shelf life. Vapor heat or ethylene dibromide fumigation are approved quarantine treatments for the fly. The latter as worked out by USDA and University of Hawaii researchers is the more commonly used method, but this has no controlling effect on the storage decay. A hot water dip (49C for 20 min.) to control the decay worked out by Professor E. K. Akamine is now combined with fumigation as the common treatment for air as well as marine shipments.

Low dosage gamma irradiation (not yet cleared for commercial use) combined with the hot water dip, effectively controls the rot as well as the fruit fly and extends the shelf life 3 to 4 days by delaying ripening and senescence. Another 2 days can be gained by shipping fruit so treated under low oxygen refrigeration.

14... DISCUSSION

E. B. TREGUNNA

University of British Columbia

Vancouver, British Columbia, Canada

I would like to use three examples to focus your attention on one part of the plant which, except for Dr. Duncan's paper, has received very little attention at this conference—the root. Increasing crop density must include increased root density. Pitman (1962) has a particular example of the effect of root density. The roots of winter wheat are aligned along the geomagnetic lines of force, and so if the rows are also aligned this way, interactions of roots from different plants are greater than if the rows cross the lines of force. There were effects on yield and on the date of heading, presumably because of competition for water.

As Dr. Duncan has indicated, explaining the results of no-tillage planting or transplanting also requires consideration of the roots. A procedure similar to the one he described from South America can also be seen in North America; it is used to transplant tree seedlings in British Columbia. To protect the roots and lower stem from damage during the transplanting procedure, Walters (1968) has developed a mechanized procedure involving the planting of seed, germination and growth of tree seedlings in plastic bullets. After transplanting, the bullet splits open under the pressure of continued plant growth.

In the type of statistical wheel that Dr. Duncan used, the gas composition of the soil would change from the outside to the inside, and it would be affected by whether green manure or inorganic fertilizer was used. An effect that these factors may have on the microflora has been shown by Pentland Friesen (1967). She has shown that the weight of Armillaria mellea can be doubled by a continual supply of 50 ppm ethanol. More recently, she has found that methoxylated lignin degradation products, again at the part per million level, control the production of rhizomorphs. The rhizomorphs are important in the pathology of Armillaria. This fungus, therefore, would be greatly stimulated by high levels of biological activity in the soil, leading to the availability of alcohol and other organic products.

LITERATURE CITED

Pentland, G. E. 1967. Ethanol produced by Aureobasidium pullulans and its effect on the growth of Armillaria mellea. Can. J. Microbiol. 13:1631-1639.

Pitman, U. J. 1962. Growth reaction and magnetotropism in roots of winter wheat (Kharkov 22 M.C.) Can. J. Plant Sci. 42:430-436.

Walters, John. 1968. Plant gun and bullet. A mechanical system for forest regeneration. Agr. Eng. 49(6)336-339.

15

Environmental Manipulation for Higher Yields

PAUL E. WAGGONER

Connecticut Agricultural Experiment Station
New Haven, Connecticut

I. INTRODUCTION

My role in this chapter on environmental manipulations is making a prediction that can be used until experiments render the final verdict.

In chapters preceding mine, an array of physical and physiological phenomena for affecting yield has been laid before the grower of plants. Predicting whether environmental manipulation will increase yield requires that all of these phenomena be considered for foreign lands are littered with the bleaching bones of immigrant varieties and practices that were ambushed by an unsuspected environmental difference.

Interaction is the Scylla of biologic prediction. Formerly we predicted by drawing a curve or writing a formula relating yield to some factor. We used this although common sense told us that the rock of some limiting factor would surely sink us. We simply couldn't accommodate all the factors that common sense told us would be important. For example, we knew light and CO_2 would alter the relation between ventilation and yield, but considering them was beyond our capacity.

Now, however, high-speed and capacious information machines give more latitude to our common sense by permitting us to include things that formerly had to be discarded in simplification. The empirical curve is easily replaced by a simulator that not only produces a prediction but also, in its interior, works like the crop. The degree to which it works like the crop is always imperfect, but passages toward realism are now easily found, and more reefs of interaction missed. Light and CO_2, for example, can now be considered in predicting the the effect of ventilation upon yield.

The simulator required for predicting yield response to environmental manipulation must combine meteorology and physiology. The reason is easily seen in the example of CO_2. It is delivered via a meteorological thing, turbulence, and the receipt is through a physiological thing, the stomata, into a photochemical process.

Models of leaves have been drawn by electrical analogy: a current of CO_2 is driven by the difference in CO_2 concentration between the air about a single leaf and its interior, and the current is opposed by boundary layer, stomatal and mesophyll resistors (Gaastra, 1959; Moss, 1966; El-Sharkawy, Loomis and Williams, 1967; Lake, 1967; and Bravdo, 1968). A current of respired CO_2 enters the conductor, too. The model has been refined (Waggoner, 1969) by separating the mesophyll resistor into physical and biochemical parts, by separating the respiration into light and dark portions, and by making the resistors functions of light, CO_2 and temperature. Clearly this leaf model or simulator needs connection to a meteorological simulator.

The microclimate simulator that I shall use incorporates the radiation and ventilation profiles within the canopy, the leaf area and stomatal resistance, and the conditions above and below the canopy. It calculates the temperature, humidity, and evaporation within the canopy and the resistances and leaf temperatures that affect CO_2 exchange (Waggoner and Reifsnyder, 1968; Waggoner et al., 1969).

In this chapter, a simulator of the photosynthesis in a canopy is made by setting the physiological simulator of a single leaf in the framework of the microclimate simulator. The resulting photosynthesis simulator then accepts the news of environmental manipulation and predicts the changes in photosynthesis and, hopefully, yield.

In the following pages, I shall first present the entire simulator. Then its reasonableness will be tested by calculating temperature, photosynthesis and CO_2 profiles from normal characteristics of weather, stand geometry and physiology and comparing the profiles to actual observations. Then the effect of stomatal aperture, light, ventilation and CO_2 management will be predicted.

II. THE PHOTOSYNTHESIS SIMULATOR

Since our goal is a photosynthesis simulator, a mathematical guinea pig, with parts that function much like the real thing, the simulator is presented from the inside parts out. That is, considerably physiology of a single leaf is incorporated into the model of a single leaf and then this is, in turn, incorporated into a meteorological framework for the entire canopy.

An electrical conductor is shown in Fig. 15-1A. This is an analog of the leaf. The potential at one end of the conductor is, in fact, C, the CO_2 concentration at the outer edge of the boundary layer around a single leaf. At the other end of the conductor, the CO_2 concentration is zero where CO_2 becomes carbohydrate. Since the system is nonisothermal, relative concentrations, as ppm, are used.

The unit of net assimilation P of CO_2 that has become predominant is mg CO_2 dm^{-2} hr^{-1}. In the case of the single leaf the dm^2 refers to the projected area of a flat leaf, which is 2 dm^2 of leaf surface. In the following pages, this long and awkward unit is abbreviated by "F". The direction of the current is shown as inward, which it will be in the normal, illuminated leaf. On the other hand, the current will often be outward as when the leaf is not illuminated or the outside air is devoid of

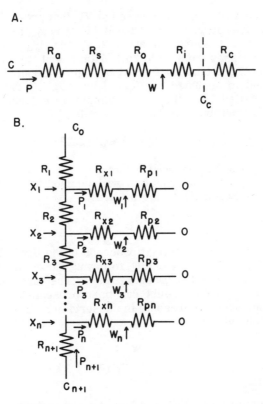

Fig. 15-1—Simulators drawn as electrical circuits for (A) a single leaf and (B) a canopy of leaves.

CO_2; no change in convention is required in this case for the current will simply appear as negative in the calculations.

The resistances have dimensions sec cm^{-1}. The net assimilation current P passes first through the resistance R_a of the boundary layer outside the epidermis of the leaf. In the epidermis, the current encounters R_S, the diffusive resistance of the stomata. Inside the leaf, the current encounters another diffusive resistance, R_O. Formally, this resistance is between the stomata and the junction where the net assimilation current P is joined by the current W of CO_2 that comes from respiration within the leaf. Physically, R_O must be in the substomatal cavity, the cell walls and the outer cell contents. Inside the outer resistance, R_O, may be an inner one, R_i. This R_i separates the junction of P and W from the biochemical site where the concentration of CO_2 has fallen to C_c. Chemical factors that lie between C_c and the final reduction to zero concentration are represented by a final resistance R_c. The resistance R_a is calculated in the microclimate simulator, and R_i and R_O are assumed independent of environment. The other parameters of Fig. 15-1A vary with environment as is now specified.

The current W of CO_2 is composed of W_d that proceeds in the dark or light and W_1 that occurs only in the light. The W_d has a well-known Q_{10} or temperature response of about 2; that is, W_d doubles when the temperature increases from 20 to 30C (Altman and Dittmer, 1966). On the other hand, W_d seems unaffected by light (Marsh, Galmiche, and Gibbs, 1965) and is assumed unaffected by CO_2. If the Q_{10} for dark respiration is called Q_{wd}, then W_d at temperature T can be calculated by an Arrhenius equation with W_{dx} as the rate at 20C.

$$W_d = W_{dx} \exp [9000 \ln (Q_{wd}) (1/293 - 1/T)] \qquad (1)$$

W_{dx} can reasonably be assigned a value of 2 F (Altman and Dittmer, 1966). Since the Arrhenius equation will be used again, it is abbreviated "arh," and equation (1) can be written

$$W_d = arh (W_{dx}, Q_{wd}, T).$$

The portion W_1 of the current W that proceeds in the light also increases with temperature. The burst of CO_2 following darkening, an indication of W_1, has a Q_{wl} of 1.4 to 3.4 (Decker, 1959). The burst was unaffected by CO_2, but its response to light can be represented by a Michaelis-Menten equation, which represents the observations in a form familiar to chemists. Thus at 20C

$$W_1 = \frac{W_{1x} L}{(K_{wl} + L)}$$

W_{1x} is the maximum W_1 at 20C, and K_{wl} is the irradiance L that causes half W_{1x} to be realized. Decker's (1959) observations indicate K_{wl} is about 1 cal cm^{-2} min^{-1} (ly min^{-1}). The parameters concerning irradiance are stated in values for insolation, i.e., the energy between 400 and 3,000 nm.

The CO_2 current W_{1x} is close to zero in maize (Zea mays) but might exceed net assimilation in tobacco (Nicotiana tabacum) at 35C (Zelitch, 1966). Jackson and Volk (1968) have reported that maize leaves take up more oxygen in the light than in the dark. Since the maize leaves do not, however, release CO_2 into CO_2-free air during photosynthesis, the existence of an O_2 current does not require an increase in the CO_2 current W in Fig. 15-1 when maize is illuminated. Thus W_{1x} of 0 and 10 mg dm^{-2} hr^{-1} are not unreasonable for an efficient and for a mediocre species, respectively. Respiration in the light can now be expressed as a realistic function of temperature and irradiance:

$$W_1 = arh (W_{1x}, Q_{wl} T) \times \frac{L}{(K_{wl} + L)}. \qquad (2)$$

Estimating R_c presents special problems. It represents the obstacle to gross photosynthesis in a photosynthetic site (unencumbered by other resistances) per unit of C_c, the CO_2 concentration at the boundary of the site. If the effects of temperature, light and CO_2 upon that photosynthesis were independent of one another, it would be reasonable to employ the familiar Michaelis-Menten and Arrhenius equations and set gross photosynthesis equal to

$$\text{arh } (P_x, Q_p, T) \; \frac{L}{K_{cl} + L} \; \frac{C_c}{K_{cc} + C_c} \; . \tag{3}$$

Then the resistance to gross photosynthesis per unit of C_c is

$$R_c = \frac{(K_{cl} + L)}{L} \; (K_{cc} + C_c) \, / \, \text{arh } (P_x, Q_p, T). \tag{4}$$

The reader will understand that the units of concentrations of CO_2 and of P_x must be converted to obtain R_c in sec cm^{-1}.

Since no naked photosynthetic sites without respiration are available for observation, the parameters of equation (4) were estimated from observations of maize, which has small resistance and respiration. The Q_p is 2 to 3 (Moss, 1965). The maximum photosynthesis at 20C, P_x, is about 120 F; K_{cl}, 0.5 ly min^{-1} and K_{cc}, 300 ppm (Hesketh, 1963; Hesketh and Moss, 1963).

R_S varies with both illumination and CO_2. Since the effect of CO_2 is much less than illumination (Gaastra, 1959), calculating R_S as follows is reasonable:

$$R_s = R_{sm} \; \frac{K_{sl} + L}{L} \; . \tag{5}$$

R_{sm} is the minimum stomatal resistance, which is attained in bright light, and K_{sl} is the insolation that makes R_s twice R_{sm}.

As stated in the Introduction, the goal is to incorporate as much physiology and as much common sense as possible into the model, making it run something like a real leaf. Equations (1) through (5) have taken us in that direction. Boundary layer, stomatal resistance, light and dark respiration, diffusive resistance in the leaf interior, and the response of the photosynthetic apparatus itself can all be identified explicitly in the equations or model. To facilitate the connection of Fig. 15-1A to the simulator of the canopy, some symbols are combined. The sum of the resistors external to W is called R_x, and the sum of those inside W is called R_p. Thus, Fig. 15-A becomes simpler and is seen in Fig. 15-1B where it represents the leaf strata of a canopy.

A canopy of leaves is conceived as a ladder of conductors, Fig. 15-1B, between a CO_2 concentration C_0 at the top of the plants and a concentration C_{n+1} near the soil. The canopy is divided into n strata. Later, when the simulator has been assembled and calculations are possible, I shall demonstrate that the stratified canopy is practically equal to the continuous one in the real field or forest.

By integrating the reciprocal of the diffusivity from the upper to lower boundary of each stratum, the resistance R is obtained. This is the diffusive resistance offered to CO_2 as it moves through the bulk air in a stratum and is the same resistance employed for water vapor or sensible heat (Waggoner and Reifsnyder, 1968). On its way down the ladder, CO_2 may pass on to another rung or stratum, or it may move into the leaves of a stratum, encountering R_X and, after joining W, passing through R_p to a sink and concentration zero.

At this point, the effect of leaf area upon R_X, W, and R_p must be mentioned. In Fig. 15-1A, a unit area of leaf surface was tacitly assumed. That is, the R_a and R_s pertain to a cm^2 of epidermis, while the other resistors and the W pertain to the cm^2 of mesophyll enclosed between 2 cm^2 of epidermis (i.e., 2 cm^2 of total surface of a flat leaf). In the full canopy, however, the R_X, R_p, and W pertain to the variable areas encountered at the different levels. Thus, R_a and R_s, which pertain to epidermis, are divided by twice the projected leaf area index in each stratum. The other resistors pertain to the leaf interior and are divided by leaf area index in each stratum. Respiration is multiplied by leaf area index in each stratum. In this way, the parameters for 1 cm^2 of leaf in Fig. 15-1A are adapted to the variable areas in the strata of the canopy in Fig. 15-1B and now pertain to 1 cm^2 of land.

At the bottom of the canopy, another sink or source is encountered. The diffusive resistance among the bare stems is R_{n+1}. If these stems are long and ventilation penetrates poorly to this recess, R_{n+1} will be great. At its bottom, the end of the conductor is reached, and the CO_2 concentration near the soil is specified. If it is CO_2-rich, an upward current P_{n+1} will move into the canopy.

If we are to simulate CO_2 fertilization, external sources X of CO_2 must also be considered. These are shown as X_1, X_2, ..., X_n entering the strata of Fig. 15-1B. Like the respiratory currents W, the advected currents X are considered independent of CO_2 concentration. Physically, the X could be the respiration of an ear of grain, gas from a flue, or evaporating dry ice measured in a stratum as mg CO_2 per dm^2 of land per hour or F.

The model of the canopy and its leaves have now been presented in words and graphs and must be reduced to equations that can be solved for the P_1, P_2, ..., P_{n+1}. The equations will also provide values for C_1, C_2, ..., C_n, which are the CO_2 concentrations at the junction of R_1 and R_{X1}, R_2 and R_{X2}, ..., R_n and R_{Xn}. These are assumed to be the concentrations that a micrometeorologist would measure within the canopy.

The equations are simply obtained from the assumed equality between concentration differences and the products of currents and resistances. Thus, between the air at the top and the interior of the leaves in the first stratum,

$$C_o - 0 = P_o R_1 + P_1 R_{x1} + (P_1 + W_1) R_{pl} \qquad (6)$$

where

$$P_0 = P_1 + P_2 + \ldots P_n - P_{n-1} - (X_1 + X_2 + \ldots + X_n). \qquad (7)$$

Between the interiors of the leaves in the first and second strata

$$0 - 0 = - (P_1 + W_1) R_{p1} - P_1 R_{x1} \tag{8}$$

$$+ (P_0 - P_1 + X_1) R_2 + P_2 R_{x2} + (P_2 + W_2) R_{p2}.$$

Finally, at the bottom,

$$0 - C_{n+1} = - (P_n + W_n) R_{pn} - P_n R_{xn} \tag{9}$$

$$- P_{n+1} R_{n+1}.$$

Equation (6) from the canopy top, the n-1 equations like (8) from the canopy interior, and equation (9) from the canopy bottom can be written in matrix form:

$$[A] [P] + [B] - [D] [X] = [C]. \tag{10}$$

The elements A_{kj} of the (n+1) x (n+1) matrix [A] are

$$0 \qquad\qquad\qquad j < k-1$$

$$- R_{x, k-1} - R_{p, k-1} \qquad\qquad j = k-1$$

$$R_k + R_{xk} + R_{pk} \qquad\qquad j = k \text{ and } k < n-1$$

$$R_x \qquad\qquad\qquad j = k = n+1 \text{ or } j > k.$$

The elements of the column vector [P] are $P_1, P_2, \ldots, P_{n+1}$.

The elements of the column vector [B] pertain to respiration and are

$$W_1 R_{p1}, (-W_1 R_{p1} + W_2 R_{p2}), \ldots, (-W_{n-1} R_{p,n-1} + W_n R_{pn}), - W_n R_{pn}.$$

The elements of D_{kj} of the (n+1) x (n+1) matrix [D] are

$$0 \qquad j < k$$

$$R_k \qquad j \geq k.$$

For the column vector [X], the elements are the external CO_2 sources $X_1, X_2, \ldots X_n$, 0. Finally, the elements of the column vector [C] are $C_0, 0, \ldots, 0, - C_{n+1}$.

Equation (10) is easily solved for net assimilation in each stratum:

$$[P] = [A]^{-1} [C] - [A]^{-1} [B] + [A]^{-1} [D] [X]. \tag{11}$$

These values of net assimilation cannot be accepted, however, until their effect upon the concentration C_C at the photosynthetic site and hence upon R_C and R_p have been considered. C_C for each stratum is calculated as the product of $(P + W)$ times R_C. This statement does not, of course, require that all of W go inward: If P is negative, $P + W$ will be less than W, and CO_2 will escape from the leaf. This C_C then permits a revised R_C to be calculated by means of equation (4) for each stratum. Then the calculation of P_1, P_2, ..., P_{n+1} by equation (11) is repeated. This repeated refinement of the net assimilation values is repeated until the refinement in all strata is less than or equal to 1% or, in the case of small values, less than or equal to 0.1 F. In five calculations with 14 to 23 F net assimilation in the entire canopy, equation (11) was applied four times in each example. The fourth and last refinement changed the canopy sum .06 to .3 F.

With values of P_1, P_2, . . ., P_n at hand, the CO_2 concentrations C_1, C_2, ..., C_n within the canopy can be calculated. For example,

$$C_3 = (R_{x3} + R_{p3}) P_3 + R_{p3} W_3.$$

This completes the specification of the model by parameters that are identified meteorological or physiologic factors.

At the conclusion of this derivation of the photosynthesis simulator, the differences between it and models designed to consider only the manipulation of light (e.g., Loomis et al., 1968) is clear. The present simulator considers several physiological factors that were not incorporated into the light models. Equally important, it considers ventilation, temperature and CO_2 in the environment. In its meteorological nature, the present simulator is more closely related to the proposals of Inoue (1965) than to the light models.

Now it is time to test the microclimate and photosynthetic simulators operating in tandem. If they are logical and the published information about the parameters is adequate, the simulation should be realistic both in function and in calculated values.

III. THE RUNNING OF THE SIMULATORS

Within a few minutes of 1400 hours on September 11, 1963, Lemon (1967) and his colleagues observed the wind, temperature, humidity and CO_2 concentration within a maize crop in New York State and then calculated the photosynthesis. Simultaneous observations made nearby by L.H. Allen, K.W. Brown, and J.L. Wright have generously been furnished to me.

If the microclimate and photosynthesis simulators described above are valid, I should be able to put into them the physiological characters of maize, e.g., lack of light respiration and low stomatal resistance, together with the ventilation, radiation and plant size observed by Lemon, and then synthesize the humidity, temperature and CO_2 profiles that he observed. I should also obtain the same rate of photosynthesis that he did if our methods are compatible.

When I set out the known factors, however, two are missing: stomatal resistance and leaf temperature. In 1963 we were not aware of the great importance of stomata and had no handy porometer available. In the case of temperature, the objective was to measure transport in the air, and hence, air—not leaf—temperature was reported. The microclimate simulator comes to the rescue, however. I can enter in it the observations that are available and various stomatal resistances and then select the stomatal resistance that causes the microclimate simulator to mimic the temperature and humidity profiles within the canopy. Leaf temperatures will automatically be calculated by the microclimate simulator.

The next paragraph is necessary because it concerns my choices and adjustments among Lemon's data. But it is tedious, and the reader who is uninterested in detail can skip a paragraph.

The highest leaf was evidently about 225 cm above the ground, and I have assumed that the lowest 25 cm of stem was leafless. K.W. Brown measured the leaf area as follows: 250 to 200 cm above the ground, 0.20 $cm^2 cm^{-2}$, 200 to 150, 1.27; 1.50 to 100, 1.30; 100 to 50, 1.00; 50 to 0, 0.55. I have assigned the area to nine 25-cm-thick strata from bottom to top: 0.20, 0.65, 0.62, 0.65, 0.65, 0.50, 0.50, 0.55, 0. Lemon (1967) gave the distribution of 300-700 nm radiation in his Fig. 20. The absorption of this radiation in each stratum divided by the leaf area provides an estimate of the equivalent irradiance perpendicular to the leaf. K.W. Brown observed the net, all-wave radiation as follows: 250 cm above the ground, 0.639 ly min^{-1}; 200, 0.643; 150, 0.411; 100, 0.160; 50, 0.150. I have assigned the absorption to the nine strata from top to bottom: 0.5 ly min^{-1} per stratum, 1.7, 1.6, 1.4, 1.2, 0.9, 0.8, 0.7, 0. The wind at canopy top was 246 cm sec^{-1}, and Lemon (1967) shows its average extinction within the canopy during the day was 3. This coefficient pertains to an exponential equation and relative height within the canopy (Uchijima, 1962). To calculate the boundary layer resistance, I assumed that the leaf dimension was 1 cm and that the wind was extinguished exponentially with height and a coefficient of 3. The specification of the diffusivity presents a greater problem. When Lemon (1967) calculated it from the wind and leaf area profiles, he found that diffusivity decreased very little with height in the upper and then very greatly in the lower canopy. Since the wind profile is opposite—i.e., it decreases greatly in the upper and little in the lower canopy—and since wind speed is observed directly, I have accepted Lemon's estimate of diffusivity at canopy top (1,140 $cm^2 sec^{-1}$) but have extinguished it within the canopy in the pattern Lemon observed in the wind. Thus, the resistances of the bulk air within the strata were calculated from the following diffusivities: 1,140 $cm^2 sec^{-1}$, 810, 480, 380, 290, 280, 260, 260, 260. This concludes the specification of the canopy, its ventilation and its absorption of radiation. Now the effects of different stomatal resistances can be calculated by means of the microclimate simulator.

In Connecticut maize, N.C. Turner and J.E. Begg measured stomatal resistance with an agitated diffusion porometer described by Slatyer (1966). The resistance approximately doubled between very bright sunlight and 0.3 ly min^{-1} insolation. In my calculations, this rule has been employed, equation (5). When minimum stomatal resistance for water vapor was set at 2 sec cm^{-1} expressed per surface area of epidermis, the synthetic air temperature at midcanopy was about 0.5C cooler than observed. On the other hand, when the minimum stomatal resistance was set at 6 sec cm^{-1}, the synthetic air temperature was nearly a degree warmer than observed. Finally, when the minimum stomatal resistance was set at 3 sec cm^{-1}, synthetic and observed temperatures were nearly identical, the synthetic was near the observed vapor pressure in the lower canopy (Fig. 15-2), and 90% of the radiant energy absorbed by the canopy was expended in evaporation.

The microclimate simulator has led us to stomatal resistances for the canopy and has also calculated the corresponding leaf temperatures. When Lemon was observing the microclimate, the air temperature at canopy top was 22.3C and the temperature of the leaves according to the simulator varied from 22.3 at canopy top to 23.1 in the lowest stratum. If the CO_2 concentration above and below the canopy and the physiology of corn leaves are specified, the photosynthesis simulator should now produce CO_2 profiles similar to Lemon's observations and photosynthesis rates similar to his calculations.

Since maize was used to obtain the characteristics of a photosynthetic apparatus devoid of resistances, its interior physical resistances are set at zero. Further, maize seems the classic case of no light respiration. The dark respiration is set at 2 F and its Q_{10} at 2. The inner photosynthetic mechanism of maize is specified by a maximum of 180 F and Michaelis parameters of 300 ppm and 0.5 ly min^{-1} for CO_2 and insolation. Its Q_{10} is set at 2, which will apply between 20 and 30 C.

The CO_2 concentrations at canopy top and bottom were 284 and 281 ppm. The sources of CO_2 outside the leaf were the respiration of the stalk and ear. First, the respiration of the stem is estimated from Begg and Jarvis's (1968) observation that a stem of Stylosanthes humilis respired 4 F where area is the projected lateral area of the stem. If maize stalks respire at the same rate, 5 stalks m^{-2} that are 225 cm tall and have average width of 2 cm would respire 1 F where area is now of the land. This was assigned to 25-cm strata according to the width of Connecticut corn stalks in mid-September. An ear that contained 45% water had a net respiration of about 0.7 mg CO_2 g^{-1} hr^{-1} (Hesketh and Musgrave, 1962); and in mid-September, Connecticut corn had 45 g of ear in the fifth stratum, 125 g in the sixth 25-cm stratum from the top, and the ear was 45% water. The respiration of stalk plus ear in 25-cm strata from top to bottom was thus set at: .06, .06, .08, .11, 1.72, 4.53, .14, .14, .16 F. (The Connecticut maize was measured by J.E. Begg.) The respiration within the leaf had already been embodied in the simulator of the individual leaf, and the preceding specifications of sources X; complete the preparation for the photosynthesis simulator.

The insolation normal to the leaves and the leaf area in each stratum is shown in Fig. 15-2 as employed in the photosynthesis simulator. According to the simulator, the canopy of leaves fixed 72 F. Of this total, 49 F was obtained from the air above, 16 F from the soil, and 7 F from the stalk and ear of the canopy. How well does all this agree with observation?

The observations that can be compared to the calculations are those of CO_2 concentration, Fig. 15-2. The minimum concentration according

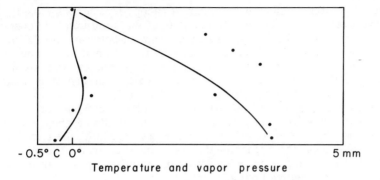

Temperature and vapor pressure

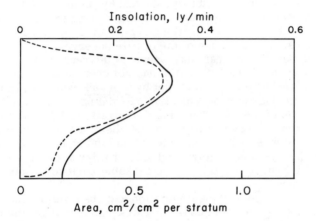

Area, cm²/ cm² per stratum

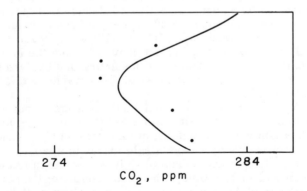

CO_2, ppm

Fig. 15-2—Observations (Lemon, 1967) of temperature, water vapor pressure, and CO_2 concentration in maize at midday are shown by dots. The simulations of these three factors are shown by curves. The measured leaf area is shown by a dashed curve, and the insolation per unit leaf area inferred by the areas and the observed extinction of insolation is shown by a solid curve.

to the simulator (-8.5 ppm less than at canopy top) agrees closely with the observed -8.0. Further, the heights of the simulated and observed minima are nearly the same. The disagreement between simulation and observation is about 150 cm from canopy top. There Lemon observed a sharp enrichment of CO_2, and only a slight enrichment was simulated. In general the simulator behaved realistically, but can it be made to produce a CO_2 enrichment just below midcanopy?

Since I decreased diffusivity rapidly in the upper but not the lower canopy—as the wind decreased, while Lemon calculated great diffusivities in the upper and slight ones in the lower canopy, the effect of his diffusivities upon the enrichment should be examined. Unfortunately, increasing upper and decreasing lower diffusivities causes an impoverishment, not the desired enrichment.

Another possibility is effectiveness of the lower leaves caused by old age. To test this possibility, the photosynthesis of the leaves in lower strata was decreased from 1/3 in midcanopy to 2/3 at the bottom. This raised the CO_2 concentration in midcanopy by 2 ppm but did not simulate the sharp curvature of the profile observed.

A final possibility that may occur to the reader is increasing the respiration of stalk and ear. This has not been pursued, however, because the rates employed were set by a priori evidence, and changing them would be the sort of a posteriori fiddling that makes simulation cunning instead of useful. Thus, the CO_2 profile is left with the conclusion that a priori evidence on the metabolism of single leaves plus the logical frameworks of the microclimate and the photosynthesis simulators mimicks the temperature and CO_2 profiles within the canopies in general, failing only to explain the remarkable enrichment observed just below midcanopy.

In addition to comparing simulation and observation, the simulated photosynthesis can be compared to rates calculated by the observer. Lemon calculated the net uptake of CO_2 by the canopy, stalk and ear at 1358 hours to be 65 F, entirely from the air. The simulator calculates precisely the same 65 F, but it says that 16 F came from the soil. The disagreement between Lemon's calculation and mine concerning the CO_2 from the soil seems caused by two things: First, my inability to find a physiological basis for a large evolution of CO_2 from the lower canopy and a micrometeorological basis for insulating that evolved CO_2 from the sink in the upper canopy; and second, his convention of showing no CO_2 flux from the soil.

The differences between our calculations seem minor, however, when the difficulties of both calculations are reviewed. Lemon has had to skate on the thin ice of estimating diffusivities within a canopy. And I have undertaken to take data from single leaves in a laboratory to calculate how an entire canopy works when it is growing in Nature's soil, under her sun and in her wind. The clear identity of the parameters, the logical nature of the simulators, and the realism of their behavior all argue that they are useful means of predicting the outcome when we manipulate the environment of a crop. First, a standard case is established for comparison.

IV. THE STANDARD CASE

Canopy height, 100 cm; stem height, 10 cm; LAI, 4; foliage distributed as Normal Curve (Stephens, 1969).

At canopy top; air temperature, 20C; vapor pressure deficit, 10
mm Hg; full insolation, 1.2 ly min^{-1}; net all-wave radiation, 0.68 ly
min^{-1}; wind, 225 cm sec^{-1}; diffusivity, 2,000 cm^2 sec^{-1}.

Within the canopy; extinction coefficients for insolation, 0.5, net
radiation, 0.4, and ventilation, 3. Minimum diffusivity, 200 cm^2 sec^{-1}.

Near the soil; air temperature, 20C; vapor pressure deficit, 7 mm
Hg.

Physiological factors; stomatal minimum resistance R_{sm}, 2 sec
cm^{-1}, and K_{sl}, 0.28 ly min^{-1}; P_x, 180 F; K_{cc}, 300 ppm; K_{cl}, 0.5 ly
min^{-1}; Q_p, 2; W_{dx}, 2 F; Q_{wd}, 2; Efficient species: W_{lx}, R_i and Ro are
0. Inefficient species: W_{lx}, 10 F; Q_{wl}, 2; R_i and R_0 are 1 sec cm^{-1}.

Results: canopies consume 95% of absorbed radiation in transpira-

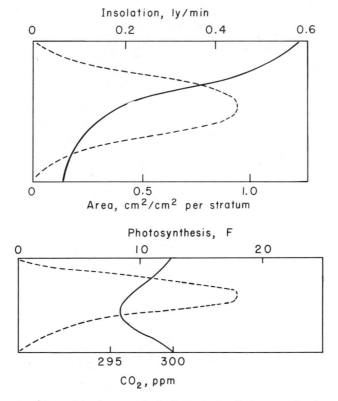

Fig. 15-3—Profiles of leaf area (dashed, top), insolation per leaf area (solid,
top), CO_2 in the air (solid, bottom), and photosynthesis per land area (dashed,
bottom) in the standard case.

tion, and leaves are within 0.5C of air temperature. Efficient species fixes 76 F, obtaining 21% from the soil while depleting the air by 4.3 ppm CO_2. Inefficient species fixes 58 F, obtaining 22% from the soil while depleting the air by 3.4 ppm CO_2.

Subdividing the canopy into 8 or 18 strata for purposes of calculation causes no more than 3% difference.

Results are portrayed in Fig. 15-3.

Now that the simulators of microclimate and photosynthesis in a canopy have been established and the standard case defined, environmental manipulations can be made and compared in their effects upon photosynthesis.

V. MANAGING STOMATA

Stomatal management is a means of affecting photosynthesis and water use, too. True, stomata are on the plant's side of the boundary between environment and plant. But the simulators are especially suited to analyze the feedback that follows a stomatal change, and I arrogate "stomatal management" for this chapter.

At the beginning of this decade, confusion over diffusion theory caused many of us to believe stomata did not affect transpiration as long as they were open the weest crack. The discovery of chemicals that would shrink stomatal width without destroying the plant (Mateus Ventura, 1954; Zelitch, 1961) was soon followed by experiments that showed stomatal widths mattered throughout their range (Zelitch and Waggoner, 1962; Shimshi, 1963b; Slatyer and Bierhuizen, 1964). This salutary experience opened our eyes to sound theory that we had been overlooking (e.g., Penman and Schofield, 1951).

Outdoors, the transpiration of single plants (Shimshi, 1963a) of a barley (Hordeum vulgare) crop (Waggoner, Monteith, and Szeicz, 1964) and even of a large forest (Waggoner and Bravdo, 1967; Turner and Waggoner, 1968) have all been decreased significantly by stomatal management.

In a symposium concerning yields, however, one must remember that the CO_2 for growth must also pass the stomatal resistance. Usually, the yield will be decreased, while water is saved by stomatal closure. There are two possible escapes from this predicament.

The first escape is to assume that the plant is suffering from dehydration that could be relieved by insulating it from the arid air with a net result of increased photosynthesis. This fortunate result seems most likely in the case of a brief period of drought susceptibility, as when maize is flowering. Ing. A. Munoz O. of Chapingo, Mexico (personal communication) and Waggoner (1966) have tried unsuccessfully to increase maize yields in this fashion.

Unfortunately, the chemical that they employed, phenylmercuric acetate (PMA), is toxic to the leaves. Thus it is unclear whether the the failure to increase yields by stomatal management was caused by the stomatal resistance to CO_2 or by the toxicity of PMA.

The other escape from the predicament is to consider yields per gallon of water transpired. Because more things resist the gain of CO_2

than oppose the loss of water by plants, photosynthesis should theoretically be decreased relatively less than transpiration by stomatal narrowing (Zelitch and Waggoner, 1962). This prediction has been verified in the laboratory and in controlled environments (Zelitch and Waggoner, 1962; Shimshi, 1963b; Slatyer and Bierhuizen, 1964; Davenport, 1966).

Outdoors, stomatal shrinking has decreased the growth of trees relatively more than it has decreased their evaporation (Turner and Waggoner, 1968). Here again, however, the toxic PMA was used, and we are uncertain whether growth was decreased mainly by the stomatal closure or by the toxicity of PMA. Fortunately the simulators are a guide to what would follow stomatal management that left all else unchanged.

The calculations are arranged in Table 15-1 to show how the shrinking of stomata would affect the net photosynthesis in sunny and cloudy times. The table also shows how stomatal change would affect the "transpiration ratio."

The transpiration ratio is not the yield per gallon; in fact, it is the reciprocal of a yield, an index of the inefficiency of the use of water. Long experience (e.g., Briggs and Shantz, 1913) has shown that evaporation usually consumes 200 to 2,000 units of water for each unit of growth. The consumption usually includes evaporation from the soil as well as transpiration from leaves. When evaporation from the soil is excluded and only daytime is considered, as in my calculations, the ratio should be lower. A canopy that consumes all net radiation received (about 60% of the insolation) and utilizes 10% of the visible radiation in photosynthesis theoretically has a transpiration ratio of only 90 (Slatyer, 1964).

Table 15-1 shows how both a rich and a poor plant would fare, and this makes a good place to begin discussing the table. Many studies (e.g., Black, 1966) have shown that rich, well watered, abundantly fertilized plants yield more per gallon. In other words, they have lower transpiration ratios. Does this prove that stomatal management that will usually decrease yield per acre is bound to increase the transpiration ratio disadvantageously? By separating two phenomena, the simulators show that disadvantage need not follow stomatal narrowing.

"Rich" means that the plant has the standard characteristics for simulating maize; i.e., P_X, the maximum photosynthesis attainable at 20C, is 180 F. "Poor," on the other hand, means that the crop is iden-

Table 15-1—Calculated effect of stomata upon photosynthesis in full sun and upon transpiration ratio in poor plants (maximum photosynthesis capacity 90F) and rich plants (180F). The stomata have a constant resistance regardless of radiation, where noted, and otherwise vary with radiation as maize stomata do.

Stomatal resistance sec cm^{-1}	Photosynthesis F		Transpiration ratio	
	Poor plants	Rich plants	Poor plants	Rich plants
2 (constant)	41	82	300	150
2	42	76	190	100
8	28	37	90	70

tical except P_X is 90 F. The simulators mimic the many experiments mentioned above: doubling the facility of the leaf doubles yield per acre and halves the transpirtation ratio in the first line of the table.

Now let us change evaporation and yield by changing stomata. In the first line of Table 15-1 we see that a canopy of poor leaves would fix 41 F if the stomata had a resistance of only 2 sec cm^{-1} throughout the canopy. But this isn't how stomata really behave: they shrink as illumination grows dimmer. Therefore, equation (5) was employed to narrow stomata normally in the shade of the canopy, second line Table 1. The effect is surprising: although the stomatal resistance was changed from an unvarying 2 to a range from 2.4 at canopy to 13.0 at canopy bottom, the photosynthesis of a poor or rich plant was scarcely changed.

The paradox of increasing stomatal resistance scarcely changing the uptake of CO_2 is caused by two processes. First, the large increase in stomatal resistance occurred in the lower half of the canopy, which was only fixing a third of the CO_2. Second and surprising, stomatal shrinking in the shade kept the leaves from cooling 2C below and actually permitted them to warm 0.4C above air temperature at canopy top. Since gross photosynthesis far exceeded respiration and had a Q_{10} of 2, the obstruction of the stomata was compensated for by the warming of the leaves. The effect upon the transpiration ratio is, of course, spectacular because lower leaves with open stomata do transpire, fueling their evaporation with sensible heat from the air. Thus when stomata narrow naturally in the shade, the transpiration ratio in both crops decreases about a third.

If the insolation is 0.6 ly min^{-1}, i.e., half full sunlight, the effect of stomatal variation upon the transpiration ratio is even greater.

These calculations were undertaken to demonstrate whether stomatal management could improve the transpiration ratio, and I seem to have gone astray, talking about the natural (not managed) variation of stomata. If this is a diversion, however, it is a strategic one to bring Nature to my side as a witness who has successfully evolved plants that shrink their stomata in the shade and save water.

Imagine that a chemical has been found that will change the minimum stomatal resistance R_{sm} from 2 to 8 while leaving the natural response to shade. A comparison of lines 2 and 3 of Table 15-1 indicates that yields would be cut, but transpiration would be cut even more, and the transpiration ratio would decrease sharply. The outcome would be about the same in dimmer illumination or more humid air.

The transpiration ratios of 200 to 500 look very much like those observed in the USA Great Plains two generations ago by Briggs and Shantz. This testifies to the realism of the simulators. The transpiration ratio of 70, however, requires explanation since a lower limit of 90 was mentioned earlier. The limit of 90 was set by assuming that the net receipt of radiation was entirely consumed in evaporation. Where the ratio is less than 90, on the other hand, stomatal closure has decreased evaporation to less than 60% of the net receipt of radiation. And this stomatal change has been attained in the theoretical canopy without changing any other characteristic of the plants.

Stomatal closure need not be by foreign chemical. It may be natural as in the pineapple (<u>Ananas</u> <u>comosus</u>), which transpires little (Ekern, 1965), grows well, and consequently has a transpiration ratio of only 50 (Joshi, Boyer, and Kramer, 1965).

Stomatal closure need not be by foreign chemical. It may be natural piration control. Epidermal coatings can also do the job, and they have been reviewed by Gale and Hagan (1966) and Waggoner (1967). If, however, the coating is practically impervious to both CO_2 and water vapor and operates by obstructing diffusion, it merely changes R_S as stomatal shrinkage does.

This concludes my examination of stomatal closure by the microclimate and photosynthesis simulators. Clearly, increasing yields per acre depends upon an improved hydration that we have not yet seen. On the other hand, if genetic or chemical stomata shrinkers that do nothing else can be found, they are not condemned by the example of rich-plant-poor-plant, and they should—like the natural closure of stomata in the shade—increase the yield per gallon.

VI. MANIPULATING LIGHT

The management of light seems a likely means of increasing yields for we know that the photosynthesis of an entire canopy enclosed in a chamber is closely correlated with irradiance (Moss, Musgrave and Lemon, 1961), and the yield of a crop rises with increasing insolation (Stanhill, 1958). In dim light, the growth of even the shade-loving <u>Impatiens</u> increases as irradiance increases (Coombe, 1966), and in bright light the photosynthesis of even a single leaf of the efficient maize rises with rising radiation (Hesketh and Musgrave, 1962).

Two means of manipulating light come to mind. The antirainmaker could be asked to roll back the cloud. Or the light absorbed by the canopy could be increased by reflecting light that had escaped the foliage and reached the ground beneath the canopy.

Once again the simulators are the guide. The microclimate simulator should predict how the changes in radiation would alter leaf temperature and, then, the photosynthesis simulator how the changes in radiation and leaf temperature would alter the net uptake of CO_2 into the entire canopy.

The first exercise, predicting the benefit of rolling away the clouds, is essentially calculating the response of the photosynthesis of an entire canopy to increased irradiance at canopy top. In this task I can employ the familiar "light response" curve and test the simulators further.

In Fig. 15-4 the upper curve represents the simulated net photosynthesis by the efficient species, which reaches 76 F in full sunlight. In the bright light the same canopy would fix only 58 F if the leaves belonged to the less efficient species.

Two things are immediately evident. First, the more efficient leaves make a canopy that responds more profitably to increasing light. But, second, then, the less efficient leaves fix considerably more CO_2 in brighter light.

The virtue of more sunlight for an hour has, however, never been doubted by either botanists or bathers. A question more worthy of such

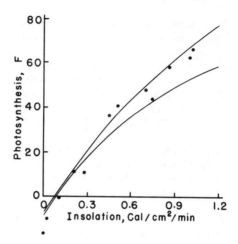

Fig. 15-4—Simulated photosynthesis in efficient and inefficient crops and the photosynthesis of maize canopy as observed by Moss et al. (1961). The simulations are shown by curves and the observations by dots.

a complicated simulator is, "In the long pull, how much yield would be added by more light?" A single day can be examined.

The simulators in tandem have only been tested by comparing them with the single instance of Fig. 15-2 and must be tested by comparison against repeated observations during a full day before being employed to predict the outcome of a day. On September 3, 1958, Moss et al. (1961) measured the uptake of CO_2 by a canopy of maize with an LAI of 4. If their observations taken periodically during the day are arranged according to the insolation received during these cloudless hours, the points of Fig. 15-4 are obtained. Since the observers included the respiration of the stem but the simulator did not, 7 F could be added to the observations; this would make the respiration in the dark nearly the same in both observation and simulation and would place the points for brighter light on or above the simulated curve. (The 7 F respired by stalks and ears of maize was calculated earlier for Fig. 15-2.) The agreement between observation and simulation is remarkable when we remember that the simulation was built up from elementary pieces of physiology and meteorology.

The next test is comparing the total simulated photosynthesis and respiration for 24 hours with actual measurements of growth. If the synthetic day were very bright, it might have 20% of its hours with full sunlight, 40% with half sunlight, and the remainder in darkness. Fully 690 ly of insolation would be received daily. If the net photosynthesis is added in the same fashion and converted into dry matter yield by multiplying by 0.65, the daily accumulation is 46 g m^{-2}. If the stem and ear respiration of 7 F is subtracted for every hour, the daily accumulation falls to 35 g m^{-2}. Increasing the temperature to 30C would increase the yield from 35 to 42 g m^{-2}.

The synthetic rates can be compared with short-term maximum

rates: Pennisteum typhoides, 54 g m^{-2} (Begg, 1965); Sorghum vulgare
and Zea mays, 51, Medicago sativa, 23 (Loomis and Williams, 1963).
Thus the simple simulation of a day produces reasonable yields of dry
matter, and calculating the effect of changed sunlight upon yields is
worthwhile.

The first simulated change is halving the insolation. That is, 20%
of the hours now receive half of full sunlight, 40% receive one-quarter
of full sunlight, and the remainder are in darkness. Changing from the
brighter day would decrease the accumulation of dry matter by the efficient canopy without stalks or ears from 46 to 19 g day^{-1}. The halving
of sunlight more than halved daily accumulation because the daytime
gains were nearly halved but the nighttime losses were unchanged.

During the 690-ly day, the less efficient species would produce 35
g m^{-2}. (Both the efficient canopy with stalks and ears and the inefficient
canopy yield 35.) In the inefficient canopy halving the insolation would
decrease the accumulation to 18 or about half. The relative loss from
halving insolation is somewhat less in the inefficient than in the efficient
species because the relation between photosynthesis and insolation is
more curved in the former than in the latter, Fig. 15-4.

The synthetic daily accumulation of 18 g m^{-1} by the inefficient species in a 350-ly day can be compared to peak growth rates of 32 to 21
in Beta maritima and Brassica oleracea in England where the daily insolation is 300 to 400 ly (Watson, 1958).

When one looks about for data to check the preceding prediction that
halving radiation means halving yields, he is reminded of the difficulties of experimenting with environment. In a geographic survey (Begg,
1965) doubled insolation and doubled yields are found, but the difference
in radiation is confounded with at least differences in temperature and
species. On the other hand, when plants were grown beneath shades,
halving insolation decreased maize grain and stover yield to about a
third (Earley et al., 1966), and the growth of wheat (Triticum vulgare)
was decreased 55% by 60% shade (Pendleton and Weibel, 1965), but the
differences in radiation are confounded with at least differences in ventilation and humidity. Thus the data seem to need the simulators almost
as much as the simulators need the data.

Taking survey, shades, and simulator together, one becomes confident that, within the range of natural insolation, increased insolation at
canopy top would increase yield of many crops almost proportionally to
the increase in light.

The foliage area affects the outcome of increased sunlight, and
only an LAI of 4 has been discussed. The increase in hourly photosynthesis in the efficient canopy when the irradiance changes from half to
full sunlight is 77% in Fig. 15-4 where LAI is 4. If the LAI were only
2, the increase would be only 68%. If the LAI were 16, net photosynthesis would more than double when insolation doubled as lower leaves left
the parasitic, shaded category and made a contribution to net photosynthesis.

This role of LAI in light relations is clearly seen in the valuable
diagram of Stern and Donald (1962) that shows growth of Trifolium
subterraneum failing to respond to brighter light at LAI 2 and respond-

ing sharply at LAI 8. LAI also has a great effect upon the outcome of tipping of leaves, which is a means of manipulating light that is discussed elsewhere in this book.

The simulators of this chapter will, of course, consider leaf angle. Leaf angle is indicated to the simulators by the extinction coefficient for net radiation of all wavelengths and the extinction coefficient for insolation.

The next subject, reflecting light into the canopy unlike managing leaf angle, is purely environmental management. Two sorts of reflectors have been employed. In one, the reflectors are placed to one side of the canopy and used to import sunlight (Pendleton et al., 1967). This resembles skip-row planting (Grissom and Spurgeon, 1963) with reflectors in the fallow rows. Since neither skip-row nor reflectors in fallow rows increases yield in proportion to the fallow area, however, I shall not consider it a means of increasing yield in a large area.

The second sort of reflector, on the other hand, does not import light from one side and seems an environmental manipulation for increasing yield. This reflector is put on the ground. It reflects back upon the canopy, especially the shaded lower leaves, light that otherwise would be wasted upon the ground or weeds.

In the standard case of full sunlight and an LAI of 4 with an extinction coefficient of 0.5 for light, 15% of the light reaches the soil. If this is reflected completely and absorbed with the same extinction coefficient as the insolation, 85% of the reflected radiation will be absorbed. Similarly the net radiation at the soil line is 21% of that above the canopy. This, too, must be reflected and considered by the simulators.

The reflection would warm the lowest leaves by 0.7C, increase transpiration by 14%, and increase photosynthesis 15% in the efficient or inefficient species. This is produced not only by warming of the lower leaves and decreasing the photochemical resistance, but also by opening the stomata in the lower leaves. In the lowest stratum, for example, the insolation per cm^2 of leaf was increased from 0.08 to 0.17 ly min^{-1} with a consequent decrease in stomatal resistance from 12.7 to 6.4 sec cm^{-1}. Now, how does this agree with observation?

In a cereal that transmitted 2 to 5% of the light through its canopy, a white plastic sheet upon the soil increased yield 5% more than did a black one. The corresponding increase in another cereal was 9% (Pendleton, Brown, and Weibel, 1965).

In maize a similar reflector beneath the canopy of 40,000 plants/ha increased yield 13% and beneath 60,000 plants/ha increased yield 6% (Pendleton, Peters, and Peek, 1966). Thus experiments bear out the prediction of the simulators that the photosynthesis of a canopy will increase in about the same proportion as light absorption is increased by the reflection of sunlight that has reached the soil.

VII. MODIFYING THE WIND

Managing the wind is a venerable way of modifying the environment of the crop. It is done by putting up a shelter belt of trees or pickets in places where the ventilation is overdone. Here, in Nebraska, the amelioration of crop environment by shelter has been studied for a long, long time. In reports that span 7 decades, Card (1897) told how a Nebraska windbreak made a crop noticeably taller, and Rosenberg (1966) related how a crop prospered within a shelter near Scottsbluff. Thorough reviews concerning windbreaks have been published (Chepil, 1965; van Eimern, 1968). In general, a shelterbelt decreases the wind downward to a distance about 20 times its height, decreases evaporation by a modest and variable amount, and improves plant growth somewhat outside the shade and inside the becalmed zone.

In recent years as we have come to think of photosynthesis as the diffusion of CO_2 into a crop, however, we have sometimes taken a different tack. Since the turbulence of the air must deliver the CO_2, a calm conceivably could limit that delivery and hence growth. No doubt the windbreaks produce their benefits by alleviating water stress and in spite of their hindering the delivery of CO_2. As we push toward higher yields by removing such deficiencies as drought, will poor ventilation become significant?

The answer for a single, prosperous leaf in the calm of a bell jar seems clear. Its photosynthesis is hindered by calm air, and ventilation will increase its photosynthesis (Waggoner, Moss, and Hesketh, 1963).

In the case of single plants growing in a greenhouse or growth chamber, on the other hand, the results are usually described in a different light. That is, the experimenter concludes, not that wind is a good thing, but that moderate wind is tolerated by the plants (e.g., Whitehead, 1957).

The canopy of a crop presents a third situation where the air within the foliage may become nearly calm. The simulators consider that microclimate becalming, of course, and can predict whether decreasing ventilation, while leaving all else unchanged, would decrease yield significantly.

Ventilation of the standard canopy is determined by four factors. At canopy top, the wind is 225 cm sec^{-1}, and the diffusivity is 2,000 cm^2 sec^{-1}. Within the canopy, the wind and diffusivity are both extinguished exponentially according to relative height and a coefficient of 3. This rule is not permitted to decrease the diffusivity below a minimum of 200 cm^2 sec^{-1}.

By varying these parameters, I shall examine how ventilation might change photosynthesis at full sunlight, when ventilation would most likely be limiting. At the same time, the relative contribution of CO_2 from the soil to the canopy's photosynthesis can be seen. Further, the relation between the CO_2 profile within the canopy and its uptake can be observed, Table 15-2.

The first, and most disappointing thing seen in Table 15-2 is the small range of the photosynthesis rates. The range in transpiration produced by this great range in ventilation is only 4%, but the range in photosynthesis is even smaller: only 1.3%. In these small differences the effect of temperature of the leaves upon photosynthesis as well as the delivery of CO_2 comes into play.

The differences in ventilation have a more profound, if less practical, importance in governing where the carbon comes from. The range of soil contribution would be nearly 4-fold as ventilation changed.

The final entries in Table 15-2 are the maximum depletion of CO_2

Table 15-2—The effects of changed ventilation upon the uptake of CO_2 by a canopy, the percentage of CO_2 that is obtained from the soil, and the maximum depletion of CO_2 within the canopy air.

Diffusivity, cm² sec⁻¹		Extinction coefficient		
Minimum in canopy	At canopy top	2	3	4
		Uptake of CO_2 , F		
0	2×10^3	76.1	75.7	75.4
	20	76.3	76.0	75.7
200	2	76.1	75.8*	75.8
	20	76.3	76.0	75.7
1,000	2	76.4	76.4	76.3
	20	76.3	76.0	75.8
		CO_2 obtained from soil, %		
0	2	24	16	11
	20	26	17	11
200	2	24	21	24
	20	26	17	15
1,000	2	39	42	42
	20	26	16	17
		Maximum depletion of CO_2 , ppm		
0	2	3.0	4.7	7.4
	20	0.3	0.6	0.7
200	2	3.0	4.3	4.2
	20	0.3	0.5	0.7
1,000	2	2.0	2.1	2.0
	20	0.3	0.5	0.6

* Standard case.

within the bulk air of the canopy. It varies from only 0.3 to fully 7.4 ppm. The first implication concerns the aerodynamic estimation of crop photosynthesis from the depletion or profile of CO_2. Although the photosynthesis of this synthetic canopy varied less than 2%, the CO_2 depletion varied more than 10-fold. Estimating the 2% change from a phenomena where 10-fold differences are occurring is fraught with difficulties, and the desperate need for an accurate means of measuring diffusivity was never clearer.

Despite the 10-fold difference in CO_2 depletions, however, the actual magnitude of the depletions in the bulk air within the canopy is small relative to the 300 ppm at canopy top and bottom. That is, less than a 3% decrease in CO_2 has occurred in even the stillest air that I have specified. Therefore, one should not be surprised that the variations in photosynthesis caused by variations in ventilation are slight.

In the final calculations, the wind at canopy top was varied from 22 to the standard 225 and on to 1,225 cm sec⁻¹, a 56-fold change in wind that produces a 7.5-fold change in boundary layer resistance. Once again, the change is disappointing: photosynthesis increases from 75.4 only to 76.2 F as the wind increases. The accompanying increase in canopy evaporation was somewhat more: 15%.

In the paragraphs reporting the result of calculation, I have said that the benefits in increased photosynthesis from increased ventilation are disappointing. And surely they are for they never exceeded 2%. But if we return to the subject of windbreaks, which opened this section of the paper, we shall find the results encouraging rather than disappointing.

In the opening paragraphs, the water conservation by a shelter was mentioned, and then concern lest this exact a toll in decreased delivery of CO_2 was added. The calculations of the intervening paragraphs have calmed the concern: the decreased ventilation and water conservation will not exact a significant toll in growth. The slight decrease in CO_2 availability should be easily counteracted by the improved hydration of the crop. These logical arguments lead, of course, to exactly the same conclusion reached by experimenters.

If windbreaks are that beneficial, why are they not universally used? Van Eimern (1968) suggests that a thorough analysis of the farming system would reveal that other costs such as establishment and maintenance and the occupation of valuable land would destroy the gains from increased yield. This is, of course, an economic result that the simulators cannot anticipate.

Finally, a similarity between the effects of stomatal and wind management should be discussed. Theoretically the narrowing of stomata would decrease transpiration more than photosynthesis because there are more obstacles to the uptake of CO_2 than to the loss of water. This is shown in Table 15-1 where the transpiration ratio declines a third to a half when the minimum stomatal resistance is increased from 2 to 8 sec cm^{-1}.

Since calmer air will also impede the exchange of both CO_2 and water, it should decrease the amount of water required for the production of dry matter. This is borne out by the calculations for varied wind. Slowing the wind from 1,225 to 22 cm sec^{-1}, decreases the transpiration ratio from 108 to 96. This change in the transpiration ratio summarizes both the advantage of wind management and the modest results that can be anticipated.

VIII. FERTILIZING WITH CARBON DIOXIDE

"Carbon dioxide has given the most spectacular yield increases of any growth factor yet discovered in the culture of greenhouse crops." Wittwer (1966) begins his comprehensive review of the enrichment of the plant environment with this enthusiastic sentence.

He also writes, "Comparable long time exposures to different atmospheric levels of carbon dioxide during a full production cycle of the major field crops . . . . have not been conducted, even experimentally. This is one of the most surprising deficiencies of modern research effort . . . ." The simulator reveals the reason for the deficiency.

Three sorts of calculations will be made. First, the CO_2 concentration above and below the canopy will be increased as it is in greenhouses, and we shall see whether the field crop mimics that I have been using will behave as greenhouse crops do. Second, CO_2 fertilization in the field will be attempted both by raising the CO_2 concentration near the soil and by conducting CO_2 into the canopy at various levels. Finally, the simulator should predict how the global increase in CO_2 that man is causing will affect yields by the end of the century.

The simulators have some convenient characteristics for these calculations. Obviously the CO_2 injected into the air of the canopy is not all going to be added to the uptake of the foliage. Rather, some will go up, some down and some into the foliage. The balance among these currents depends upon concentrations or potentials and upon conductivities. These are precisely the factors that the simulators deal in. Also the increase in photosynthesis will not exactly follow the increase in concentration in the leaf interior for there will be a decreasing return. But this is all anticipated in the parameters P_X and K_{CC}.

One feedback has not been built into the simulator, however: the effect of rising CO_2 concentration in raising the stomatal resistance. This has been a particular concern of Heath and his colleagues. Heath and Russell (1954), for example, found that the viscous resistance of the leaf increased 10-fold when CO_2 increased from 290 to 840 ppm. If diffusive resistance is proportional to the cube root of viscous resistance (Waggoner, 1965), Heath and Russell's results indicate that doubling 300 ppm CO_2 would double stomatal resistance.

In the examples that follow, the effect upon stomata of CO_2 changes smaller than 50 ppm has been ignored. When, however, a change from 300 to fully 600 ppm is considered, the stomatal resistance will be doubled.

The first example, changing the concentration both above and below the canopy from 300 to 600 ppm, is the sort practiced by horticulturalists. The simulator indicates that the efficient crop without light respiration would increase its photosynthesis in bright light by 40% if the CO_2 concentration were increased to 600 ppm, Table 15-3. At half of full sunlight the increase would be 37%. At 690 ly day^{-1}, the dry matter production would be increased 40% to fully 64 g $m^{-2} day^{-1}$.

Table 15-3—The effects of changed CO_2 concentrations above and below a canopy of efficient leaves upon its uptake of CO_2, the percentage of the CO_2 that is obtained from the soil, and the maximum depletion of CO_2 within the canopy air. Full sunlight.

CO_2, ppm		Uptake, F	From soil, %	Max depletion, ppm
Above	Below			
Standard Ventilation				
300	300	75.8*	21	4.3
600	600	105.8*	21	5.9
300	315	76.5	61	1.2
315	315	78.8	21	4.4
344	344	84.4	21	4.8
Slow Ventilation†				
300	300	75.4	21	17
300	315	76.0	31	13
Slow Ventilation in Top Stratum‡				
300	300	75.9	33	7.8
300	315	77.0	65	3.4

* R_{sm} = 4.
† At canopy top, diffusivity = 500 cm^2 sec^{-1} and wind = 100 cm sec^{-1}.
‡ Standard diffusivity except 200 cm^2 sec^{-1} in top of eight strata.

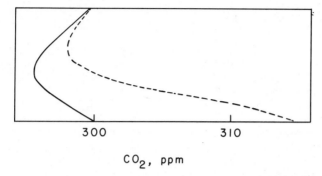

CO_2, ppm

Fig. 15-5—Profiles of CO_2 concentration in an inefficient canopy where the concentration near the ground is 300 or 315 ppm.

The less efficient species resembles more nearly the plants that have been grown in CO_2-enriched air. At 690 ly day^{-1}, the increase in yield would be 57%. At 350 ly day^{-1}, which resembles the greenhouse climate, the simulator indicates that doubling CO_2 concentration above and below the canopy would increase by two-thirds the daily production of dry matter in this synthetic species. In fact, increases up to 88% were achieved in lettuce (Lactuca sativa) where the CO_2 concentration was quadrupled (Wittwer, 1966).

The significant result of this exercise with the simulator is that field crops, even efficient ones such as maize, should respond greatly to CO_2 fertilization. Recently Egli, Pendleton, and Peters (1968) reported that the daily photosynthesis of soybeans (Glycine max) was increased fully 72% when they were enclosed in a chamber and the CO_2 concentration was maintained at 600 ppm rather than the usual 300 ppm. Thus the potential for increased yields in field crops is available for CO_2 enrichment and was rationalized by the simulator. The only question is how to deliver the CO_2. Increasing the concentration near the ground as by heavy application of manure is tried first.

The consequence of increasing the CO_2 near the soil from 300 to 315 ppm is seen in the CO_2 profiles of Fig. 15-5. The minimum concentration in mid-canopy is raised from 295.7 to 298.8. The concentration in the lower canopy is increased more, but these lower leaves are in limited light and can scarcely increase their photosynthesis. The consequence is a disappointing 1% increase in net photosynthesis.

The dramatic change is in the source of the CO_2 taken into the leaves. Formerly 21% of the 76 F was taken from the soil line where the CO_2 concentration near the soil conserves atmospheric CO_2! What would happen if the canopy were less porous?

The porosity of the standard canopy is, of course, determined by the ventilation parameters: at canopy top a diffusivity of 2000 cm^2 sec^{-1} and wind of 225 cm sec^{-1} and in the canopy an extinction coefficient of 3 and a minimum diffusivity of 200 cm^2 sec^{-1}. This is not severe ventilation. Nevertheless, they can be decreased to the very quiet conditions of 500 cm^2 sec^{-1} and 100 cm sec^{-1} at canopy top and a minimum of 50 cm^2 sec^{-1} within the canopy. The extinction coefficient is left at 3.

WAGGONER

The transpiration from the canopy in full sunlight is decreased by 8% and the leaves in midcanopy are warmed 0.8C by the decrease in ventilation.

The effect upon CO_2 exchange is tabulated in the lower lines of Table 15-3. The CO_2 is depleted to 283 ppm or 13 ppm more than in the standard ventilation. The greater depletion of the CO_2 decreases the photosynthesis from 75.8 to 75.4.

The effect of the enrichment of the CO_2 near the soil beneath a poorly ventilated canopy can now be seen. It is no greater than in a better ventilated canopy because the decreased diffusivity has insulated the active and numerous middle leaves from both the soil and the air at canopy top. The air in the top stratum can be made an insulator by decreasing its diffusivity to 200 cm^2 sec^{-1} while leaving the rest of the ventilation as in the standard case. This would warm the leaves somewhat and increase photosynthesis from 75.8 to 75.9 F. Then raising the CO_2 concentration near the soil from 300 to 315 ppm would increase the photosynthesis from 75.9 to 77.0. That is, even this improbable ventilation does not permit a significant increase in CO_2 uptake from an enrichment near the soil. We are left, therefore, with the inescapable conclusion that increasing the CO_2 concentration near the soil will have little effect upon the photosynthesis in a canopy outdoors.

Another means of fertilizing with CO_2 is piping gas into the field or scattering dry ice about. The experience of David Jordan of Tipton, Indiana is described in the July-August 1968 issue of The Furrow published by John Deere Co. In August he dropped 1-pound chunks of dry ice 25 feet apart in every direction in his maize field. The yield around the places where he dropped the dry ice was a third greater than in the rest of the field. The simulators can help us decide whether, in Mr. Jordan's words, the increased yield was "a stroke of luck."

The application was 78 mg CO_2 per dm^2 or 78 kg ha^{-1}. I have calculated the effect upon the photosynthesis that would accompany additions of 5 F at full sunlight. If the dry ice applied by Jordan evaporated in 16 hours, the rate would have been 5 F. Allowing the sun to shine at its full brightness for the full time should give the maximum response to the fertilization.

The calculation was accomplished by making the external source X of CO_2 at the junction of stem and canopy equal to 5 F. The result, Table 15-4, is a 0.1 enrichment of the air at midcanopy and a 0.02 F increase in photosynthesis. The increase represents a 0.4% recovery of the 5 F dry ice.

If the CO_2 were added to the bottom of the poorly ventilated canopy, the increase would be somewhat more, 0.06 F, but still too small to be significant, Table 15-4.

An alternative is adding the CO_2 at midcanopy, i.e., about 60 cm from the canopy top. This is the bottom edge of the 38 cm of canopy that fixes 70% of the CO_2 and is where CO_2 depletion is greatest, Fig. 15-3. By adding the 5 F among these active leaves that have impoverished the air, one causes a somewhat greater increase in concentration and net photosynthesis. Nevertheless, the recovery of the 5 F of added CO_2 would be only 4% in the poorly ventilated and 1% in the well-ventilated canopy.

Table 15-4—The effects of external sources of CO_2 within a canopy of efficient leaves upon its uptake of CO_2, the percentage of CO_2 that is obtained from the soil, and the maximum depletion of CO_2 within the canopy air. Full sunlight.

External source, F	Uptake, F	From soil, %	Max depletion, ppm
Standard Ventilation			
None	75.83	21	4.3
5 at midcanopy	75.89	19	3.8
5 at canopy bottom	75.85	15	4.2
Slow Ventilation			
None	75.38	21	17
5 at midcanopy	75.61	19	15
5 at canopy bottom	75.44	15	16

Thus the simulators indicate that Jordan was most fortunate in getting such a large increase in maize yield or succeeded in concentrating the CO_2 near the harvested plants.

In more general terms, crops would surely yield more if they grew in a richer CO_2 environment, but our schemes seem sunk by the rock of delivery. This, not a lack of industry, is probably why agronomists have not shared the horticultural success with CO_2 fertilization.

Although I have added 31 F (0.5 tons dry matter $ha^{-1} day^{-1}$) by raising the CO_2 concentration near the soil or 5 F (120 kg $CO_2 ha^{-1}$ day^{-1}) within the synthetic canopies, I have been unable to increase the photosynthesis in full sun substantially. The only way to manipulate the CO_2 environment for higher yields seems to increase its concentration above as well as below the canopy. This is, of course, what is done in the greenhouse. It is also what we seem to be doing to the globe, and allows me to end by seeing a silver lining in the cloud of pollution.

During 1960-62 the CO_2 concentration in the air over the northern Pacific Ocean was increasing 0.06 ppm per month. At $41^{\circ}N$ during December, 1961 the concentration was 315 ppm, not the 300 ppm that we usually speak of (Bolin and Keeling, 1963). How has the increase to 315 ppm affected photosynthesis?

The increase in the CO_2 concentration both above and below the canopy from 300 to 315 ppm has, according to the simulators, increased photosynthesis by 4%, Table 15-3.

If the increase continues, the concentration will reach 344 ppm at the turn of the century. According to the simulator, this would raise photosynthesis about one-tenth above the rate of 300 ppm, Table 15-3, an increase that would be slightly moderated by narrower stomata. Thus, from what must be the only benefit ever attributed to pollution, we are receiving small and will receive somewhat larger yield increases from the CO_2 generated by our furnaces and autos.

IX. SUMMARY

The effect of environmental manipulation upon the photosynthesis and the yield of a crop canopy is explored by the use of mathematical models. These models or crop simulators use logical rules for calculation that not only estimate the amount of photosynthesis but also work in many ways like an actual crop.

The first or microclimate simulator accepts news of the weather above, the temperature and humidity of the air beneath the canopy, as well as the canopy architecture, stomatal resistance, absorption of radiation, and ventilation. From these factors the simulator calculates evaporation and the temperature of the air and the leaves within the canopy.

The second or photosynthesis simulator accepts the output of the first plus the following characteristics of the individual leaves:

1) Photochemical facility and how it varies with temperature, light and CO_2 concentration

2) Dark respiration and how it varies with temperature

3) Light respiration and how it varies with temperature and light

4) The physical resistances to the current of CO_2.

The second simulator also accepts the CO_2 concentration above and below the canopy and currents of that gas that are injected or advected into the canopy at different levels. From this information, the simulator calculates the CO_2 concentrations in the air and the photosynthesis in the leaves of the canopy.

Manipulating the leaf pores or stomata can decrease evaporation, and the simulators indicate that photosynthesis will be decreased relatively less. This is a different outcome than from a decrease in photochemical facility, which would decrease photosynthesis relatively more than evaporation.

Increasing the light either from above or below the canopy would increase assimilation nearly proportionally.

Since great differences in ventilation have little effect upon assimilation, the conservation of water by shelter extracts no hidden tax of decreased delivery of CO_2 for photosynthesis.

Naturally ventilated canopies are very porous. Hence, the recovery by photosynthesis of CO_2 released from dry ice or decay below or within the canopy is inefficient. On the other hand, the general increase of 0.72 ppm CO_2 per year in the earth's atmosphere will increase photosynthesis in efficient species and full sunlight by 7% between now and the end of the century.

LITERATURE CITED

Altman, P. L., and D. S. Dittmer. 1966. Environmental biology. Fed. Am. Soc. Exp. Biol., Bethesda, Md. 694 p.

Begg, J. E. 1965. High photosynthetic efficiency in a low-latitude environment. Nature 205:1025-1026.

Black, C. A. 1966. Crop yields in relation to water supply and soil fertility, p. 177-206. In W. H. Pierre et al. (ed.) Plant environment and efficient water use. Amer. Soc. Agron., Madison, Wis. 295 p.

Bolin, B., and C. D. Keeling. 1963. Large-scale atmospheric mixing as deduced from the seasonal and meridional variations of carbon dioxide. J. Geophys. Res. 68:3899-3920.

Bravdo, B. 1968. Decrease in net photosynthesis caused by respiration. Plant Physiol. 43:479-483.
Briggs, L. J., and H. L. Shantz. 1914. The relative water requirement of plants. J. Agr. Res. 3:1-65.
Card, F. W. 1897. Windbreaks. Nebraska Agr. Exp. Sta. Bull. 48:69-96.
Chepil, W. S. 1965. Transport of soil and snow by wind. Meteorol. Monogr. 6(28):123-132.
Davenport, D. C. 1966. Effects of phenylmercuric acetate on transpiration and growth of small plots of grass. Nature 212:801-802.
Decker, J. P. 1959. Comparative responses of carbon dioxide outburst and up-take in tobacco. Plant Physiol. 34:100-102.
Duncan, W. G., R. S. Loomis, W. A. Williams, and R. Hanau. 1967. A model for simulating photosynthesis in plant communities. Hilgardia 38:181-205.
Earley, E. B., R. J. Miller, G. L. Reichert, R. H. Hageman, and R. D. Seif. 1966. Effects of shade on maize production under field conditions. Crop Sci. 6:1-7.
Egli, D. B., J. W. Pendleton, and D. B. Peters. 1968. Photosynthetic rates of three natural soybean communities as related to carbon dioxide levels and solar radiation. Agron. Abstr. 1968:32.
Ekern, P. C. 1965. Evapotranspiration of pineapple in Hawaii. Plant Physiol. 40:736-739.
El-Sharkawy, M. A., R. S. Loomis, and W. A. Williams. 1967. Apparent reasim-ilation of respiratory carbon dioxide by different plant species. Physiol. Plan-tarum 20:171-186.
Gaastra, P. 1959. Photosynthesis of crop plants as influenced by light, carbon dioxide, temperature, and stomatal diffusion resistance. Mededel. Landbou-whogesch. Wageningen. 59:1-68.
Gale, J., and R. M. Hagan. 1966. Plant antitranpirants. Ann. Rev. Plant Phy-siol., p. 269-282.
Grissom, P. H., and W. I. Spurgeon. 1963. Skip-row plan increases yield on good land. Mississippi Farm Res. 26(1):1,8.
Heath, O.V.S., and J. Russell. 1954. Studies in stomatal behavior. VI. An inves-tigation of the light responses of wheat stomata with the attempted elimination of control by the mesophyll. Part 2. Interactions with external CO_2, and gen-eral discussion. J. Exp. Bot. 5:269-292.
Hesketh, J. D. 1963. Limitations to photosynthesis responsible for differences among species. Crop Sci. 3:493-496.
Hesketh, J. D., and D. N. Moss. 1963. Variation in the response of photosyn-thesis to light. Crop Sci. 3:107-110.
Hesketh, J., and R. B. Musgrave. 1962. Photosynthesis under field conditions. IV. Light studies with individual corn leaves. Crop Sci. 2:311-315.
Inoue, E. 1965. On the CO_2-concentration profiles within crop canopies. J. Agr. Meteorol. (Tokyo) 20:137-140.
Jackson, W. A., and R. J. Volk. 1968. Oxygen uptake by illuminated corn leaves. Agron. Abstr. 1968:35.
Joshi, M. C., J. S. Boyer, and P. J. Kramer. 1965. Growth, carbon dioxide ex-change, transpiration, and transpiration ratio of pineapple. Bot. Gas. 126:174-179.
Lake, J. V. 1967. Respiration of leaves during photosynthesis. I. Estimates from an electrical analogue. Aust. J. Biol. Sci. 20:487-493.
Lemon, E. R. 1967. Aerodynamic studies of CO_2 exchange between the atmos-phere and the plant, p. 263-290. In A. San Pietro, F. A. Greer, and T. J. Army (ed.). Harvesting the sun. Academic Press, New York.
Loomis, R. S., and W. A. Williams. 1963. Maximum crop productivity: an esti-mate. Crop Sci. 3:67-72.
Loomis, R. S., W. A. Williams, W. G. Duncan, A. Dovrat, and F. Nunez A. 1968. Quantitative descriptions of foliage display and light absorption in field com-munities of corn plants. Crop Sci. 8:352-356.

Marsh, H. V., Jr., J. M. Galmiche, and M. Gibbs. 1965. Effect of light on the tricarboxylic acid cycle in Scenedesmus. Plant Physiol. 40:1013-1022.

Mateus Ventura, M. 1954. Action of enzymatic inhibitors on transpiration and the closing of stomata. II. Arsenite, 2, 4-dinitrophenol and janus green on isolated leaves of Stizolbium atterrimum. Rev. Brasil. Biol. 14:153-161.

Moss, D. N. 1965. Capture of radiant energy by plants. Meteorol. Monogr. 6(28):90-108.

Moss, D. N. 1966. Respiration of leaves in light and darkness. Crop Sci. 6: 351-354.

Moss, D. N., R. B. Musgrave, and E. R. Lemon. 1961. Photosynthesis under field conditions. III. Some effects of light, carbon dioxide, temperature, and soil moisture on photosynthesis, respiration, and transpiration of corn. Crop Sci. 1:83-87.

Pendleton, J. W., C. M. Brown, and R. O. Weibel. 1965. Effect of reflected light on small grain yields. Crop Sci. 5:373.

Pendleton, J. W., D. B. Egli, and D. B. Peters. 1967. Response of Zea mays L. to a "light rich" field environment. Agron. J. 59:395-397.

Pendleton, J. W., D. B. Peters, and J. W. Peek. 1966. Role of reflected light in the corn ecosystem. Agron. J. 58:73-74.

Pendleton, J. W., and G. E. Smith. 1967. Corn plant of the future. Crops and Soils Mag. 19(8):9.

Pendleton, J. W., and R. O. Weibel. 1965. Shading studies on winter wheat. Agron. J. 57:292-293.

Penman, H. L., and R. K. Schofield. 1951. Some physical aspects of assimilation and transpiration. Symp. Soc. Exp. Biol. 5:115-129.

Rosenberg, N. J. 1966. Microclimate, air mixing and physiological regulation of transpiration as influenced by wind shelter in an irrigated bean field. Agr. meteorol. 3:197-224.

Shaw, R. H., and C. R. Weber. 1967. Effects of canopy arrangements on light interception and yield of soybeans. Agron. J. 59:155-159.

Shimshi, D. 1963. Effect of chemical closure of stomata on transpiration in varied soil and atmospheric environments. Plant Physiol. 38:709-712.

Shimshi, D. 1963. Effect of soil moisture and penylmercuric acetate upon stomatal aperture, transpiration and photosynthesis. Plant Physiol. 38:713-721.

Slatyer, R. O. 1964. Efficiency of water utilization by arid zone vegetation. Ann. Arid Zone. 3:1-12.

Slatyer, R. O. 1966. In situ measurements of stomatal resistance, p. 5-6. In Conference on instrumentation for plant environment measurements. CSIRO Div. Meteorol. Physl. Aspendale, Australia.

Slatyer, R. O., and J. F. Bierhuizen. 1964. The effect of several foliar sprays on transpiration and water use efficiency of cotton plants. Agr. Meteorol. 1:42-53.

Stanhill, G. 1958. Effects of soil moisture on the yield and quality of turnips. II. Response at different growth stages. J. Hort. Sci. 33:264-274.

Stephens, G. R. 1969. Dry matter productivity of red pine. I. Foliage distribution in tree crown and stand canopy. Agr. Meteorol. In press.

Stern, W. R., and C. M. Donald. 1962. Influence of leaf area and radiation on the growth of clover in swards. Aust. J. Agr. Res. 13:615-623.

Turner, N. C., and P. E. Waggoner. 1968. Effects of changing stomatal width in a red pine forest on soil water content, leaf water potential, bole diameter and growth. Plant Physiol. 43:973-978.

Uchijima, Z. 1962. Studies on the micro-climate within the plant communities. 1. On the turbulent transfer coefficient within plant layer. J. Agr. Meteorol. (Tokyo) 18:1-9.

Van Eimern, J. 1968. Problems of shelter planting, p. 157-166. In Agroclimatological methods. Proceedings of the Reading symposium. Unesco, Paris. 392 p.

Waggoner, P. E. 1965. Calibration of a porometer in terms of diffusive resistance. Agr. Meteorol. 2:317-329.

Waggoner, P. E. 1966. Decreasing transpiration and the effect upon growth, p. 49-72. In W. H. Pierre et al. (ed.) Plant environment and efficient water use. Amer. Soc. Agron., Madison, Wis.

Waggoner, P. E. 1967. Moisture loss through the boundary layer, p. 41-52. In S. W. Tromp and W. H. Wiche (ed.). Biometeorology, Vol. 3. Proc. 4th Int. Biometeorol. Congr., New Brunswick. Swets and Zeitlinger Publ. Co., Amsterdam.

Waggoner, P. E. 1969. Predicting the effect upon net photosynthesis of changes in leaf metabolism and physics. Crop Sci. In press.

Waggoner, P. E., and B. Bravdo. 1967. Stomata and the hydrologic cycle. Proc. Nat. Acad. Sci. 57:1096-1102.

Waggoner, P. E., G. U. Furnwal, W. E. Reifsnyder. 1969. Simulation of the microclimate in a forest. Forest Sci. 15:37-45.

Waggoner, P. E., D. N. Moss, and J. D. Hesketh. 1963. Radiation in the plant environment and photosynthesis. Agron. J. 55:36-39.

Waggoner, P. E., J. L. Monteith, and G. Szeicz. 1964. Decreasing transpiration of field plants by chemical closure of stomata. Nature 201:97-98.

Waggoner, P. E., W. E. Reifsnyder. 1968. Simulation of the temperature, humidity and evaporation profiles in a leaf canopy. J. Appl. Metrol. 7(3):400-409.

Watson, D. J. 1958. The dependence of net assimilation rate on leaf-area index. Ann. Bot., N.S. 22:37-54.

Whitehead, F. H. 1957. Wind as a factor in plant growth, p. 84-95. In J. P. Hudson (ed.) Control of the plant environment. Academic Press, Inc., N.Y.

Zelitch, I. 1961. Biochemical control of stomatal opening in leaves. Proc. Nat. Acad. Sci. U.S. 47:1423-1433.

Zelitch, I. 1966. Increased rate of net photosynthetic carbon dioxide uptake caused by the inhibition of glycolate oxidase. Plant Physiol. 41:1623-1631.

Zelitch, I., and P. E. Waggoner. 1962. Effect of chemical control of stomata on transpiration and photosynthesis. Nat. Acad. Sci. Proc. 48:1101-1108 and 1297-1299.

16

Germ Plasm Manipulations of the Future[1]

GEORGE F. SPRAGUE

Agricultural Research Service, USDA

Beltsville, Maryland

The topic, Germ Plasm Manipulations of the Future, could cover the entire field of genetics. This would be a very difficult assignment and, were I willing to attempt it, one that might not best serve the specific purpose of this symposium. I shall take a much more restrictive view and consider only certain phases of genetics which, in my opinion, will become of increasing importance in crop improvement.

In the period since 1900 genetics has achieved close and reciprocally productive relations with several fields of science. A partial listing of these would include genetics and cytology to yield cytogenetics; genetics and statistics to yield quantitative and population genetics; and genetics and biochemistry to yield biochemical genetics. These fields have already contributed greatly to agricultural improvements and their usefulness will undoubtedly increase.

In the past the geneticists interested in crop improvement have been concerned largely with final product evaluation with yield receiving primary attention. Tremendous advances have been made in the last 20 years in experimental design, and they permit an increased degree of precision in the estimation of mean yields. Developments in quantitative genetics have contributed to a better understanding of the genetic basis of variability, and of how such variability can be effectively manipulated in a breeding program. Given a high and a low yielding stock, a study of the F_1 and subsequent progeny permits of certain conclusions as to the genetic difference between the parents. Such an analysis, however, tells us little as to why one parent is low and the other inherently high yielding. Information on the underlying causes of such differences must come from detailed studies combining biochemistry or physiology and genetics. This field has been relatively neglected in crop plants, and it merits greatly increased attention and support. If such an expansion occurs it could well be called biochemical genetics. I would prefer,

---

[1]Contribution from the Crops Research Division, Agricultural Research Service, U.S. Department of Agriculture, Beltsville, Maryland.

however, to label it physiological genetics. Obviously the expansion of this field will draw heavily upon biochemistry. It would differ from biochemistry, however, in that biosynthetic pathways and the isolation and characterization of enzymes would not be an end in themselves, but would be extended to explore the effects of individual enzymes or of enzyme systems on all aspects of growth, development and reproductive capacity.

I. THE TRANSFER OF GENETIC INFORMATION

I shall present a very brief and selective review of the tremendous advances made within the broad field of genetics in recent years; selecting only those areas which: (i) illustrate the current state of the art or, (ii) have direct implications to the area I am calling physiological genetics.

The Watson-Crick model for the structure of deoxyribonucleic acid (DNA) has been verified. The genetic code has been solved, at least in its major details. DNA is composed of 4 nucleotides; 2 purines, adenine and guanine, and 2 pyrimidines; thymine and cytosine. The two strands of DNA are complementary and are held together by hydrogen bonding between the purine-pyrimidine pairs; A-T, and G-C. In replication, each DNA strand forms a complementary strand under the control of the enzyme DNA polymerase. Nucleotide sequence is read in triplets (codons). The genetic code resides in the 64 possible arrangements of the 4 nucleotides.

One of the complementary DNA strands serves as a template for the production of an ribonucleic acid (RNA) strand. The DNA specifies the sequence of the nucleotides and controls the production of RNA polymerase. RNA is quite similar to DNA, differing in the sugar backbone of the molecule and in the substitution of uracil for thymine.

Three types of RNA are formed. Messenger RNA is a complementary copy of a segment or the entire DNA template, with the exceptions mentioned above, and therefore carries the genetic information. Soluble or transfer RNA (sRNA) performs the function of supplying amino acids to the developing polypeptide chain in the sequence specified by the nucleotide triplets of the genetic message. sRNA is a small molecule with two active sites; one to attach to the activated amino acid and the other to recognize the codon. Each amino acid has at least one specific sRNA, but some amino acids have more than one. The third RNA type is ribosomal RNA (rRNA). Ribosomes are composed of two subunits, each composed of RNA and protein. The function of rRNA is to bring together the RNA bearing the genetic message and the activated amino acid molecules in the sequence called for by the template codons to produce proteins.

Mutation has been related to one of three events: substitution, deletion, or addition of base pairs within the DNA chain. Genetic changes may also be effected by means of transformation or transduction. (Transformation involves the incorporation of purified DNA, transduction involves the incorporation of DNA by means of virus infection.)

The important developments detailed above have used microorganisms as test material. Two questions logically arise: Are the findings equally applicable to higher organisms, and what is their utility to plant breeding?

The first question is the easier to answer. Evidence from several types of experiments indicate that the essentials of the genetic code are universal. Protein formation, through the intermediary of the three types of RNA, also appears to be universal.

Genetic control through the use of either transduction of transformation was first demonstrated and has been extensively used in genetic studies involving bacteria. The success achieved has led some to believe that the control of undesirable heritable effects in mankind is just around the corner. If this be true, the same techniques should be available for the improvement of crops on which mankind depends for food, feed, and fiber. For this reason it may be desirable to give further consideration to both transduction and transformation.

Transduction involves the transfer of DNA material (genetic information) to the bacterial genome through the intermediary of phage. The first step in this process involves the incorporation of bacterial DNA into the phage DNA. Under proper conditions this combination of bacterial and phage DNA are incorporated into the genome of a newly infected bacterium. The frequency of such a successful event is very low but because of the large numbers of bacterial cells which can be handled, transduction has proven to be a very useful technique for genetic mapping in both bacteria and phage.

At the moment there is no clear evidence that the same series of events occurs in higher organisms. Most plants are susceptible to one or more viruses. There is, however, only limited evidence to suggest that these viruses can induce genetic changes (Sprague and McKinney, 1966). Where such genetic changes are indicated there is no direct evidence that transduction is the mechanism involved.

Transformation involves the incorporation of DNA, usually after special purification, into the genome of the recipient cell. Such incorporation occurs in low frequency and has been a much less useful tool to bacterial geneticists than transduction.

One would need to be a confirmed optimist to assume that either of these techniques could be useful to the plant breeder in the near future. Several problems would need to be resolved. First, a high degree of control would be essential. Such control would require a greater detail of genetic information involving both host and virus than is currently available or apt to become available in the near future. Without such control, and assuming that the mechanics can be solved, the induced changes would be as random as mutations. Such changes could parallel mutations or duplications, depending upon the length of the DNA molecule involved. Changes of this type can be induced more readily by radiation or chemical mutagens. Secondly, the bacterial chromosome is apparently a naked DNA molecule while the chromosomes of higher organisms have a complex structure. The DNA core is enclosed in a highly organized protein coat. For either transduction or transformation to be both effective and specific this coat must be removed at the appropriate site and time. Problems relating to the effective use of transduction and transformation will eventually be solved, but it appears unlikely that these methods of transferring genetic material can become useful breeding tools within the next few years.

Biochemical genetics, as developed in bacteria and phage, offers little immediate utility to the plant breeder. This situation arises largely from the general lack of biochemical information leading to a lack of precision in the interpretation of genetic data in the higher organisms. The accumulation of such background information will be a time-consuming operation but one which must eventually be accomplished.

A classical study by Jacob and Monod (1961) may serve to illustrate the power of a combination of biochemistry and genetics in the analysis of an operon. Four genes, occupying adjacent sites on the chromosome, were involved in the study. Each is involved in the utilization of lactose by E. coli. Two of these genes produce enzymes: z produces β galactosidase and y produces a permease which controls the permeability of the cell to lactose. The remaining two genes were designated o and i. The o gene is described as an operator and is adjacent to the z gene. As an operator it controls the action of the structural genes, z and y. In the presence of o⁺, normal amounts of the z and y enzymes are produced. In the o⁰ form, production of both enzymes is inhibited. The common situation in bacteria is for metabolically sequential genes to occupy adjacent sites on the chromosome. The o gene, therefore, may be visualized as the point of origin for a segment of mRNA which specifies the enzymes needed for lactose utilization. The i gene is visualized as blocking RNA transcription of the operator and sequentially related structural genes.

In the absence of a galactoside the organism produces very limited quantities of the enzymes controlled by z and y. In the presence of galactoside, however, enzyme production increases several thousandfold. The i gene regulates this behavior; the wild type allele i⁺ is inducible while the recessive allele, i-, is constitutive.

The purpose in presenting this very brief resume of a brilliant research study is to emphasize the detail made possible through the combined genetic and biochemical approach. Had this study been restricted to techniques commonly used in genetic studies with higher plants, most of the details would have remained obscure. Possibly one could have done no more than postulate the presence of a compound locus or a locus with multiple alleles which conditioned the organism's ability to utilize lactose as a carbon source. Thus although we have a great mass of information on the inheritance of traits in higher plants, such information is not directly and immediately useful in an understanding of the underlying biochemical principles and processes.

II. ENZYMES AND HETEROSIS

Heterosis is commonly observed in seedling vigor. Ashby (1930, 1932) has interpreted this early vigor as a reflection of differences in 'initial capital' of embryo tissue in the hybrid seed. This assumption is not supported by data presented by Sprague (1937) or Grossman and Sprague (1948). Therefore the increased dry weight of F_1 hybrid seedlings must be related to either greater amounts or greater efficiency of enzyme systems.

Studies on enzymes and heterosis have been under way at the Illinois Station for some years. Much of this work has recently been summarized by Hageman et al. (1967). The general objectives in the studies reported by these workers was to relate certain enzyme systems to heterosis in corn (Zea mays L.). Two groups of enzymes were studied: one group was concerned with the energy transfer system in germinating seeds and young seedlings, and the second with nitrogen metabolism. The first group included the enzymes triosephosphate dehydrogenase (TPD), aldolase (ALD), and glucose-6-phosphate dehydrogenase (G-6-PD). The second enzyme was nitrate reductase (NR) which is involved in nitrogen metabolism.

TPD and G-6-PD are the sites of the first energy conversion; ALD and TPD are involved in the glycolytic pathway relating the stored endosperm starch to the Krebs cycle. Two single-cross hybrids and their inbred parents were utilized in the studies. Hybrid vigor for seedling growth was observed in each cross. In WF9 × M14, hybrid vigor was also observed for TPD and possibly ALD. The hybrids were intermediate for G-6-PD activity. Activity in the Hy2 × Oh7 hybrid was intermediate for all three enzymes. On first consideration these results appear somewhat disappointing. One might have hoped for a greater and more uniform manifestation of heterosis at the enzyme activity level. It must be remembered, however, that the genetic materials used were chosen on the basis of seed availability, rather than because of any prior demonstration of genetic divergence of enzyme activity between the parental lines. Possibly the most that can be concluded is that, for these three enzyme systems, heterozygosity, per se, is not an important factor conditioning the expression of hybrid vigor in the seedling stage.

Considerable information has become available on the response of inbred lines and hybrids to population density. For a variety of reasons tolerance or intolerance of high plant populations was assumed to be related to nitrate reductase (NR) activity. An extensive screening of inbred lines indicated large differences in seasonal means which were reasonably repeatable over seasons. Lines were grouped into three categories: high, medium, and low. High × high, high × low and low × low single-crosses were produced. NR assays were then conducted on these hybrids and their inbred parents. Five of seven low × low crosses gave values exceeding either the mid- or high-parental values. In the high × low category all of the values were intermediate except for one (Hy2 × Oh7) which exceeded the midparental value. In the high × high group none of the NR activity values exceeded the midparental value. In one case, R181 × M14, the value for the hybrid was lower than for either parent. Additional tests reported by Beevers et al. (1964) indicated no qualitative differences among the NR enzymes from several diverse maize sources.

In a later study Warner et al. (1969) a more detailed genetic analysis has been made of one of the low × low crosses exhibiting heterosis for NR activity. The genetic analysis indicates two complementary loci. One locus is assumed to represent a structural and the second a regulator site. Each inbred is dominant at one locus and recessive at the other. In the dark, the enzyme from Oh43 exhibits a very rapid decay rate; three-fold greater than that for B14. In the light, Oh43 synthesizes NR very rapidly while the rate in B14 is much slower. On the basis of the genotypes assumed, heterosis for NR activity would be expected. Similarly, stable F_2 and F_3 lines should be found which possess the activity of the F_1. These expectations were realized.

An increasing efficiency of agricultural production requires a better understanding of nitrogen metabolism. The need for such understanding assumes even greater significance in light of the current world-wide deficiency of protein. We use ever-increasing quantities of nitrogen to maintain or increase yield levels. We know that under many conditions nitrogen fertilization results in an increased protein percentage in the harvested crop. Research findings from the wheat (Triticum aestivum L.) program here at Nebraska indicate that varieties differ in their ability to extract nitrogen from the soil. Genetic differences also exist in the use made of this nitrogen. Some cereals retain higher percentages in the foliage and straw while others transfer proportionally larger amounts of nitrogen to the developing grain to be transformed into protein. In certain stocks genetic control of both quantity and quality of protein has been established. Other aspects of nitrogen metabolism presumably also have a genetic basis but adequate evidence is still largely lacking.

Miflin and Hageman (1963) have developed a technique for isolating chloroplasts from young corn leaves capable of carrying on photophosphorylation. In subsequent studies the same authors (1966) compared three assays: Hill reaction, noncyclic and cyclic photophosphorylation. Comparable results were obtained for each and the cyclic photophosphorylation was used to evaluate a group of inbred lines and their F_1 hybrids. Marked differences were observed in chloroplast activity. The activity of the hybrids tended to be intermediate between the parental values.

The tests by Hageman and his coworkers involving the three enzymes and chloroplast activity indicate a general tendency for the hybrid to be intermediate. These results may be disappointing to those seeking a simple explanation for heterosis. Two points are deserving of emphasis. First, heterosis does not require complete dominance. Cumulative effects of individual loci, each exhibiting values above the midparent, will lead to heterosis. Second, we must remember that no single reaction occurs in isolation in a living cell. Each reaction is modified by both substrate and metabolites. It is not too surprising, therefore, that single enzyme heterosis was not demonstrated. Variability was noted, however, for each of the enzyme systems used and in each case there was evidence that the variation was gene controlled.

Considerable evidence has been reported for the genetic control of isozymes for specific enzymes. Schwartz (1960, 1964, 1965a, 1965b) has reported 7 alleles for the pH 8.6 esterase in maize. In each case the heterozygotes exhibit the parental isozymes and a new hybrid type. This hybrid type does not appear to be formed by an association between the two parental forms. The interpretation of these results is still quite uncertain. In vivo treatment of tissue with sodium borohydride also gives rise to nonparental isozyme forms, paralleling in migration rate previously identified isozyme forms. Furthermore in vitro treatment with glyceraldehyde converts all isozyme forms to a common type.

Beckman et al. (1964a) have demonstrated the presence of four alleles conditioning isozyme forms of leucine aminopeptidase. In a subsequent paper (1964b) they reported three hybrid catalase isozymes. Scandalios (1965) reported tissue specific isozymes for leucine aminopeptidase, esterase, catalase and peroxidase.

Studies in Drosophila (Ursprung et al., 1968) exhibit a similar pattern but the analysis has been carried somewhat further. Isozyme forms exist for the enzymes aldehyde oxidase and alcohol dehydrogenase. Hybrids exhibit the parental forms and a new hybrid type. A fact of possibly greater significance is that each of these enzymes exhibits a characteristic pattern during development. Alcohol dehydrogenase is low in the egg, increases rapidly during the larval instar stages, falls to a low level during the midpupal stage and rises again during metamorphosis and after hatching. Aldehyde oxidase is high in the egg, falls to a low level during the first larval instar and then increases rather gradually until the adult stage is reached.

The significance of such variations is not clear. The genes responsible are present at all developmental stages. The mechanisms affecting control are the subject of continuing study. The answers may throw light on the whole problem of development.

Stuber and Levings (1969) have demonstrated eight peroxidase isozymes in subapical coleoptile sections of oats (Avena sativa L.). One of these isozymes was repressed by the application of either IAA or 2,4-D. The same growth regulator treatments induced a second isozyme. Genetic variability was indicated for the inducible isozyme. It was suggested that this induction-repression system provides a mechanism for control of the normal growth regulator system.

The results with isozymes are of great interest but many aspects remain unclear. The sometime occurrence of hybrid isozymes is particularly intriguing, because it provides a conceptual basis for overdominance; the hybrid exhibiting a form not present in either parent. However, this attractive possibility thus far receives little support from the published results. This may not be too surprising, since as yet the studies have been concerned primarily with electrophoretic migration rates with little evidence on either qualitative or quantitative characterization of the isozymes involved.

Sarkissian and his coworkers (1966, 1967, 1968) have demonstrated complementation involving mitochondrial preparations derived from inbred lines of maize which, in hybrid combination, produce heterotic hybrids. The activity of the mitochondrial mixture approaches that of mitochondrial preparations from the hybrid in oxygen uptake or oxidadative phosphorylation. The enzymes involved are closely associated with the mitochondrion membrane and have, therefore, not been purified or individually characterized. From the studies thus far reported, complementation appears to be restricted to combinations of lines capable of exhibiting heterosis. As heterosis is commonly presumed to have a quantitative genetic basis, studies of this sort provide some insight into at least one component of the underlying mechanism but do not resolve any of the genetic complexities.

III. MINERAL NUTRITION AND GENETICS

Some genetic information is available on certain aspects of mineral nutrition. Sayre (1955) has demonstrated that inbred lines of maize accumulate mineral elements differentially. This finding has been extended. Gorsline, and his associates at Pennsylvania (1961, 1964a, 1964b),have demonstrated that the differential ear-leaf accumulation of P, K, Mg, Cu, B, Zn, Mn, Al, and Fe was highly heritable. Additive gene effects were of major importance, though varying amounts of non-additivity were also indicated. Ear-leaf and grain accumulations were not correlated, suggesting that different control mechanisms were operative. The possible relation between differential accomulation and efficiency of use remains to be established.

IV. PLANT DESIGN AND BIOLOGICAL EFFICIENCY

Over the years the question has often been raised as to whether our crops are properly designed for maximum efficiency. Initially such queries received little serious consideration. Recent studies, some of which have been reviewed at this Symposium, indicate consideration must be given to both plant design and function.

Several studies have indicated the importance of leaf angle and crop canopy on grain yield and apparent photosynthetic efficiency. I shall cite only a few of the studies in this area which appear to have strong genetic implications. Pendleton et al. (1968) compared isogenic single crosses differing in leaf angle. The hybrid having nearly upright leaves gave a significant increase in yield amounting to about 40%. A simply inherited character, lg_2, was used to provide the differential for leaf angle. The significant difference in yield is the more impressive as many simply inherited traits tend to condition pleiotropic effects, some of which are deleterious. Somewhat less striking effects were obtained with a normal hybrid through an artificial change in leaf angle. In this case, yield differences were less pronounced, but the plots in which the leaves were in an upright position tended to produce increased yields. Wide differences in leaf angle can be observed in any corn breeding nursery. If this trait has the importance indicated by the studies of Pendleton et al. commercial utilization should not be difficult or long delayed.

Eastin and Sullivan (1969) have demonstrated a significant difference in apparent photosynthetic efficiency by compact and open-headed sorghum types (Sorghum vulgare). These same studies indicated the importance of the flag leaf as an important photosynthetic organ.

V. THE PHYSIOLOGICAL GENETICS APPROACH

The preceding review has dealt briefly with certain aspects of physiology, biochemistry, and genetics. It will have served its purpose it if calls attention to two facts. First, there is a growing body of evidence either establishing or suggesting that many conditions related to biological efficiency are under genetic control. Second, the body of such evidence is quite inadequate to indicate the maximum efficiency which may be attainable. There can be little question but that increased activity in this area would be highly productive.

Physiological genetics, as I am using the term, would be a very broad and somewhat utilitarian discipline. It would include any aspect of physiology involving form or function which has an influence on economic worth or biological efficiency. Similarly it would include any aspect of genetics that was required for the efficient manipulation of the traits of interest. Progress, therefore, will be highly dependent upon the close cooperation between research workers in these two fields.

Differences in inherent yielding ability (dry matter production) could arise from inefficiencies in any one or more of the following broad areas: (i) energy transfer mechanisms; (ii) net assimilation rate; (iii) translocation and utilization of photosynthate; (iv) nutrient uptake and use; (v) plant growth substances; (vi) response under stress conditions; and (vii) efficiency of water use. The investigator choosing any of these areas for detailed study would make extensive subdivision based on both relative importance and feasibility of study. My knowledge of physiology is too limited to permit any meaningful suggestions.

Two factors of great importance deserve stress. First, if the research is to be productive in terms of physiological genetics, it is imperative that a simple and rapid analytical procedure be available for any reaction or trait of interest. Ideally, this analytical procedure would have a high degree of repeatability to minimize sampling and environmental problems. This is a major requirement because the genetic analysis and possible eventual incorporation into breeding stock will require large numbers of determinations. Second, an extensive survey of the germ plasm of the species should be undertaken to identify the range of variability that exists. The assessment of the potential contribution to biological efficiency can be studied more readily when extreme types are involved. Each enzyme of a system may be subject to individual induction or repression so mean or net values may have little value or meaning. Natural selection would have operated on the system as a whole, so that a common end product provides no assurance that the component steps are also equal.

I shall turn now to the more strictly genetic aspects which may be required. Information is required on the influence of the two alternative states (low activity vs. high activity, low leaf angle vs. high leaf angle, etc.), on plant performance; and the more favorable characteristic must eventually be introduced into superior breeding stocks. In some cases these two objectives may be achieved through one transfer operation. Under other circumstances two separate operations may be required and we shall consider the two operations separately.

Appropriate techniques for comparing strains differing in efficiency of a particular enzyme or some other trait of interest will be influenced by the complexity of inheritance, the sources of the contrasting types, and the time requirements of the analytical procedures. It would appear that if the trait involves the primary gene product (an enzyme) inheritance will tend to be monogenic. The greater the number of steps between the primary product and the expression of the character the greater will be the likelihood for multigenic inheritance or interactions.

If inheritance is simple the most efficient evaluation of differences will be obtained through use of isogenic lines. Several sets of such lines, differing in origin, would be desirable to minimize the background genotype effects. This approach has two possible limitations. First, the term isogenic is relative rather than absolute. Even long-time inbred lines exhibit some degree of genetic variability, presumably arising through mutation, so that either long-continued selfing or back-crossing can only be expected to narrow but not completely eliminate extraneous genetic differences. Second, the development of such contrasting pairs is a time-consuming operation requiring identification of the contrasting types in each segregating generation.

If the trait of interest occurs in adapted lines, a diallel analysis may supply the desired information. This method requires the utilization of a series of "high" and "low" lines to permit the expression of phase of the trait at the F_1 level. This method suffers from the limitation that the variances estimated are influenced by the lines comprising the diallel set. Therefore, interpretations must be made with some degree of caution.

Under conditions where one phase of the contrast of interest is rare, comparisons may be made in the F_2 generation. This approach requires that each F_2 plant be assayed. A simple analysis of variance involving the 'between-' and 'within genotype' contrast provides the significance test of interest. If the F_2 population is large, one may assume, except for linkage, that extraneous genetic differences are averaged within each subpopulation, thus minimizing the background genetic influence.

If the trait is inherited in a quantitative manner alternative procedures must be used. The development of isogenic lines becomes impractical or impossible. The diallel approach remains a possibility but one must be concerned with covariances as well as variances. This is true because the F_1 array will exhibit a range in expression of the trait under study. It would be desirable to include the parental types in the diallel analyses (Griffing, 1956) which would permit the estimation of both reciprocal and parent-progeny relations.

The examination of F_2 populations may also be useful. As the array will represent a continuous distribution rather than two discrete classes a different system of analysis is required. A simple regression of Y on X would appear to be appropriate.

Additional tests and details of suitable experimental designs may have to be developed to fit special needs or circumstances.

After the establishment of the superiority of the variant type the problem of incorporation into useful breeding stocks remains. This task requires the continued cooperation of the physiologist and the geneticist. The complexity of inheritance of the trait under study as well as breeding objectives will influence the choice of transfer methods. Basically the choice lies between incorporation into existing populations of known characteristics (lines, varieties, synthetics or composites) or the development of new populations with the attendant task of evaluating merit for other traits of agronomic importance. The first alternative will normally be the most economical in terms of total effort required.

In a recent review (Sprague, 1966) of Quantitative Genetics in Plant Breeding, I have used the term population improvement as a general term to include all operations within a system designed to develop an improved type, whether this be a random mating population or an improved line. The procedures reviewed there in some detail encompass the several alternatives that would be most useful in the present context.

If the trait is simply inherited, transfer to a stable line or composite is readily accomplished by backcrossing. The heterozygous individuals must be identified in each generation through either appropriate genetic tests or physiological evaluations. Transfer to a stable inbred line poses the fewest problems. Such a procedure, however, should be viewed as a short-term solution. Relatively few inbred lines or self-pollinating varieties have a long expectancy of commercial usefulness. Furthermore genetic modifiers peculiar to the recurrent parent may limit the expression of the desired trait. Transfer to random-mating populations (natural or induced) will normally provide the most satisfactory long-term solution. Obviously the populations chosen as recipients should represent the best synthetics or composites currently available and preferably those which are undergoing active selection for further improvement.

The two objectives, further improvement and incorporation, are not incompatible. The donor strain can be grown as a separate entry within the recipient population and hand-emasculated or detasseled depending upon the morphology of the crop. The crossed seed would then be used to produce an F_2 generation. The desired individuals within this population could again be crossed to the current generation of the recipient population. Thus the incorporation utilizes, in each back-cross cycle, the most advanced generation of the recipient population. After the required number of generations of backcrossing a new subpopulation can be derived which is homozygous for the trait of interest but which otherwise carries the gene frequency of the recipient population.

If the desired attribute is conditioned by many genes, transfer of the entire complex by backcrossing will be very difficult. Under such conditions some type of recurrent selection or an alternation of backcrossing and recurrent selection may be appropriate. The final choice of procedures can best be made after detailed information is at hand on mode of inheritance.

In this brief review I have not attempted any long-range projections for new genetic techniques which may reach the stage of usability. I have not attempted to give detailed information on many aspects of genetics; present developments of theory far exceed their effective utilization. Rather, I have attempted to indicate that the available genetic knowledge is adequate to provide the necessary support of a productive cooperative effort involving physiology and genetics. A major expansion is needed in this combined area to provide: (i) a better understanding of crop response, and (ii) a more sound basis for further increases in agricultural efficiency. The research required will demand time, funds, and facilities but should achieve a high order of productivity.

LITERATURE CITED

Ashby, E. 1930. Studies in the inheritance of physiological characters. 1. A physiological investigation of the nature of hybrid vigour in maize. Ann. Botany (London) 44:457-467.

Ashby, E. 1932. Studies in the inheritance of physiological characters. 2. Further experiments upon the basis of hybrid vigour and upon the inheritance of efficiency index and respiration rate in maize. Ann. Botany (London) 46:1007-1032.

Beckman, L., J. G. Scandalios, and J. L. Brewbaker. 1964a. Genetics of leucine aminopeptidase isozymes in maize. Genetics 50:899-904.

Beckman, L., J. G. Scandalios, and J. G. Brewbaker 1964b. Catalase hybrid enzymes in maize. Science 146(3648):1174-1175.

Beevers, L., Dounce Flesher, and R. H. Hageman. 1964. Studies on the pyridine nucleotide specificity of nitrate reductase in higher plants and its relationship to sulfhydryl level. Biochem. Biophys. Acta 89:453-464.

Eastin, J. D., and C. Y. Sullivan. 1969. Carbon dioxide exchange in compact and semi-open sorghum inflorescences. Crop Sci. 9:165-166.

Gorsline, G. F., J. L. Ragland, and W. I. Thomas. 1961. Evidence for inheritance of differential accumulation of calcium, magnesium, and potassium by maize. Crop Sci. 1:155-156.

Gorsline, G. W., W. I. Thomas, D. E. Baker, and J. L. Ragland. 1964a. Relationships of strontium-calcium accumulation within corn. Crop Sci. 4:154-156.

Gorsline, G. F., W. I. Thomas, and D. E. Baker. 1964b. Inheritance of P, K, Mg, Cu, B, Zn, Mn, Al, and Fe concentrations by corn leaves and grain. Crop Sci. 4:207-210.

Griffing, B. 1956. Concept of general and specific combining ability in relation to diallel crossing systems. Aust. J. Biol. Sci. 9:463-493.

Grossmann, A., and G. F. Sprague. 1948. Comparative growth rates in a reciprocal maize cross. 1. The kernel and its component parts. J. Amer. Soc. Agron. 40:88-98.

Hageman, R. H., E. R. Leng, and J. W. Dudley. 1967. A biochemical approach to corn breeding. Advance. in Agron. 19:45-86.

Jacob, F., and J. Monod. 1961. On the regulation of gene activity. Cold Spring Harbor Symposium 26:193-209.

McDaniel, R. G., and I. V. Sarkissian. 1966. Heterosis: Complementation by by mitochondria. Science 152:1640-1642.

McDaniel, G. F., and I. V. Sarkissian. 1968. Mitochondrial heterosis in maize. Genetics 59:465-475.

Miflin, B. J., and R. H. Hageman. 1963. Demonstration of photophosphorylation in maize chloroplasts. Plant Physiol. 38:66-70.

Miflin, B. J., and R. H. Hageman. 1966. Activity of chloroplasts isolated from maize inbreds and their F_1 hybrids. Crop Sci. 6:185-187.

Pendleton, J. W., G. E. Smith, S. R. Winter, and T. J. Johnson. 1968. Field investigations of the relationships of leaf angle in corn (Zea mays L.). Agron. J. 60:422-424.

Sarkissian, I. V., and H. K. Skrivaslava. 1967. Mitochondrial polymorphism in maize. II. Further evidence of correlation of mitochondrial complementation and heterosis. Genetics 57:843-850.

Sayre, J. D. 1955. Mineral nutrition of corn. In G. F. Sprague (ed.) Corn and corn improvement. Agronomy 5:293-314.

Scandalios, J. G. 1964. Tissue specific isozyme variations in maize. J. Hered. 55:281-285.

Schwartz, D. 1960. Genetic studies on mutant enzymes in maize: Synthesis of hybrids enzymes by heterozygotes. Proc. Nat. Acad. Sci. USA 46:1210-1216.

Schwartz, D. 1964. Genetic studies on mutant enzymes in maize. V. In vitro interconversion of allelic isozymes. Proc. Nat. Acad. Sci. USA 52:222-226.

Schwartz, D., Lucy Fuchsman, and K. H. McGrath. 1965a. Allelic isozymes of the pH 7.5 esterase in maize. Genetics 52:1265-1268.

Schwartz, D. 1965b. Genetic studies on mutant enzymes in maize. VI. Elimination of allelic isozyme variation by glyceraldehyde treatment. Genetics 52:1295-1302.

Sprague, G. F. 1937. Hybrid vigor and growth rates in a maize cross and its reciprocal. J. Agr. Res. 53:819-830.

Sprague, G. F. 1966. Quantitative genetics in plant improvement, p. 315-354. In K. J. Frey (ed.) Plant breeding. Iowa State Univ. Press.

Sprague, G. F., and H. H. McKinney. 1966. Aberrant ratio: An anomaly in maize associated with virus infection. Genetics 54:1287-1296.

Stuber, C. W., and C. S. Levings. 1969. Auxin induction and repression of peroridase isozymes in plant tissue. Crop Sci. 9:000-000.

Ursprung, H., K. D. Smith, W. H. Sofer, and D. T. Sullivan. 1968. Assay systems for the study of gene function. Science 160:1075-1081.

Warner, Robert, R. H. Hageman, J. W. Dudley, and R. J. Lambert. 1969. Inheritance of nitrate reductase activity in Zea mays L. Proc. Nat. Acad. Sci. USA. (in press)

16... DISCUSSION

NEAL F. JENSEN

Cornell University
Ithaca, New York

Dr. Sprague is to be congratulated for his thoughtful analysis and clear exposition of a difficult and neglected area of vital importance to crop improvement. Especially valuable are the many illustrations and references to published work. I found provocative his fine distinction between biochemical genetics and physiological genetics and his preference for the latter where "biosynthetic pathways and the isolation and characterization of enzymes would not be an end in themselves, but would be extended to explore the effects of individual enzymes or of enzyme systems on all aspects of growth, development, and reproductive capacity." Plant breeders, particularly, would applaud the growth of a form of genetics that would show a clear relationship to plant improvement.

One cannot read or hear Dr. Sprague's paper without being led to interesting speculations such as, what happens to an efficient primary gene product that has the misfortune to be associated with less efficient gene products in a multistep process? Or, what is the relation between hybrid vigor or unusual activity in the seedling stage and end product productivity?

However useless it would be for me to pose as a physiological geneticist I believe I may lay claim legitimately as a plant breeder to an appreciation for this type of research, in fact, I find that in 1968 on no fewer than eight occasions I used physiological ecology as the theme for public talks or espoused its cause in meetings concerned with crop improvement. The committee on biological efficiency of the USDA-State Experiment Station Joint Task Force that last year assessed the research needs of the small grains for the next 10 years gave this subject its highest priority. In addition, the completed task force document carries in its recommendations a statement which I quote in part:

"The yield, quality, physical traits and other characteristics of the cereal varieties grown on millions of USA acres are the result of a continuing interaction between the genotype of the plant and its changing total environment; in fact, they are the result of a sequence of biochemical reactions monitored by enzymes, themselves under the control of genes. This whole area of the physiological ecology of the cereals is not well understood; high yielding varieties have been bred without fully understanding why they are superior in performance. For crop scientists to progress in the future it is essential that favorable plant metabolic processes be recognized and used in variety development and crop production.

"Biological efficiency involves a host of important subject areas but the Task Force wishes to stress the need for research on the basic biological processes, morphological traits, response characteristics and genotype-environment interactions in the cereals so that these traits will become as well known as an useable in plant improvement as are, for example, genes for height, disease resistance or stiff straw."

I want now to give you 2 postulates that in my view emphasize the necessity to expand research in the areas Dr. Sprague has designated as physiological genetics. These are:

1) The rate of progress in plant improvement will decrease with time.

2) Our breeders are exhausting resource materials suitable to present systems and must soon receive supplementary research information of a nature suitable to more complex and sophisticated procedures.

Taking these in order, the first postulate that the rate of progress in plant improvement will decrease with time is another way of saying, "Yes, Virginia, there is a ceiling." Plant improvement in its manifold forms is, after all, finite. Yield is finite. One can, if he wishes, speculate as to what the ultimate yield limit of a given crop might be under the most favorably endowed environment. While we do not need to concern ourselves here with such figures, nor the question of time scale, it is important to recognize during this present period of significant productivity advances that each move to higher yield levels uses up some of the finite potential. The question I raise here is a curious one: can we increase the rate at which we use up this remaining finite resource? We note the quantum jumps being made in wheat and rice yields, for example. While giving proper due to the breeder let us also

be aware of the element of fortune inherent in such successful samp-
lings of our world germplasm resources. In the case of wheat these
successes indicate a sizeable as-yet-unexploited variability pool; certain other crops do not show this favorable aspect. A proper topic for
discussion by geneticists and plant breeders would be a consideration
of possibly better ways to sample and use the variability present in
world germplasm collections than our present haphazard and subjective
ones.

The second postulate that our breeding methods are exhausting resource materials to the point that supplemental assistance is needed, is
based upon knowledge of a characteristic inseparable from the methodology of almost all breeding programs, that of empiricism. As Hageman, Leng, and Dugley pointed out in the paper referred to by Dr.
Sprague, "Yield testing in the field is the major selection tool." I mean
by the empirical method that plant breeders long ago found that by using
standard plot techniques superior genotypes as we define them would be
sorted out by the process and identified in the data sheets, almost automatically. Indeed, as we all know, empirical methods have given successful results but now we recognize a deficiency in the method: it adds
little to our store of knowledge or understanding as to how the results
were obtained and, particularly, why a superior genotype yields and
performs as it does. Not knowing why we are unable to identify and use
the responsible traits as genetic building blocks in further breeding.
This weakness of the empirical method will become more apparent as
performance levels are raised. To illustrate from my own work two
decades ago it was possible to release a superior wheat variety in New
York and then look within the project with confidence for the appearance
of its successor; today, with the release of Yorkstar, and projected
cumulative yields at levels 60% higher, I am not so sure that empiricism can play the same role. We are seeking for direction for future
breeding programs retaining, if possible, the empirical framework.
Two avenues, particularly, appear to me to offer promise of help.
These are:

1) A modification of breeding methods to increase predictability
and odds of successfully reaching objectives, and

2) An increase in our knowledge of the form and function components of productivity. The latter has been the subject of Dr. Sprague's
talk.

In conclusion, I have pointed out two characteristics of varietal
development for crop improvement, namely, (i) prospects for an eventual decline in the rate of growth of crop productivity, with the suggestion that we reverse conservation concepts and work to exploit this
finite resource as rapidly as possible, and (ii) a flaw in the empirical
breeding method. Dr. Sprague offers hope that we can supplement our
present procedures by adding to the available tools and building blocks
of the plant breeder. He is asking that physiologists establish with
geneticists and plant breeders the same kind of close working cooperation that has already been in existence for decades with plant patholo-
gists, entomologists, and agronomists. Specifically, he is asking that
information be obtained on the influence of alternative states of form or
function on plant performance.

SUBJECT INDEX

391